D1195394

FISH
BIOMECHANICS

FISH BIOMECHANICS

Edited by
Paul W. Webb
Daniel Weihs

PRAEGER

PRAEGER SPECIAL STUDIES • PRAEGER SCIENTIFIC

JEROME LIBRARY–BOWLING GREEN STATE UNIVERSITY

Library of Congress Cataloging in Publication Data
Main entry under title:

Fish biomechanics.

  Bibliography: p.
  Includes indexes.
  1. Fishes—Physiology. 2. Fishes—Locomotion.
3. Animal mechanics. I. Webb, Paul W., 1923–
II. Weihs, Daniel.
QL639.1.F55 1983   597′.01852   83-11209
ISBN 0-03-059461-8

Published in 1983 by Praeger Publishers
CBS Educational and Professional Publishing,
a Division of CBS Inc.
521 Fifth Avenue, New York, NY 10175, U.S.A.

© 1983 by Praeger Publishers

All rights reserved

3456789   052   987654321

Printed in the United States of America on acid-free paper.

CONTENTS

PREFACE

The spate of reviews and books on fish locomotion in recent years is indicative of the growing importance of the biomechanical approach to zoologic problems for both zoologists and physicists; however, the biomechanical approach can be useful over a much wider range of subjects than locomotion. Discussion of many of these other aspects of fish biomechanics is mainly fleeting and scattered in divers texts. With the exception of R. McNeill Alexander's classic text *Functional Design in Fishes* (Hutchinson, 1967) and to a lesser degree Y. G. Aleyev's *Nekton* (Junk, 1977), no single text has attempted to examine the breadth of fish biomechanics problems. Our objective is the production of a text on fish biomechanics that explains and applies fundamental principles for a wide range of fish structures and functions. We wanted a text that would not only be up-to-date but also a vehicle toward future research and instruction, while providing a summary of basic knowledge that could be broadly applied to an understanding of the lives of fishes.

Fish are the oldest group of vertebrates. The earliest remains, toothlike structures, and fragments of dermal bone in Ordovician strata, are aged at about 500 million years. Fish remains become more common and complete towards the end of the Silurian, ushering in the Devonian 400 million years ago (sometimes called "the Age of Fishes"). In 500 million years there have been many "experiments" and changes in structures and functions in fish, leading to a diversity among some 20,000 extant species in about 450 families that is unparalleled by any other vertebrate group.

Biomechanics studies, including those on fish, also have a long history, and they can serve an increasing role in understanding adaptation and evolution; thus, a common result of biomechanics studies is the definition of boundaries within which an animal can operate, boundaries that in turn must help define the niche breadth. Borrowing terms from metabolism, biomechanics studies can define functional scope, which has great potential for developing new hypotheses as to the biological role of systems and for understanding animal life styles. The interaction between the physical sciences and biology should be a two-way street with new mathematic and technologic insights triggered by ideas and observations from the results of experiments by natural selection.

In order to treat the various areas of fish biomechanics and to try and place these in context, we have organized the book to build from functional components through successively higher levels of organization and integration. The book begins with a concise history of the subject, placing the various chapters in their appropriate temporal perspective. Chapter 2 deals with fish muscle, summarizing recent advances in the understanding of the properties and physiologic capabilities of myotomal muscle systems. The next chapter examines the structural components that with the muscles allow a fish to apply and resist forces in manipulating its environment. Chapter 4 discusses the motion of fluids within body compartments, such as the cardiovascular system and the gills. Through the transport of nutrients and gases these systems are essential to physiological responses to the environment. The book moves on to examine some of the systems evolved by fish in dealing with special problems of vertebrate life in water. Chapter 5 summarizes the physical principles related to buoyancy and examines their consequences to the behavior and ecology of fishes. Locomotion is the subject of the next two chapters, recognizing the very different roles played by the body and caudal fin (Chap. 6) compared to the paired and other median fins (Chap. 7). Chapter 8 looks at the problem of heat exchange between a fish and water, highlighting the difficulties of controlling body temperatures in an environment of high heat capacity.

Energy flow through any animal determines growth and reproductive potential. Chapter 9 describes how energy is obtained, and Chapter 10 shows how it is distributed (both food capture and use of energy vary with habits and habitat). The last chapter shows how energy obtained by a fish might be optimally utilized by appropriate behavior. The book closes with an epilogue designed to sum up what has been achieved in the area of fish biomechanics and suggests critical areas for further study.

Some relevant fields are not covered in this book, including sensory systems, larval adaptations, and reproduction. Biomechanical aspects of reproduction do not appear ripe for discussion at this time. The subject could include problems of sperm and egg dispersion and distribution and certain aspects of thermodynamics of egg production. The increasing importance of knowledge of early life history is witnessed by several international symposia in recent years; here, biomechanical aspects include scaling and feeding, propulsion, and respiration functions. Studies in these areas may make major contributions toward understanding the well-known high mortality of fish larvae. Sensory systems, especially vision and acoustic-lateralis systems, are the subjects of intensive research deserving more attention than is possible in this single volume. These subjects will undoubtedly play an important role in future volumes on fish biomechanics.

The symbols in each chapter largely follow the conventions of their parent disciplines. We decided that facilitating interaction with a wider literature was more desirable than forcing uniformity of symbols throughout this volume of broad scope.

Fish biomechanics is a very active field, evidenced by the fact that the majority of the references in most chapters were published in the 5 years preceding the writing of the chapters (1981). We expect future volumes in the subject to become necessary within a few years. Furthermore, the exponential increase in the number of active researchers and their output necessitates a multiauthored approach. The topic is dynamic, and because the various subjects have advanced by differing degrees, we have refrained from restricting the enthusiasms of the contributors by the natural desires of editors for bland uniformity.

We have found that biomechanics is an interdisciplinary field that asks its practitioners to make forays into novel fields and disciplines. Although this may require some effort, any exchange between disciplines can be enormously fruitful; therefore, we hope this volume will help biologists and non-biologists towards further collaboration. Preparing this book has been fun for us, and we hope the readers will find it equally enjoyable.

Paul W. Webb
Daniel Weihs
Ann Arbor
February, 1983

ACKNOWLEDGMENTS

This book would never have been completed without the labors of several colleagues who read each chapter for us. It is a pleasure to thank J.J. Childress, S. Corrsin, T.L. Daniel, M.R. Hebrank, S.R. Kerr, W.H. Neill, J.J. Videler, D.R. Wilkie, and T.Y. Wu for reviewing one or more of the contributions.

CONTRIBUTORS

R. McN. Alexander

The University of Leeds
Department of Pure and Applied
    Zoology
Leeds LS2 9JT
England

A. Anantaraman

University of Guelph
Department of Zoology
Guelph, Ontario N1G 2W1
Canada

R. W. Blake

University of British Columbia
Department of Zoology
Vancouver, British Columbia V6T 1W5
Canada

J. H. Gee

University of Manitoba
Department of Zoology
Winnipeg, Manitoba R3T 2N2
Canada

J. B. Graham

Scripps Institution of Oceanography
Physiological Research Laboratory
University of California at San Diego
La Jolla, CA 92093
U.S.A.

I. A. Johnston

University of St. Andrews
Department of Physiology
St. Andrews, Fyfe KY16 9ST
Scotland

Dr. J. F. Kitchell

University of Wisconsin
Center for Limnology and Department
    of Zoology
Madison, WI 53706
U.S.A.

Dr. L. Langille

University of Western Ontario
Department of Physiology
London, Ontario N6A 5C1
Canada

G. V. Lauder

University of Chicago
Department of Anatomy
Chicago, IL 60637
U.S.A.

Sir James Lighthill

University College London
Gower Street
London WC1E 6BT
England

E. D. Stevens

University of Guelph
Department of Zoology
Guelph, Ontario N1G 2W1
Canada

S. A. Wainwright

Duke University
Department of Zoology
Durham, NC 27707
U.S.A.

D. Weihs

Technion—Israel Institute of Technology
Department of Aeronautical Engineering
Haifa 32000
Israel

P. W. Webb

University of Michigan
School of Natural Resources
Ann Arbor, MI 48109
U.S.A.

G. T. Yates

California Institute of Technology
Engineering Science Department
Pasadena, CA 91109
U.S.A.

FISH
BIOMECHANICS

Chapter 1
THE HISTORY OF FISH MECHANICS
R. McNeill Alexander

CONTENTS

Subsequent chapters discuss the present state of knowledge about fish and consider separately topics such as swimming, feeding, and blood circulation. This chapter tries to show how we reached the present state of knowledge, considers all branches of fish mechanics in a single time sequence, and tries to show how progress was affected by developments in basic mechanics and by the invention of new equipment.

FISH MECHANICS BEFORE 1660

Aristotle's works include *History of Animals,* which is a compendium of ancient zoologic knowledge, *Movement of Animals* and *Progression of Animals* (Aristotle, fourth century BC a, b, and c). These works discuss the numbers of fins that fish have (four in *Dicentrarchus,* two in *Anguilla,* none in *Muraena,* etc.). It is clear from the context that only pectoral and pelvic fins are included, and it is implied that they are used for swimming. Fish without fins swim by using the sea in the way that snakes use dry ground (and snakes in water also swim this way). *Raia* and *Dasyatis* have no fins but swim by the undulatory movement of their flat bodies. "All creatures that

1

are capable of motion move with four or more points of motion; the blooded animals [i.e. vertebrates] with four only: as, for instance, man with two hands and two feet, birds with two wings and two feet, quadrupeds and fishes severally with four feet and four fins. Creatures that have two winglets or fins, or that have none at all like serpents, move all the same with not less than four points of motion; for there are four bends in their bodies as they move, or two bends together with their fins" (Aristotle a, book I, chap 5). This passage may seem to owe more to intellectual tidiness than to observation, but the bends in the body are more numerous and more obvious in swimming snakes and eels than in carangiform fish.

Aristotle remarked that animals with gills have no lungs, and he described the different numbers and positions of gills in different kinds of fish. He knew that water passes over the gills, entering by the mouth and leaving by the gill openings. He wrote a brief description of the hearts of fish but nothing about blood movement. Surprisingly, he wrote nothing about the swimbladder except in a passage about *Trigla* and other sound-producing fish. He wrote that these fish have air inside them and that some of them produce their sounds by rubbing or moving this air.

It was a very long time before fish mechanics made much more progress. Pliny (first century AD) wrote four centuries after Aristotle, but his account of fish swimming is a mere précis of Aristotle's. Very little progress was made in any branch of zoology in the Middle Ages, and the works of the ancient authors were not widely available until the Renaissance. Then, Guillaume Rondelet (1554) wrote a book about marine animals, referring frequently to Aristotle, Pliny, and other ancient authors (Aristotle is cited several times on each of very many pages). Rondelet described how some fish swim by movements of their bodies and some by fins; he mentioned the swimbladder and explained it as a buoyancy organ.

Fish were important in William Harvey's (1628) discovery of the circulation of the blood. He dissected living fish, cut the ventral aorta, and observed that blood squirted out from the end nearer the heart, at every beat of the heart. In other experiments he tied ligatures around veins of snakes and fish and observed that the vein between the ligature and the heart became empty. These experiments clearly indicated that blood travels from the veins through the heart to the ventral aorta.

EARLY ACADEMICIANS (1660–1700)

There was a burst of activity in fish mechanics late in the seventeenth century, among scientists who were members of the Royal Society of London (founded 1660) or of the Accademia del Cimento in Florence (active 1657–1667). To appreciate their achievements, it is necessary to know something of the state of physical mechanics at the time (Dugas, 1957; Forbes and Dijksterhaus, 1963). The works of Archimedes (third century BC) had been available since publication of the first printed edition in 1543; they present Archimedes' principle, the principle of levers, and a lot of information about centers of gravity. Stevin (1548–1620) established the concept of hydrostatic pressure; Roberval (1602–1675) explained the parallelogram of forces; Galileo (1564–1642) showed that bodies fall with uniform acceleration. Little other mechanics was known. Newton's *Principia* with his laws of motion was not published until 1687. Torricelli had in 1643 performed the experiment that produced the mercury barometer and so demonstrated one method of producing a vacuum. Van Guericke had invented his air pump, and Robert Boyle had used one for the experiments that led to Boyle's law, published in 1662.

This background was peculiarly favorable for research on swimbladders. Members of the Accademia del Cimento used a column of mercury to reduce the pressure over barbels (*Barbus*) and other fish in water; the fish swelled up and was unable to swim downward from the surface. When atmospheric pressure was restored, the shape of the fish returned to normal, but the fish sank to the bottom. Dissection revealed that abnormally little air was left in the swimbladder. When the pressure was reduced over a fish that had been weighted to keep it submerged, bubbles escaped from its mouth. These observations were published anonymously (Accademia del Cimento, 1666). Boyle (1670) exposed a gudgeon (*Gobio*) to low pressure, using his air pump, but derived no useful conclusions. He saw air bubbles forming all over the fish but failed to realise that they were coming out of solution in the water.

A few years later, a perceptive suggestion was published in the *Philosophical Transactions* of the Royal Society. Its author was identified only by the initials A.I. (A.I., 1675). These are not the initials of any seventeenth century fellow of the Royal Society. According to Fischer (1795) the article was reprinted in a posthumous edition of the works of Francesco Redi, published in 1762, but I have not seen the edition in question. Redi had been a member of the Accademia del Cimento, and he published some good drawings of swimbladders (Redi, 1684). A.I. wrote:

> If the fish in the middle region of the water, be of equal weight to the water that is commensurate to the bulk of it, the fish will rest there without any tendency upwards or downwards: but if the fish be deeper in the water, the bulk of the fish becoming less by the compression of the bladder, and yet retaining the same weight, it will sink and rest at the bottom: and, on the other side, if the fish be higher than that middle region, the air dilating itself, and the bulk of the fish consequently increasing, but not its weight, the fish will rise upwards, and rest at the top of the water. Perhaps the fish, by some action, can emit air out of this bladder, and afterwards out of its body, and also, when there is not enough, take in air and convey it to this bladder; and then it will not be wondered, that there should be always a due proportion of air in the bodies of all fishes, to serve their use, according to the depth of water they are bred and live in: perhaps by some muscle the fish can contract this bladder beyond the pressure of the weight of water: perhaps the fish can by its sides or some other defence keep off the pressure of the water, and give the air leave to dilate itself. In these cases the fish

will be helped in all intermediate distances, and may rise or sink from any region of the water, without moving one fin.

Notice that A.I. suggested two ways in which an ability to adjust swimbladder volume could be used: statically, to equilibrate the fish at a chosen depth, and dynamically, to cause changes of depth.

A.I. wrote that Boyle had suggested to him an experiment to test the dynamic theory. A fish was to be put in water in a flask, the neck of the flask was to be drawn out into a capillary, and more water was to be added to bring the meniscus up into the capillary. Movements of the meniscus would then indicate any volume changes that occurred when the fish changed its depth in the water. The experiment was left untried for nearly 200 years (Harting, 1872).

A.I.'s article inspired one from John Ray (1675), who wrote that he found in Willoughby's notes, which he was editing for publication, that a fish whose swimbladder has been emptied by pricking sinks and cannot swim. Also, Pleuronectidae live on the bottom and have no swimbladder. There is a pneumatic duct in "most fishes," and Ray wondered whether it could be used to let air into and out of the swimbladder. A comparison with Cartesian divers led to the erroneous conclusion that "those fishes that descend by contracting the bladder, letting the contracting muscle cease to act, will rise again of their own accord, the air within dilating itself" (the air would not dilate to its original volume because of the additional hydrostatic pressure).

The swimbladder was also discussed by Giovanni Borelli (1680), who had been a prominent member of the Accademia del Cimento and had established his reputation as a physicist and astronomer. Remarks in his book *On The Movement Of Animals* seem to show that he had been involved in the Accademia's experiments on swimbladders. He favored both the static and the dynamic theories of swimbladder function and illustrated his discussion with Figure 1-1. He also discussed the mechanism of fish swimming. He argued that fish do not row themselves along with their paired fins as Aristotle had implied. He observed that fish swim with their pectoral fins against their sides, and he found that they could still swim after he had torn off their pectoral fins. He stated that the paired fins are used for braking and turning and to keep the fish the right way up. He knew that fish have their centers of mass dorsal to their centers of buoyancy and are therefore apt to roll over.

Borelli's explanation of fish swimming seems highly unsatisfactory today, but it is hard to see how the mechanics of his day could have produced a better one. He described the movement simply as transverse wagging of the tail (Fig. 1-1, right). He interpreted the lateral movement of the tail from *D* to *G* as a preparatory stroke; all the thrust was produced by the movement back toward the midline. The tail fin is furled for the preparatory stroke and spread for the power stroke; also, it is bent during the preparatory stroke in order to present a convex surface to the water.

Borelli was also interested in the mechanics of the human skeleton (which

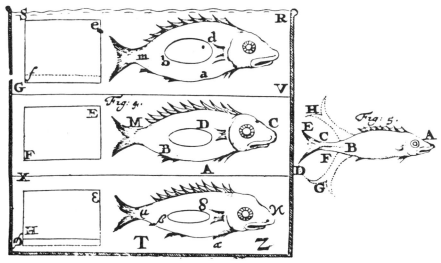

Figure 1-1

Diagrams from Borelli (1680). *Left,* a discussion of swimbladder size. The three fish are in water of different densities. The one at the top is in the least dense water and needs the largest swimbladder. *Right,* an explanation of swimming.

he treated as a system of levers) and of pennate muscles. He concerned himself with equilibrium of forces, but Nicolaus Steno (another member of the Accademia del Cimento) discussed the geometry of muscle contraction (Steno, 1667). One of Steno's illustrations shows the complex pennate arrangement of muscle fibers in the myotomes of a shark, anticipating part of Alexander's (1969a) description by three centuries. Du Verney (1701) described, to the French Académie des Sciences, how teleost fish pump water over their gills. He compared the function of the operculum to that of the valve of a bellows. He had carefully observed breathing movements without making any experiments. This period was one of profitable interaction between colleagues in the academies of science, some of whom were active both in biology and in physical science. It was followed by a long hiatus in which fish mechanics made hardly any progress.

THE LONG HIATUS (1700–1870)

Great progress was, however, made in physical mechanics. Daniel Bernoulli (1700–1782), Euler (1707–1783), d'Alembert (1717–1783), Lagrange (1736–1813), Navier (1785–1836), Stokes (1819–1903), and Poiseuille (1797–1869) established the equations and other work known by their names (see Dugas, 1957; Forbes and Dijksterhuis, 1963). By the end of the period, classical mechanics and classical hydrodynamics were essentially complete.

Some remarkable work was done at this time on the mechanics of blood flow, but not with fish. Stephen Hales (1733) performed a series of brilliant but cruel experiments in which he measured arterial blood pressures of farm animals. Thomas Young (1809) made rough calculations of the pressures required to drive blood through the various vessels of the human blood system and concluded that the capillaries offer most of the resistance to flow.

In 1809, Sir George Cayley was trying to discover the ideal streamlined shape. He measured the girth of a trout (*Salmo*) at intervals along its length and drew in his notebook a body of revolution with the same distribution of girths (Gibbs–Smith, 1962, Fig. 23[A]). In the following year he published a discussion of streamlining (Cayley, 1810) in which he suggested that natural shapes, such as those of trout and woodcock (*Scolopax,* a bird), gave the best available indication of the "solid of least resistance."

Delaroche (1809) published a long paper on the physiology of the swimbladder, arguing against the dynamic theory of swimbladder function. He stated that swimbladder compressibility is not a useful aid to vertical movement, but actually restricts the rate at which fish can change depth. Fish with swimbladders probably have to change depth slowly enough to allow time for secretion or resorbtion of gas. A small committee headed by Cuvier (1809) commented that if this were the case, nature would not have produced the swimbladder but would simply have made fish the same density as water without the bladder. This was obviously possible because all fish, with or without swimbladders have densities close to that of water. Delaroche had seen the comment before publication and added a footnote to his paper, showing that various species that lack swimbladders have about the same density as fish whose swimbladders has been deflated.

Shortly afterward, E.H. Weber (1820) published his account of the bones in fish that have since become known as the *Weberian ossicles.* He wrote a detailed account of these bones and of their connections with the ear, in Cyprinidae, Cobitidae, and *Silurus.* He injected a little mercury into the inner ear of a dissected *Cyprinus* and observed the inner ear and the ossicles while he squeezed air from the posterior to the anterior sac of the swimbladder. He showed in this way that changes of swimbladder volume cause movements of the ossicles that are transmitted to the fluid of the inner ear. He suggested that the swimbladder functions like an eardrum and the ossicles like mammalian ear ossicles.

THE KYMOGRAPH AND THE CINE CAMERA (1870–1910)

Experimental physiology became a busy field of study in the midnineteenth century. A particularly important group of physiologists in Berlin was led by Johannes Müller, who wrote a textbook (Müller, 1834–1840) describing much of their work. Müller himself performed experiments on the mechanics of the human larynx and on the acoustics of the ear. Schwann, his pupil and assistant, measured the force exerted by the frog gastrocnemius muscle in isometric contraction at different lengths. Another distinguished pupil commented that this "was the first time that an evidently vital force was investigated in a similar manner to a physical force, and that the laws of this force were mathematically expressed in figures" (duBois–Reymond, 1859; quoted in Science Museum, 1876). Helmholtz was another pupil, and Ludwig was an associate of Müller (Nordenskiold, 1928).

This activity led to the invention of a wide range of physiological apparatus. The most important item was the smoked-drum kymograph introduced by Ludwig (1847), which is still used for teaching and occasionally for research; this made it possible for the first time to produce an automatic record of a physiological experiment. Several variants that made records on flat plates were produced, but the drum has been generally preferred.

Many instruments were invented for use with the kymograph. Ludwig used the device shown in Figure 1-2 to record blood pressure; it is a manometer with a piston floating on the mercury. A wire from the piston ends

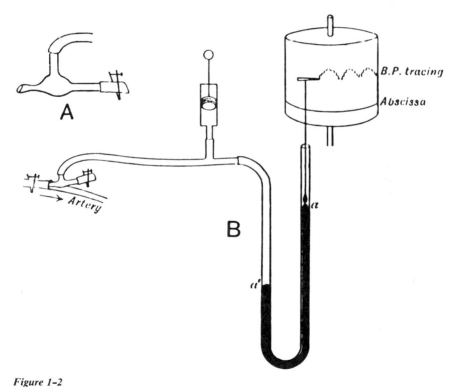

Figure 1–2
A diagram of Ludwig's apparatus for recording blood pressure. *aa'* is a mercury manometer, with a float at *a* connected to a stylus that writes on smoked paper on a drum, which is rotated by clockwork. (From Halliburton, 1903).

in a stylus that touches the smoked surface of the rotating drum. E.–J. Marey introduced various devices involving levers connected to tambours. The device shown in Figure 1-3 makes a lever writing on a smoked drum imitate the movements of another lever attached to a specimen some distance away. The mechanism is pneumatic, and movements of the first lever move a flexible membrane in and out, causing pressure changes that are transmitted along the connecting tube to the other membrane and lever.

Figure 1-4 shows a device used by Chauveau and Marey (1861) for recording pressures in the heart and thorax of a horse. The tubes end in rubber bulbs that are placed where the pressure is to be sensed. Pressure on the bulbs actuates the tambours and is recorded on the drum. The bottom tambour is connected to a single tube and bulb, but the other two are connected to a device with two bulbs for sensing the pressures in the auricle and ventricle. A curious feature of this illustration is that the drum is represented as revolving toward the bases of the writing levers, in the reverse of the usual direction. An impression can be gained of the range of physiological equipment available in the late nineteenth century by examining the catalogue of an exhibition held in 1876 (Science Museum, 1876) or slightly later textbooks of physiology (for instance, Halliburton, 1903). There were even instruments for measuring rates of blood flow in arteries.

Paul Bert (1870) used rubber bulbs connected to tambours for experiments on the breathing movements of fishes (Fig. 1-5). He put a rubber bulb between the jaws to record mouth movements and another under the operculum to record opercular movements. In other experiments he put a bulb into the mouth cavity to record pressure changes. His records seemed to show that the mouth and operculum open and close simultaneously (Fig. 1-5c), contrary to the then current view that they opened alternately.

François–Franck (1906 a and b) criticized Bert's experiment, remarking

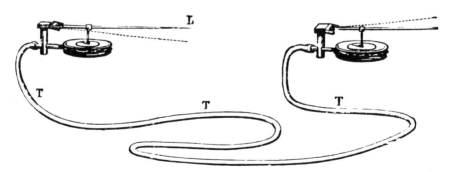

Figure 1–3
Apparatus used by Marey. The two tambours are connected by the tube (T) so that downward movement of one of the levers (L) causes upward movement of the other. (From Marey, 1873).

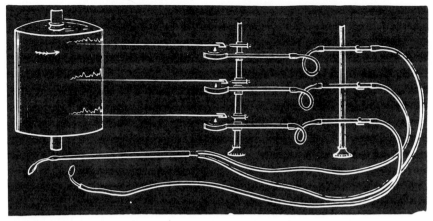

Figure 1-4
Chauveau and Marey's apparatus for recording pressures in the heart and thorax. (From Halliburton, 1903).

that a fish so encumbered with rubber bulbs was unlikely to breathe normally. He used the equipment shown in Figure 1-3 and so avoided having to put anything inside the fish. He put the recording lever of one double tambour under the mouth to record jaw movements and another against the operculum. His kymograph records of *Cyprinus, Tinca,* and *Perca* showed that the mouth began to open before the operculum (records obtained by modern methods confirm this; Hughes & Shelton, 1958). François–Franck released India ink into the water to show that the water flow goes in at the mouth and out by the opercular openings. He also used a small manometer submerged in the aquarium to show that the pressure just in front of the mouth falls below ambient pressure at inspiration and that the pressure just outside the opercular openings rises above ambient pressure at expiration.

Jolyet (1872) seems to have been the first to measure blood pressures of fish. He inserted a T-shaped cannula into the ventral aortas of eels (*Anguilla*) and connected it, through a tube filled with a hemostatic solution, to a "manometre de Magendie," which seems to have been a mercury manometer. It is not clear whether the manometer was connected to a kymograph or whether he observed the movements of the mercury directly. He observed systolic and diastolic pressures. Schoenlein & Willem (1895) used a Marey tambour to make kymograph records of blood pressure in *Torpedo.* Greene (1904) used Ludwig's manometer for recording blood pressure in Pacific salmon (*Oncorhynchus*).

Harting (1872) designed equipment for measuring the changes of volume of a living fish as it was moved up and down in a tall jar of water. He intended to perform the experiment suggested by Boyle to A.I. (1675), but his experi-

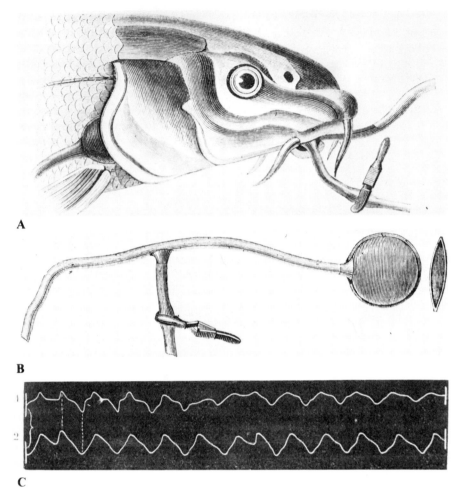

Figure 1-5

A, A gudgeon (*Gobio*) with rubber bulbs in its mouth and under its operculum, for Bert's experiments on respiration. *B,* The bulb that fits under the operculum. The side tube, closed by a clip, makes it possible to adjust the quantity of air in the bulb. *C,* A kymograph record obtained in this experiment, showing movements of 1, the mouth, and 2, the operculum. (From Bert, 1870).

ment did not match Boyle's apparent intention: the fish did not change depth voluntarily but was moved up and down in a small cage. He also made experiments with isolated swimbladders and found that an *Abramis* swimbladder changed volume less with changes of depth than Boyle's law predicted for unrestrained gas.

Armand Moreau (1876) made an outstandingly good series of experiments on fish with swimbladders. He set out to test the static and dynamic hypotheses of swimbladder function suggested by A.I. (1675; to whom he does not refer) and Borelli (1680). He performed Boyle's experiment with *Perca* swimming freely in a cylinder full of water. The volume of the fish increased as it swam up and decreased as it swam down, but the volume changes always accompanied the depth changes and did not anticipate them. The dynamic hypothesis predicted that volume changes should anticipate depth changes. The volume was not restored to its original value after a depth change even by *Trigla,* which has large muscles on the swimbladder.

In the experiment shown in Figure 1-6, Moreau enclosed a fish in a close-fitting cage that prevented fin movements, with a glass float above and a pan of mercury below. He adjusted the quantity of mercury to make the overall density of the assembly about equal to that of water. He put this assembly in a jar of water connected to an air pump on the left of the diagram and a manometer on the right. The pump could be used for suction or compression, as required. Reduced pressure made the swimbladder expand so that the fish floated; increased pressure compressed the swimbladder and made the fish sink. Moreau found that the difference between the pressure required to cause sinking from the surface and that required to cause rising from the bottom equaled the difference in hydrostatic pressure between bottom and top. This is

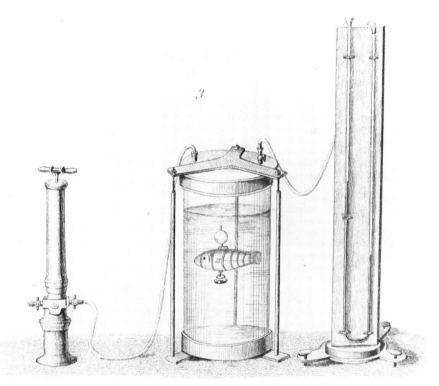

Figure 1–6
Apparatus used by Moreau for an experiment on the effect of pressure changes on the volume of a fish. (From Moreau, 1876).

how a Cartesian diver would behave: the volume changes seem to be passive responses to the pressure changes.

Figure 1-7 shows another of Moreau's experiments, designed to find out whether the muscles are capable of adjusting the volume of the swimbladder. The fish is fastened to a stand in a closed container that is completely full of water, with a meniscus in the capillary tube (AB). The small handle behind A is attached to a tight-fitting piston that can be used to adjust the position of the meniscus, if required. In some experiments tube AB was connected to a Marey tambour to obtain a record of volume changes. An electric battery (the flask on the right) is connected through an induction coil to electrodes in contact with the fish. Electric shocks caused small, brief changes of volume that were presumably caused by muscles compressing the swimbladder. Further experiments showed similar volume changes when fish struggled to get past obstacles, but these changes were also brief and very small.

Moreau also held *Labrus bergylta* in a cage in the sea for periods of a few days alternately at 7 m to 8 m depth and at the surface. From time to time he attached a float and pan of mercury to the fish (as in Fig. 1-6) and treated it like a hydrometer, observing how much of the float protruded above the water when it floated. In this way he measured volume changes and showed that gas was secreted slowly into the swimbladder after the fish had been lowered to a greater depth and resorbed slowly when it was brought back to the surface.

The new methods that Moreau made so effective in his experiments on swimbladders were not suitable for investigating swimming. Pettigrew's (1874) account of fish swimming is as unsatisfactory as is Borelli's (1680). He claimed that the body always formed an integral number of S bends. He

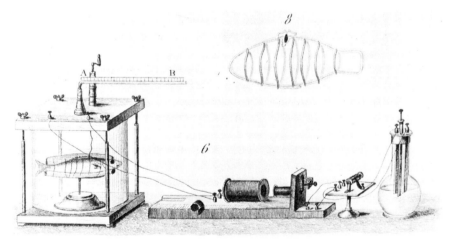

Figure 1-7
Apparatus used by Moreau to find out whether muscular contraction can affect the volume of the swimbladder. (From Moreau, 1876).

believed that the body formed standing (not traveling) waves and that there were stages in its cycle of movement when the body was straight. Further, he believed that fish roll about their long axes as they swim so that the tail moves broadside-on to the water in its effective stroke but obliquely in its recovery stroke. (At one point he wrote that there is no noneffective stroke, but the rest of his account seems to imply that only the movement towards the midline produces thrust.) Pettigrew compared the action of the tail to that of the propeller of a steamship. He stated that its path, in each cycle of swimming movements is 8-shaped. He was right (see Fig. 1-10A), but one of his peculiarities was a tendency to find waves, figures of eight, and helical screws wherever he looked in all forms of locomotion.

It must have been extraordinarily difficult to study locomotion without cine photography. Muybridge studied animal movement from 1877 onward by taking a series of photographs with 12 or more cameras fired in rapid succession (Muybridge, 1887). Marey took the first motion pictures with a single camera in 1882, using a "photographic gun," which took 12 exposures on a rotating plate of glass (Marey, 1894). Marey was also one of the first to take motion pictures on a strip of celluloid film (he was doing this by 1889).

Muybridge did not study fish, but in 1890 Marey exhibited some strips of film taken at the Naples Aquarium (Marey, 1890). They included sequences of *Raia* making swimming movements while tethered and of *Hippocampus* swimming (for reproductions, see Marcy, 1894). The pictures of *Raia* showed waves travelling posteriorly along the pectoral fins; those of *Hippocampus* seemed to show waves travelling anteriorly (*i.e.*, upward) along the dorsal fin, and because the fish was sinking slowly Marey (1894) interpreted this as active downward swimming. He may have been right, but an alternative explanation is that this was an early example of the illusion that sometimes makes wheels seem to turn backwards in films. The pictures of *Hippocampus* were taken with an exposure time of $1/2000$ s, short enough to freeze very rapid movement, but the framing rate was only 20 Hz. The much later films of Breder and Edgerton (1942), taken at 300 frames per second, showed waves travelling posteriorly along the dorsal fin with a frequency of 35 Hz. A film of the same waves, taken at 20 frames per second, would appear to show waves travelling anteriorly with a frequency of 5 Hz.

By 1894 Marey had also filmed *Anguilla* and *Scyliorhinus* (Fig. 1-8). He wrote of *Anguilla:* "Actual measurement shows that the velocity of the waves is greater than the rate of progress of the animal, and that they move in the opposite direction. There must be, therefore, a recoil, as in the case of the screw of a steamer, and it is due to the mobility of the resisting point." He seems to have formed the idea that the waves push against the water.

Shortly afterwards, François-Franck (1906b) used cinematography to study the respirations of *Cyprinus* and *Tinca;* he drew particular attention to the movements of the opercular valve.

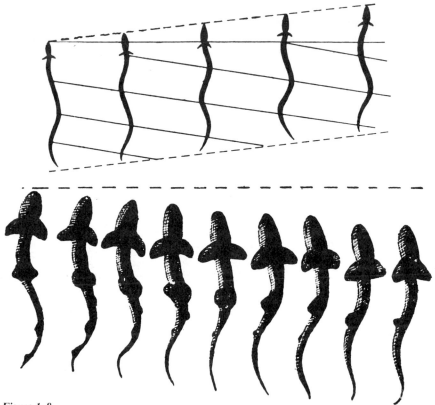

Figure 1-8
Illustrations from Marey (1894), based on his films of (*above*) an eel (*Anguilla*) and (*below*) a dogfish (*Scyliorhinus*) swimming. The pictures of the eel read from left to right and those of the dogfish from right to left. Lines on the pictures of the eel emphasize that waves travel backwards as the eel swims forwards.

ENGINEERS AND JAMES GRAY (1910–1950)

Until this time, investigation of fish swimming had involved only qualitative observations. A new, quantitative approach was inaugurated by Houssay (1912). None of his actual results seem useful now, but the new attitude was important. Houssay harnessed fish and measured the speeds at which they could swim against different forces. He multiplied the speed by the force to calculate power output. His apparatus is shown in Figure 1-9. The wheels R and r are mounted on a horizontal axle over a tank of water. The rods T and T' are also attached to the axle. The fish is harnessed to T, and a weight is hung from T' so that if the fish swims away, trying to escape, it lifts the weight. Wheel r is attached rigidly to the axle, but R has a ratchet that allows rotation in only one direction. Both wheels have blocks of ebonite inlaid in their rims. When they revolve they make and break electrical circuits, moving the pointers A and A', which write on a kymograph, thereby recording speed and direction of revolution. The system was highly artificial, and it measured only power exerted on the machine, missing power dissipated in the water.

Houssay towed wooden models of more or less fishlike shape through water. He found that they travelled in unstable (wobbling) fashion but that stability could be obtained by attaching fins in the positions where fish have them. These experiments with models towed by the snout have little relevance to free swimming fish.

Houssay's work was continued by his colleague Magnan, who eventually published an account of the whole program of research (Magnan, 1929–1930). He accumulated geometrical data about fish. He also tried to measure the drag on fish by filming weighted, dead fish sinking head first in a tank of water. A clever optical arrangement gave him an image of a calibrated grid and a pendulum on the same film, so he was able to draw graphs of distance sunk (x) against time (t). His argument (paraphrased) was that if the fish had mass M and weight in water W, the drag was

$$W - (M.d^2x/dt^2)$$

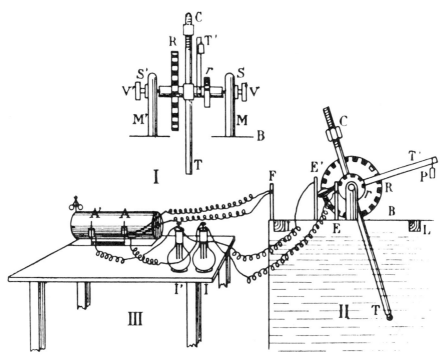

Figure 1-9
Apparatus for measuring the power output of swimming fish. (From Houssay, 1912).

He found in many cases that x was about proportional to t^2, implying that d^2x/dt^2 and therefore also drag were constant. It seems likely that most of the "drag" measured in this way was actually the inertia force on the added mass of water accelerating with the fish. The tank was too shallow for the fish to reach speeds at which the drag would have been a large fraction of the weight.

Magnan realized that it would not be meaningful to make direct comparisons of speed or power output between fish of different sizes. He tried to use considerations of physical similarity to establish a basis for comparison. Because he had observed fish sinking with about constant acceleration, sinking distances proportional to (time)^2, he argued that if one fish had λ times the length of another it should take $\lambda^{1/2}$ times as much time for any particular movement. This led to the prediction that similar fish of different sizes should swim at speeds proportional to (length)$^{1/2}$ or (mass)$^{1/6}$ and produce power proportional to (mass)$^{7/6}$. The initial assumption that fish of different sizes should move with equal acceleration may not be unrealistic (Webb, 1976), but it had no satisfactory basis in Magnan's data. Much later, Wu (1977) showed how the analysis should have been done.

Just before Magnan's paper appeared, Breder (1926) published the review of fish swimming, which gave us the useful terms *anguilliform*, *carangiform*, *ostraciiform*, and so on. He built a model boat with a wagging tail that demonstrated the ostraciiform propulsive mechanism.

The development of airplanes prepared the way for some kinds of study of fish locomotion. The Wright brothers had made their first flight in 1903, and in the same year the first wind tunnel was built (Prandtl and Tietjens, 1957). Thereafter, wind tunnel measurements of lift and drag and investigations of aerodynamic stability became common. Some aviation pioneers, including Lilienthal (1889) and Lanchester (1908), had studied birds as well as aircraft, and in due course a few of these engineers became interested in fish. Magnan's (1929–1930) investigation was sponsored by the French Air Ministry, and Magnan had previously worked on aircraft performance.

Shoulejkin (1929) (an engineer) made a model of the flying fish *Exocoetus*, put it in a wind tunnel, and measured lift and drag at various angles of attack. He calculated that an *Exocoetus* that took off at 16 m · s^{-1} could glide close above the sea surface at a gradually decreasing speed until it stalled and fell back into the water after travelling 68 m. He judged that this theoretical performance was realistic. Kempf and Neu (1932), also engineers, measured the drag of dead pike (*Esox*) in the testing tank of a nautical engineering laboratory at speeds up to 5 m · s^{-1}. They found that the drag was about three times the calculated friction drag, so the fish compared unfavorably with manmade streamlined bodies. Removing the mucus increased the drag slightly.

Richardson (1936) was yet another engineer, and he also investigated the drag on dead fish, apparently in ignorance of the work of Kempf and Neu. He wondered whether the mucus or the flexibility of the fish would reduce drag and suggested that if they did, there would be important implications for aircraft and ship design. He measured the rates at which weighted fish sank and found (in contrast to Magnan) that drag increases rapidly with increasing speed. He also carried out an experiment with a sheet of rubber vibrating in a wind tunnel, which illustrated the principle of undulatory propulsion. He tried to calculate the Froude efficiency of undulatory swimming by assuming that water is driven backwards at the speed of the traveling waves. This assumption was misguided because by the law of conservation of momentum a fish swimming at constant velocity imparts no net momentum to the water. Similar calculations are appropriate for screw-driven ships because the water in the wake of the ship that is dragged forward by the hull is largely distinct from the narrow jet of water driven backward by the screw.

While these engineers studied fish, James Gray began his influential work on animal locomotion (summarized in Gray, 1968). Trained as a zoologist, his earlier research was cytological. The first of his papers on locomotion presented and analyzed films of fish swimming, taken with the help of J.E. Harris, who had recently graduated (Gray, 1933a). In this paper, Gray wrote, "The principles of propulsion of a fish are much more readily derived from a study of the transverse movements of each section of the body than from a direct investigation of the propagated waves of contraction." This was a marked change from the attitude of Marey (1894) and Breder (1926) and a most important insight.

Gray superimposed outlines of successive frames of a film of an eel (*Anguilla*), as shown in Figure 1-10A. He showed that if waves were traveling posteriorly along the body, the left side of any segment that was traveling to the left and the right side of any segment that was traveling to the right, were always inclined posteriorly. These sides are indicated by thick lines on certain segments in Figure 1-10A. Gray went on to consider the forces on a segment, using Figure 1-10B. The segment AB travels laterally as the fish undulates, but the fish is traveling forwards, so the segment is moving about in direction OE. Let vector OE represent the velocity of the segment relative to the ground; this implies that the initial velocity of the water relative to the segment is represented by EO. This vector has two components, a normal one (EF) and a tangential one (FO). Water that strikes the fish and is deflected along its body loses its normal component of velocity and has its tangential component reduced by friction to a value represented by OH. If the mass of water deflected in unit time is m, the net force on the segment owing to the changed momentum of the water is the result of a normal component $-m \times EF$ and a tangential component $m \times (OH - FO)$. A fish that starts from rest and makes undulatory swimming movements will travel with increasing speed until the forward components of the normal forces on its body segments are equaled by the backward components of the tangential forces. This approach

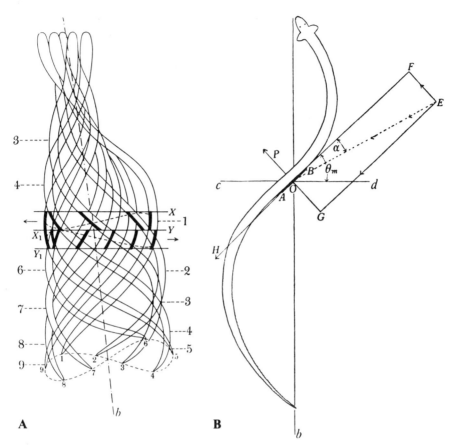

A   **B**

Figure 1-10

Illustrations from Gray (1930a). *A*, Outlines traced from a film of an eel (*Anguilla*) swimming. The eel was swimming forwards but the outlines have been superimposed with their heads side by side. The segments emphasized by thick lines on one side are discussed in the text. *B*, A diagram used in a discussion of forces on a segment of an eel.

was novel and pointed the way for further advances, but had a major shortcoming. In taking the important step of looking at a single small segment, Gray forgot that the water approaching the segment would have been influenced by more anterior segments.

The machine shown in Figure 1-11 was built for Gray's early research on swimming but has apparently never been illustrated or described in detail. It serves to impart any desired wave motion (within wide limits) to a model or dead fish. The rods impaling the fish are moved from side to side by cams when the handle is rotated. The cams can be adjusted to vary the phase differences between successive rods, and the amplitude of vibration of each rod can also be adjusted. The machine seems to have been used first by Professor G. Varley (then an undergraduate).

Gray (1933b) filmed the swimming movements of a whiting (*Merlangus*), intact and after amputation of the caudal fin. He describes how Varley used the machine to simulate swimming movements with a dead whiting immersed in a tank of water. The experiment was performed with the fish intact and after amputation of the caudal fin. It was estimated from the water movements in the tank that 40% of the thrust came from the caudal fin. The machine was used again by Gray (1936), with a rubber model instead of a real fish, to study the pattern of water movements produced by undulation. It was also used by Harris (1936) for an experiment with a heterocercal tail.

Harris had been working at Cambridge (England) but was awarded a fellowship to visit New York, to work with Breder at the New York Aquarium, and to perform a series of experiments at the Gugenheim School of Aeronautics. (Here was a very promising situation: an associate of Gray working in an engineering laboratory.) At the Gugenheim school, Harris fixed a cast of a small shark (*Mustelus*) in a wind tunnel with the wind speed adjusted to give a realistic Reynolds number and investigated its aerodynamic stability in pitch and yaw (Harris, 1936). The model had stiff, removable fins. With all of the fins in place, the model had neutral equilibrium in yaw when facing into the wind. Harris suggested that *Mustelus* may control its stability in yaw by using fin muscles to make individual fins stiff or limp. With the anterior dorsal fin limp and the posterior one stiff, it would be stable in yaw, but with the

Figure 1-11
Gray's machine for simulating undulatory swimming movements.

converse arrangement it would be unstable. Stability would be desirable when gliding along on a straight path, but instability could assist turning. In another of his papers on fish swimming, Harris (1938) made a very neat mathematical analysis of braking. He considered how the positions of the pectoral and pelvic fins affect the ability of a teleost to maintain a level course without pitching as it brakes. Harris was outstanding among the zoologists of his time for his excellent grasp of mechanics.

Even though so much sophisticated work was done in the 1930s on the mechanics of fish swimming, the same decade saw an extraordinary controversy that would have been resolved far more quickly if zoologists in general had had a reasonable appreciation of physical principles. Two French zoologists published a series of experiments in and after 1931, purporting to show that the swimbladder has no hydrostatic function. They do not seem to have realized that the presence of gas in the swimbladder inevitably reduces the density of a fish. They removed swimbladders surgically and found that swimming was not impaired, but it was later shown that by performing the operation in air, they had allowed the space that the swimbladder occupied to refill with air. They subjected fish to reduced pressure and repeated Boyle's (1670) error of supposing that the gas bubbles that formed on the fish came mainly from their tissues rather than from the water. Controversy about their experiments raged for 10 years and became so bitter that it had to be referred to an impartial jury. The controversy was reviewed in detail by Jones and Marshall (1953).

THEORETICAL DEVELOPMENTS SINCE 1950

This section and the next are about quite recent developments in fish mechanics. Many of the papers mentioned are discussed in detail in subsequent chapters, which present the current state of knowledge. These sections give a general impression, showing (in this section) how new theoretical ideas have developed and (in the next) how progress has depended on new techniques.

Before 1950, no attempt was made at quantitative hydrodynamic analysis of undulatory swimming. At about that time, Sir James Gray's work excited the interest of Sir Geoffrey Taylor, the distinguished mathematician, who was also working at Cambridge. Taylor began his work by analyzing the motion of microscopic organisms but went on (Taylor, 1952) to consider the swimming of larger animals such as snakes and worms. He made no direct use of Gray's data on eels, but his analysis was applicable to eels and was largely inspired by them. The films of other animals that he analyzed were supplied by Gray.

Taylor treated eel-like animals as chains of short segments, as Gray had done in his qualitative analysis (Fig. 1-10). He assumed that the force on each segment was the same as if that segment were part of a long, straight cylinder moving with the same velocity. He multiplied the force by the velocity of the segment to obtain the power required to move it and integrated over the length of the body to obtain the total power requirement for swimming. He considered the effects of waves of different shapes (different ratios of amplitude to wave length) and concluded that snakes swim very nearly in the optimum fashion, minimizing the power requirement at its particular speed.

In the same year, Gadd (1952) made a quite different analysis of the swimming of snakes and eels. He did not try to calculate the resistance offered by the water to a segment moving with a particular velocity. Instead, he calculated the reaction needed to change the transverse momentum of the water as the animal passed through it. He obtained the disconcerting result that an animal that tapers gently to a point at each end ought not be able to swim and tried to explain why snakes nevertheless can swim. He made no reference to the work of Gray or of any other biologists.

Taylor (1952) had mentioned correspondence with another distinguished mathematician, Sir James Lighthill. In due course and after discussion with Gray, Lighthill (1960) devised his own theory of eel-like swimming. It is a reactive theory like Gadd's, not a resistive one like Taylor's. He calculated the Froude efficiency of swimming, as Gadd had done, but took his theory much further and obtained conveniently simple equations. He does not seem to have been aware of Gadd's work.

Lighthill (1960) argued that for high efficiency, large-amplitude movements should be confined to the posterior part of the body and should include at least one complete wavelength. He later (Lighthill, 1970) modified these conclusions, showing that a deep caudal fin on a slender peduncle gives an advantage and necessitates a complete wave of large amplitude. This helps to explain why the carangiform mode of swimming is so widely used. Lighthill (1971) extended his theory to make it a better model of the large-amplitude movements of real fish and applied it to a film of a dace (*Leuciscus*) made by Bainbridge in Gray's department at Cambridge. (Bainbridge's equipment is described in the next section of this chapter.) Lighthill showed that the dace produced far more thrust than would be needed to drive a rigid body of the same size and shape at the same speed. This helped to explain the high metabolic rate cost of fish swimming, which had previously seemed to imply very low efficiency (Alexander, 1967a). Dr. Quentin Bone had suggested to Lighthill that undulatory swimming might keep the boundary layer thinner than on a rigid body and so increase the drag, and Lighthill made a rough calculation that confirmed that this was plausible.

Lighthill's papers provided the theoretical basis for much subsequent work. Webb (1971a) and Wardle and his colleagues (Wardle and Reid, 1977; Videler and Wardle, 1978) used Lighthill's theory to calculate the mechanical power consumption of swimming fish. Their experimental methods are described in the next section. Webb's (1971b) ingenious measurement of the efficiency of conversion of metabolic energy to mechanical work by swimming fish made it possible to reconcile power outputs calculated from Lighthill's theory with power consumption calculated from oxygen consumption. Weihs (1972, 1973a) applied Lighthill's theory to turning and to acceleration from rest, using film supplied by Gray. He also explored the consequences of the enhanced drag in undulatory swimming (Weihs, 1974); he argued that fish could save energy by using bursts of swimming alternately with periods of gliding with the body rigid.

Other work on the hydrodynamics of fish swimming has taken different directions. Alexander (1966) made rough estimates of differences in power requirements for swimming for fish with different buoyancy adaptations. McCutchen (1970) pointed out the structure of teleost caudal fins, with half-rays separated by a layer of "squidge," and considered how they should bend during swimming. Weihs (1973b) considered the trail of vortices behind swimming fish and showed that energy might be saved by swimming in schools. (Schooling fish do not seem, however, to space themselves appropriately to take advantage of this [Partridge and Pitcher, 1979]). Blake (1979 and subsequent papers) has analysed the power requirements for rowing with pectoral fins. Webb (1976) discussed the theory of pursuit of prey by predatory fish.

Hydrodynamics has been applied to other aspects of fish biology, as well as to swimming. Hughes (1966) used a modified form of Poiseuille's equation in a discussion of water flow through gills. Alexander (1967a) and others estimated the power requirements for pumping water and blood through gills, by multiplying the volume flow rate by the pressure drop in each case. Satchell (1971) adapted a simple electrical analogue of mammalian blood circulation for a discussion of the effect of elastic properties of the bulbus and ventral aorta on blood flow in teleosts. Jones, Langille, Randall, and Shelton (1974) used this model and a hydraulic one to interpret records of blood pressure and blood flow in cod (*Gadus*).

The hydrodynamics of fish feeding presents formidable difficulties. Alexander (1967b) made a very crude attempt to estimate the distances from which teleosts can suck food into their mouths. Osse (1969) used Bernoulli's theorem in a first attempt to calculate the pressures involved. These simple calculations have been superseded by Muller and Osse's (1978) remarkable theory of fish feeding, the first to take into account the unsteadiness of the flow by using the Navier–Stokes equations.

While these advances were being made in fish hydrodynamics, sensory physiologists had become aware of the theory of vibration of damped, linear systems. De Vries (1950) applied the theory to teleost otolith organs. He clamped fish heads to x-ray plates, which he exposed while vibrating or rotating them. The displacements of the otoliths relative to the skull enabled him to assess response times and degrees of damping. At about the same time,

Groen and his colleagues had been applying the theory to human semicircular canals, and in due course Groen, Lowenstein, and Vendrik (1952) applied it to the semicircular canals of *Raia*. Problems of damped vibration also arise in discussion of the swimbladder, of its roles in sound production and hearing (Alexander, 1966), and also of its response to echo sounding (Farquhar, 1971). This field is not discussed in detail here because fish acoustics is excluded from the scope of this book.

During the past 20 years, many other branches of mechanics have been applied to particular problems concerning fish. For instance, knowledge of rubberlike viscoelasticity has been applied to swimbladder walls (Alexander, 1961). The protrusible jaws of teleosts were analysed in terms of the kinematics of machines (Alexander, 1967c); solid coordinate geometry was used to model the contraction of muscle fibers in the myomeres of fish (Alexander, 1969a); and the skulls of teleosts were treated as assemblies of bars and plates joined by frictionless hinges in calculations of the stresses required in head muscles to generate pressures observed in feeding (Alexander, 1969b).

Knowledge of mechanics has been made more accessible to zoologists by publication of Alexander's *Animal Mechanics* (1968); Wainwright, Biggs, Currey, and Gosline's *Mechanical Design of Organisms* (1976); and Caro, Pedley, Schroter, and Seed's *The Mechanics of the Circulation* (1978). Zoologists, physical scientists, and mathematicians met to discuss animal mechanics at the conference reported by Wu, Brokaw, and Brennen (1975) and at several subsequent conferences. The prospects seem excellent for further progress in applying theoretical mechanics to the study of fish.

TECHNIQUES SINCE 1950

Pressure Transducers

Much of the physiological equipment invented during the midnineteenth century continued in use for a very long time; smoked-drum kymographs are still used. As late as 1961, one of the most respected textbooks of physiology (Bell, Davidson, and Scarborough, 1961) illustrated a recording mercury manometer like the one shown in Figure 1-2 and a pneumatically operated kymograph stylus like the Marey tambour. This textbook was published during a revolution in physiological methods and includes many records made with much more modern equipment.

The rapid development of electronics for military purposes during the second world war made possible the introduction of many new recording devices after the war. Among these, pressure transducers have been particularly useful in fish mechanics. Many physiological investigations require records of rapidly fluctuating pressures, but an adequate record is possible only if the natural frequency of the recording equipment is high compared to the frequency of the pressure fluctuations. Mercury manometers cannot be made with high natural frequencies: for instance, a manometer with a column of liquid 0.2 m long has a natural frequency of only 1.1 Hz. Other purely mechanical devices for recording pressures have to be made with high compliances to obtain adequate sensitivity, so their natural frequencies are also low. The problem was recognized by Frank (1903), who introduced a membrane manometer. The pressure being recorded caused slight distortion of a membrane, which had a tiny mirror mounted on it. Pressure fluctuations were indicated by movements of a beam of light reflected from the mirror. A version with a metal membrane, introduced in 1934, gave natural frequencies up to 200 Hz, but was very sensitive to vibrations because a long beam of light was necessary (Hamilton, Brewer, and Brotman, 1934). Roberts (1950) and Mott (1951) used membrane manometers for their measurements of respiratory pressures in lampreys (*Lampetra*) and blood pressures in eels (*Anguilla*).

Hansen (1949) designed a pressure transducer working on a different principle. The pressure distorted a metal membrane that served as one plate of an electrical condenser, and the resulting changes of capacity were detected by an appropriate circuit. This was not the first instrument of its kind, but it was very carefully designed and was capable of giving natural frequencies up to 100 Hz in physiological applications. Shortly afterward, another type of pressure transducer was introduced in which strain gauges sense distortion of a membrane.

Hughes and Shelton (1958) used a Hansen manometer for recording the pressure fluctuations associated with breathing in the mouths and opercular cavities of teleost fish. Satchell (1960) and Johansen (1960) used strain-gauge manometers for recording blood pressure in fish, and similar transducers have been in use ever since. In the early experiments, the fish were immobilized, but Johansen, Franklin, and von Citters (1966) recorded blood pressures from selachians swimming in a large aquarium. Transducers had been surgically implanted in the fish and were connected by fine wires to apparatus alongside the aquarium. Alexander (1969b) used a strain-gauge manometer to record the very rapid pressure changes that occurred in the mouth of a teleost fish during feeding. In his experiments, the fish took the food from the end of a tube connected to the transducer, but Liem (1978) recorded feeding pressures from free-swimming fish, using a long flexible cannula inserted through the ethmoid. By this time, miniature pressure transducers were available. Du Bois and Ogilvy (1978) measured the pressures on either side of the caudal fins of swimming fish by attaching miniature transducers directly to the fin.

Displacement transducers, which sense movements, have been less generally useful than have pressure transducers; one type is the RCA 5734, an electronic valve with its anode mounted in a flexible diaphragm. Hughes and Shelton (1958) used the RCA model in their study of fish breathing, in the same way as François–Franck (1906b) used the double tambour system.

Several other types of displacement transducer have also come into use since the second world war.

Several devices for measuring rates of flow in blood vessels were already in use during the late nineteenth century (see Halliburton, 1903), but they required insertion of objects into the vessels and would have been very difficult to use with fish small enough to be kept conveniently in laboratories. The data on cardiac outputs recorded in Brown's *The Physiology of Fishes* (1957) had all been obtained by crude methods such as comparison of the volumes of ventricles (of different individual fish) isolated by ligatures during systole and diastole. By this time, two flowmeters had been invented that did not require penetration of the blood vessel (see McDonald, 1960). The electromagnetic flowmeter had been used by physiologists since Kolin (1936) applied one to a dog's aorta, but it does not seem to have been applied to fish until Johansen (1962) put one on the aorta of a cod (*Gadus*). An ultrasonic flowmeter was used by Johansen, Franklin, and van Citters (1966) for their work on free-swimming sharks. Flowmeters have also been used by Holeton and Jones (1975) and others to measure water speeds in the mouths of fishes.

Strain gauges have already been referred to as components of pressure transducers. Since 1970, they have been glued to bones of various living animals and used to discover the strains experienced in various activities. Early uses were reviewed by Lauder and Lanyon (1980), who attached strain gauges to opercula of teleost fish in an investigation of the mechanics of feeding. Accelerometers have also had little use in fish mechanics but were used by Du Bois and Ogilvy (1978) to measure the accelerations of swimming bluefish (*Pomatomus*) at different stages of the tail beat cycle.

The experiments made possible by all of these kinds of transducer are typified by the one shown in Figure 1-12, which involved four strain-gauge manometers connected to different parts of the heart of a shark. A flexible beam with attached strain gauges was used as a displacement transducer, and an electromagnetic flowmeter was fitted round the ventral aorta. Electrical potentials detected by an electrode on the heart were amplified by an electrocardiograph (ECG) amplifier. The outputs of all these instruments were displayed and recorded by means of a cathode ray oscilloscope (CRO) and a pen recorder.

Electromyography has become an important technique for discovering the patterns of activity of muscles since Inman, Saunders, and Abbott's (1944) pioneering study of the human shoulder (Basmajian, 1962). It was used by Roberts (1950) to show that the respiratory muscles of lampreys are active only during expiration and that inspiration is driven by an elastic recoil. I am not aware of its application to fish again until Hughes and Shelton (1962) used it to elucidate the role of the geniohyoideus in teleost respiration. These and many subsequent observations were made on clamped fish, but Osse (1969) achieved the remarkable feat of implanting electrodes into eight muscles in the head of a perch (*Perca*) and then recording from them as the fish

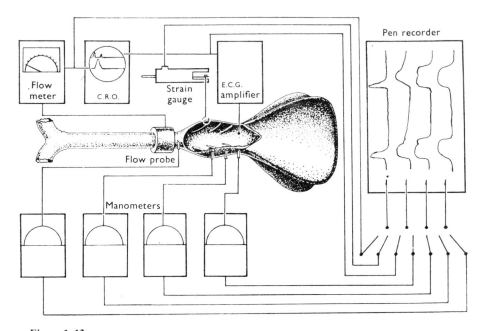

Figure 1-12
A diagram of an experiment on a shark, in which several kinds of transducer were connected to the heart. Four pressure transducers (labeled *manometers*), an electromagnetic flow meter (*flow probe*) and a displacement transducer (*strain gauge*) are in use, and an electrocardiograph record is being made. (From Satchell and Jones, 1967).

swam in an aquarium, trailing the leads. This enabled him to obtain electromyographs of feeding as well as breathing.

Marcy (1890) took his early cine films at 10 to 20 frames per second, but Breder and Edgerton (1942) were able to film *Hippocampus* at 300 frames per second. Since then, cine cameras capable of much higher framing rates have been developed; they have been used in investigations of the jumping and flight of insects but do not seem to have been found necessary for studying fish.

Mott (1950) used a simple form of x-ray cinematography in an investigation of blood flow in eels. He injected an x-ray opaque material into the blood and observed the times it took to travel through the circulation. He took only two x-ray films per second. Anker, Simons, and Dullemeijer (1967) built x-ray cine equipment that enabled them to film stickleback (*Gasterosteus*) breathing movements at 42 frames per second. They implanted particles of lead at selected points in the heads of their fish to make accurate measurements easier. Bishop and Foxon (1968) used similar framing rates in an investigation of lungfish (*Lepidosiren*) breathing movements. They were able to take advantage of the difference in x-ray contrast between air and the tissues of the fish, as well as between soft tissues and bone. Since then, much higher framing rates have become possible. Liem (1978) used a rate of 200 frames per second to study mastication in cichlid fishes.

Fish can be made to swim long distances in laboratories simply by making them swim in circles (*e.g.,* Regnard, 1893). An alternative technique is to train a fish to swim in a rotating annular tank, remaining stationary relative to the laboratory. Fry and Hart (1948) used this method to investigate the relationship between swimming speed and temperature. Bainbridge's fish wheels were also rotating annular tanks, but the fish were allowed to choose their own swimming speeds (Fig. 1-13; Bainbridge, 1958; Bainbridge and Brown, 1958). The aim was to keep the fish constantly in view of cine cameras so that their swimming movements could be studied. The cameras were trained at a point on the righthand side of the wheel (Fig. 1-13), which was filled with water, and a fish was put in. A powerful electric motor was used to rotate the wheel when the fish swam to keep the fish in view of the cameras. Vertical gates were arranged so that at least one was always in the water, forcing the water to move with the same angular velocity as the wheel. As a gate approached the cameras it was raised by a ramp in order not to block the path of the fish. The wheel shown in Figure 1-13 had two gates: one is shown open and one closed. The larger wheel, which had three gates, had a diameter of 2.3 m; the annulus of water was 15 cm wide and could be driven at speeds up to 6 m/sec. This remarkable machine has been dismantled, and nothing like it has been used since.

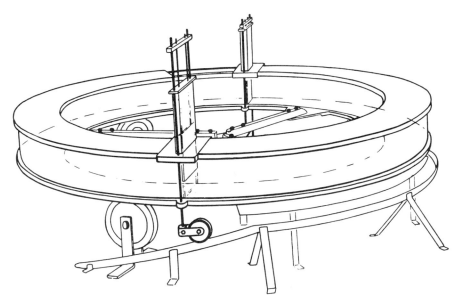

Figure 1-13
One of Bainbridge's fish wheels. (From Bainbridge, 1958).

The water tunnel is another device for keeping fish swimming in the laboratory. Blazka, Volf, and Cepela (1960) used a simple water tunnel, and Brett (1964) built the more elaborate one shown in Figure 1-14. The pump drives water counterclockwise around the circuit. The fish is confined to an 11-cm diameter chamber by two wire screens. The one behind the fish is electrified, so the fish learns to keep swimming to avoid a mild electric shock. It has to swim at the speed of the water, which can be adjusted up to 1.1 m/sec. The Blazka-and-Brett water tunnels were used initially for measurements of oxygen consumption. Samples of water were periodically removed and analyzed for dissolved oxygen. Farmer and Beamish (1969) incorporated an oxygen electrode in their water tunnel, so that oxygen consumption could be recorded continuously. Webb (1971a) filmed trout (*Salmo*) in a copy of Brett's water tunnel to obtain the data needed to calculate mechanical power outputs from Lighthill's (1960) theory of swimming.

DuBois, Cavagna, and Fox (1974) used a very simple system to keep swimming fish stationary for short periods. They pumped water into a raised tank and then let it flow out rapidly through a pipe containing the fish. The diameter of the pipe was 30 cm so it could accommodate fish much larger than could the fish wheels and water tunnels built so far. This system was used initially for an investigation of the distribution of pressure on the external surfaces of swimming fish and exploited an important advantage that this type of equipment shares with water tunnels: a fish swimming fast can be connected by quite short wires or cannulae to stationary apparatus. In another recent

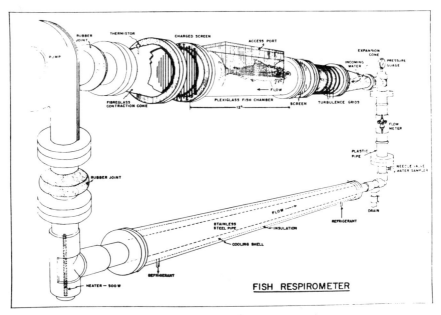

Figure 1-14
Brett's water tunnel. (From Brett, 1964).

investigation of fish swimming, Wardle and Reid (1977) made no effort to keep the fish stationary but filmed them as they swam along an 8-m track toward a flashing light that signaled the presence of food.

Flow visualization is sometimes useful in research on fish hydrodynamics. François–Franck (1906a) used India ink to demonstrate the respiratory water currents, in at the mouth and out through the opercular openings. Rosen (1959) demonstrated vortices in the wake of a teleost by making it swim along a narrow tank of water with a thin layer of milk on the bottom. McCutchen (1977) used shadowgraphs of temperature-stratified water to visualize water movements in the wake of swimming fish and used the results for an ingenious calculation of Froude efficiency. Osse and Muller (1980) obtained films of lionfish feeding, with the water flow into the mouth shown by the movements of tiny (0.5 mm) polystyrene spheres, which were silver plated and had the same density as the water.

In many recent experiments (some of them described in this section) swimming fish have been connected to physiological recording equipment by flexible wires and cannulae. In field studies such direct connections are generally not possible, and telemetric methods must be used. The development of telemetric methods for fish studies was reviewed by Stasko and Pincock (1977). In an early experiment (described in 1956) ultrasonic transmitters were attached to salmon (*Oncorhynchus*) so that they could be followed as they migrated up river. Since then, both ultrasonic and radio transmitters have been used. They have often been used merely to signal the position of the fish but have also been used to transmit information from electrodes or transducers attached to the fish. Ambient pressure (indicating depth of swimming), tail-beat frequency (indicating swimming speed), and electrical potentials from the heart and respiratory muscles have all been transmitted.

Most of the methods described in this section are not peculiar to fish mechanics but have been applied to many kinds of animals. Even the fish wheels and water tunnels have analogues in the treadmills and wind tunnels used in research on running and flight. The new methods that have been developed since the second world war have had a profound effect on all branches of physiology. Many of the opportunities they present have already been taken, but much remains to be done, and improved transducers that will make many more experiments possible continue to be developed.

REFERENCES

A.I. 1675. A conjecture concerning the bladders of air that are found in fishes. *Phil. Trans. R. Soc.* 10:310–311.

Accademia del Cimento. 1666. *Saggi di naturali esperienze.* Florence: Cocchini (English trans: R. Waller 1684. *Essays of Natural Experiments Made in the Accademia del Cimento.* London: Alsop.)

Alexander R. McN. 1961. Visco-elastic properties of the tunica externa of the swimbladder in Cyprinidae. *J. Exp. Biol.* 38:747–757.

Alexander, R. McN. 1966. Physical aspects of swimbladder function. *Biol. Rev.* 41:141–176.

Alexander, R. McN. 1967a. *Functional Design in Fishes.* London: Hutchinson.

Alexander, R. McN. 1967b. The functions and mechanisms of the protrusible upper jaws of some acanthopterygian fish. *J. Zool. (London)* 151:43–46.

Alexander, R. McN. 1967c. Mechanisms of the jaws of some atheriniform fish. *J. Zool. (London)* 151:233–255.

Alexander, R. McN. 1968. *Animal Mechanics.* London: Sidgwick & Jackson.

Alexander, R. McN. 1969a. The orientation of muscle fibres in the myomeres of fish. *J. Marine Biol. Assoc. U.K.* 49:263–290.

Alexander, R. McN. 1969b. Mechanics of the feeding action of a cyprinid fish. *J. Zool. (London)* 159:1–15.

Anker, G.C., Simons, J., and Dullemeijer, P. 1967. An apparatus for direct x-ray cinematography exemplified by analysis of some respiratory movements in *Gasterosteus aculeatus. Experientia* 23:74.

Aristotle. fourth century B.C. a. *History of Animals.* (English trans: D'A.W. Thompson. 1910. *Historia animalium.* Oxford: Clarendon.)

Aristotle. fourth century B.C. b. *Movement of Animals.* (English trans: E.S. Forster. 1937. London: Heinemann.)

Aristotle. fourth century B.C. c. *Progression of Animals.* (English trans: E.S. Forster. 1937. London: Heinemann.)

Bainbridge, R. 1958. The speed of swimming of fish as related to size and to the frequency and amplitude of the tail beat. *J. Exp. Biol.* 35:109–133.

Bainbridge, R., and Brown, R.H.J. 1958. An apparatus for the study of the locomotion of fish. *J. Exp. Biol.* 35:134–137.

Basmajian, J.V. 1962. *Muscles Alive. Their Functions Revealed by Electromyography.* London: Baillière, Tyndall & Cox.

Bell, G.H., Davidson, J.N., and Scarborough, H. 1961. *Textbook of Physiology and Biochemistry*, 5th ed. Edinburgh: Livingstone.

Bert, P. 1870. *Lecons sur la physiologie comparée de la respiration, professées au Museum d'Histoire Naturelle.* Paris: Baillière.

Bishop, I.R., and Foxon, G.E.H. 1968. The mechanism of breathing in the South American lungfish, *Lepidosiren paradox;* A radiological study. *J. Zool. (London)* 154:263–271.

Blake, R.W. 1979. The mechanics of labriform locomotion. I. Labriform locomotion in the angelfish (*Pterophyllum eimekei*): An analysis of the power stroke. *J. Exp. Biol.* 82:255–271.

Blazka, P., Volf, M., and Cepela, M. 1960. A new type of respirometer for the determination of the metabolism of fish in an active state. *Physiol. Bohem.* 9:553–560.

Borelli, I.A. 1680. *De motu animalium pars I.* Rome: Bernabo.

Boyle, R. 1670. New pneumatical experiments about respiration. *Phil. Trans. R. Soc.* 5:2011–2056.

Breder, C.M. 1926. The locomotion of fishes. *Zoologia (New York)* 4:159–297.

Breder, C.M. and Edgerton, H.E. 1942. An analysis of the locomotion of the searhorse, *Hippocampus,* by means of high speed cinematography. *Ann. N.Y. Acad. Sci.* 43:145–72.

Brett, J.R. 1964. The respiratory metabolism and swimming performance of young sockeye salmon. *J. Fish Res. Board Canada* 21:1183–1226.

Brown, M.E. (ed.). 1957. *The Physiology of Fishes.* Academic Press, London.

Caro, C.G., Pedley, T.J., Schroter, R.C., and Seed, W.A. 1978. *The Mechanics of the Circulation.* Oxford: Oxford University Press.

Cayley, G. 1810. On aerial navigation, part III. *Nicholson's J. Nat. Phil. Chem. Arts. NS* 25:161–169.

Chauveau, A., and Marey, E.J. 1861. Détermination graphique des rapports du choc du coeur avec les mouvements des oreillettes et des ventricules: expérience faite à l'aide d'un appareil enregisteur (sphygmographe). *C.R. Acad. Sci.* 53:622–625.

Cuvier, G. 1809. Rapport fait a la classe des sciences physiques et mathematiques, sur le Memoire de M. Delaroche, relatif a la vessie aerienne des poissons. *Ann. Mus. Hist. Nat.* 14:165–183.

Delaroche, F. 1809. Observations sur la vessie aerienne des poissons. *Ann. Mus. Hist. Nat.* 14:184–217; 245–289.

de Vries, H. 1950. The mechanics of the labyrinth otoliths. *Acta Otolaryngol.* 38:262–273.

DuBois, A.B., Cavagna, G.A., and Fox, R.S. 1974. Pressure distribution on the body surface of swimming fish. *J. Exp. Biol.* 60:581–591.

DuBois, A.B., and Ogilvy, C.S. 1978. Forces on the tail surface of swimming fish: thrust, drag and acceleration in bluefish (*Pomatomus saltatrix*) *J. Exp. Biol.* 77:225–241.

Dugas, R. 1957. *A History of Mechanics.* (English trans: J.R. Maddox. London: Routledge & Kegan Paul.)

du Verney, M. 1701. Mémoire sur la circulation du sang des poissons qui ont desouïes, et sur leur respiration. *Mém. Acad. Sci. (Paris)* 224–239.

Farmer, G.J., and Beamish, F.W.H. 1969. Oxygen consumption of *Tilapia nilotica* in relation to swimming speed and salinity. *J. Fish Res. Board Canada* 26:2807–2821.

Farquhar, G.B. (ed.). 1971. *Proceedings of an International Symposium on Biological Sound Scattering in the Ocean.* Washington, D.C.: Maury Center for Ocean Science, Department of the Navy.

Fischer, G. 1795. *Versuch uber die Schwimmblase der Fische.* Leipzig: Rabenhorst.

Forbes, R.J., and Dijksterhuis, E.J. 1963. *A History of Science and Technology.* Harmondsworth: Penguin Books.

François-Franck, C.A. 1906a. Analyse graphique des mouvements respiratoires des poissons téléostéens. *C.R. Hebd. Séances Mém. Soc. Biol.* 60:799–801; 801–802.

François-Franck, C.A. 1906b. Mecanique respiratoire des poissons téléostéens. I & II. *C.R. Hebd. Séances Mém. Soc. Biol.* 60:962–964; 965–967.

Frank, O. 1903. Kritik der elastischen Manometer. *Zeitschr. Biol.* 44:445.

Fry, F.E.J., and Hart, J.S. 1948. Cruising speed of goldfish in relation to water temperature. *J. Fish. Res. Board Canada* 7:169–175.

Gadd, G.E. 1952. Some hydrodynamical aspects of the swimming of snakes and eels. *Phil. Mag.* 43:663–670.

Gibbs–Smith, C.H. 1962. *Sir George Cayley's Aeronautics, 1796–1855.* London: Her Majesty's Stationery Office.

Gray, J. 1933a. Studies in animal locomotion. I. The movement of fish with special reference to the eel. *J. Exp. Biol.* 10:88–104.

Gray, J. 1933b. Studies in animal locomotion. III. The propulsive mechanism of the whiting (*Gadus merlangus*). *J. Exp. Biol.* 10:391–400.

Gray, J. 1936. Studies in animal locomotion. VI. The propulsive powers of the dolphin. *J. Exp. Biol.* 13:170–199.

Gray, J. 1968. *Animal Locomotion.* Weidenfeld & Nicolson, London.

Greene, C.W. 1904. Physiological studies of the Chinook salmon. *Bull. Bureau Fisheries, Washington* 24:431–456.

Hales, S. 1733. *Statistical Essays vol. II Containing Haemastaticks.* London: Innys.

Halliburton, W.D. 1903. *Handbook of Physiology,* 5th ed. London: Murray.

Hamilton, W.F., Brewer, G., and Brotman, I. 1934. Pressure pulse contours in the intact animal. I. Analytical description of a new high-frequency hypodermic manometer with illustrative curves of simultaneous arterial and intracardiac pressure. *Am. J. Physiol.* 107:427–435.

Hansen, A.T., 1949. Pressure measurement in the human organism. *Acta. Physiol. Scand.* 19:Suppl. 68.

Harris, J.E. 1936. The role of the fins in the equilibrium of the swimming fish. I. Wind-tunnel tests on a model of *Mustelus canis* (Mitchill). *J. Exp. Biol.* 13:476–493.

Harris, J.E. 1938. The role of the fins in the equilibrium of the swimming fish. II. The role of the pelvic fins. *J. Exp. Biol.* 15:32–47.

Harting, P. 1872. Le physomètre, nouvel instrument pour la détermination des volumes variables d'air ou d'autres corps, surtont de la vessie natatoire des poissons. *Arch. Neerl. Sci. Exactes Nat.* 7:289–327.

Harvey, W. (Harveius, G.). 1628. *Exercitatio anatomica de motu cordis et sanguinis in animalibus.* Frankfurt-am-Maine: Fitzer. (English trans: 1894. *An Anatomical Dissertation upon the Movement of the Heart and Blood in Animals.* Privately printed for G. Moreton, Canterbury.)

Holeton, G.F., and Jones, D.R. 1975. Water flow dynamics in the respiratory tract of the carp (*Cyprinus carpio* L.). *J. Exp. Biol.* 63:537–548.

Houssay, F. 1912. *Forme, puissance et stabilité des poissons.* Paris: Hermann.

Hughes, G.M. 1966. The dimensions of fish gills in relation to their function. *J. Exp. Biol.* 45:177–195.

Hughes, G.M., and Shelton, G. 1958. The mechanism of gill ventilation in three freshwater teleosts. *J. Exp. Biol.* 35:807–823.

Hughes, G.M., and Shelton, G. 1962. Respiratory mechanisms and their nervous control in fish. *Adv. Comp. Physiol. Biochem.* 1:275–364.

Inman, V.T., Saunders, J.B. de C.M., and Abbott, L.C. 1944. Observations on the function of the shoulder joint. *J. Bone Joint Surg.* 26:1–30.

Johansen, K. 1960. Circulation in the hagfish *Myxine glutinosa* L. *Biol. Bull.* 118:289–295.

Johansen, K. 1962. Cardiac output and pulsatile aortic flow in the teleost, *Gadus morhua. Comp. Biochem. Physiol.* 7:169–174.

Johansen, K., Franklin, D.L., and van Citters, R.L. 1966. Aortic blood flow in freeswimming elasmobranchs. *Comp. Biochem. Physiol.* 19:151–160.

Jolyet, F. 1872. De la pression du sang, dans l'artère branchiale chez les poissons. *C.R. Soc. Biol.* 4:254–255.

Jones, D.R., Langille, B.L., Randall, D.J., and Shelton, G. 1974. Blood flow in dorsal and ventral aortas of the cod, *Gadus morhua. Am. J. Physiol.* 266:90–95.

Jones, F.R.H., and Marshall, N.B. 1953. The structure and functions of the teleostean swimbladder. *Biol. Rev.* 28:16–83.

Kempf, G., and Neu, W. 1932. Schleppversuche mit Hechten zur Messung des Wasserwiderstandes. *Zeitschr. vergl. Physiol.* 17:353–364.

Kolin, A. 1936. An electromagnetic flowmeter. Principle of the method and its application to blood flow measurements. *Proc. Soc. Exp. Biol. Med.* 35:53–56.

Lanchester, F.W. 1908. *Aerodonetics.* Constable, London.

Lauder, G.V., and Lanyon, L.E. 1980. Functional anatomy of feeding in the bluegill sunfish, *Lepomis macrochirus: In vivo* measurement of bone strain. *J. Exp. Biol.* 84:33–55.

Liem, K.F. 1978. Modulatory multiplicity in the functional repertoire of the feeding mechanism in cichlid fishes. I. Piscivores. *J. Morphol* 158:323–360.

Lighthill, M.J. 1960. Note on the swimming of slender fish. *J. Fluid Mech.* 9:305–317.

Lighthill, M.J. 1970. Aquatic animal propulsion of high hydromechanical efficiency. *J. Fluid Mech.* 44:265–301.

Lighthill, M.J. 1971. Large amplitude elongated-body theory of fish locomotion. *Proc. R. Soc.* B179:125–138.

Lilienthal, O. 1889. *Der Vogelflug als Grundlage der Fliegekunst,* Berlin. (English trans: A.W. Isenthal. 1911. *Bird Flight as the Basis of Aviation.* London: Longman.)

Ludwig, C. 1847. Beitrage zur Kenntnis des Einflusses der Respirationsbewegungen auf den Blutlauf im Aortensysteme. *Arch. Anat. Physiol.* 1847:242–302.

Magnan, A. 1929–30. Les caractéristiques géométriques et physiques des poissons avec contribution à l'étude de leur équilibre statique et dynamique. *Ann. Sci. Nat. Zool.* ser. 10, 12:5–133; 13:355–489.

Marey, E.J. 1873. *La machine animale: Locomotion terrestre et aerienne.* Paris: Coulommiers. (English trans: 1874. *Animal Mechanism.* London: King.)

Marey, E.J. 1890. La locomotion aquatique étudiée par la chronophotographie. *C.R. Acad. Sci.* 111:213–216.

Marey, E.J. 1894. *Le mouvement.* Masson, Paris. (English trans: E. Pritchard. *Movement.* London: Heinemann.

McCutchen, C.W. 1970. The trout tail fin: A self-cambering hydrofoil. *J. Biomechanics* 3:271–281.

McCutchen, C.W. 1977. Froude propulsive efficiency of a small fish, measured by wake visualisation. In *Scale Effects in Animal Locomotion,* edited by T.J. Pedley, 339–363. London: Academic Press.

McDonald, D.A. 1960. *Blood Flow in Arteries.* London: Arnold.

Moreau, A. 1876 Recherches expérimentales sur les fonctions de la vessie natatoire. *Ann. Sci. Nat. Zool.* ser. 6, 4:1–85.

Mott, J.C. 1950. Radiological observations on the cardiovascular system in *Anguilla anguilla. J. Exp. Biol.* 27:324–333.

Mott, J.C. 1951. Some factors affecting the blood circulation in the common eel (*Anguilla anguilla*). *J. Physiol. (London)* 114:387–398.

Muller, J. 1834–40. *Handbuch der Physiologie des Menschen.* (English trans: W. Baly. 1839–42. *Elements of Physiology.* London: Taylor & Walton.

Muller, M., Osse, J.W.M. 1978. Structural adaptations to suction feeding in fish. In *Proceedings of the Zodiac Symposium on Adaptation,* edited by R.D. Politiek, 57–60, Wageningen: Centre for Agricultural Publishing and Documentation.

Muybridge, E. 1887. *Animal Locomotion. An Electro-photographic Investigation of Consecutive Phases of Animal Movements.* Philadelphia: Lippincott. (Reprinted 1979 by Dover Publications, New York.)

Nordenskiöld, E. 1928. *The History of Biology.* New York: Tudor Publishing.

Osse, J.W.M. 1969. Functional morphology of the head of the perch (*Perca fluviatilis* L.): An electromyographic study. *Neth. J. Zool.* 19:289–392.

Osse, J.W.M., and Muller, M. 1980. A model of suction feeding in teleost fishes with some implications for ventilation. In *Environmental Physiology of Fishes,* edited by M.A. Ali, 335–352. New York: Plenum.

Partridge, B.L., and Pitcher, T.J. 1979. Evidence against a hydrodynamic function for fish schools. *Nature (London)* 279:418–419.

Pettigrew, J.B. 1874. *Animal Locomotion or Walking, Swimming and Flying, with a Dissertation on Aeronautics,* 2nd ed. London: King.

Pliny. first century A.D. *Naturalis Historia.* (English trans: H. Rackham, W.H.S. Jones, and D.E. Eichhol. 1938–1963. *Natural History.* London: Heinemann.)

Prandtl, L., and Tietjens, O.G. 1957. *Applied Hydro- and Aeromechanics.* (English trans: J.P. Den Hartog. New York: Dover Publications.)

Ray, J. 1675. A letter written to the publisher by the learned Mr. Ray containing some considerations on the conjecture in numb. 114 of these tracts, about the swimming bladders in fishes. *Phil. Trans. R. Soc.* 10:349.

Redi, F. 1684. *Osservationi intorno agli animali viventi, che se trovano negli animali viventi.* Florence: Martini.

Regnard, P. 1893. Sur un disposatif qui permet de mesurer la vitesse de translation d'un poisson se mouvant dans l'eau. *C.R. Soc. Biol.* 45:81–83.

Richardson, E.G. 1936. The physical aspects of fish locomotion. *J. Exp. Biol.* 13:63–74.

Roberts, T.D.M. 1950. The respiratory movements of the lamprey (*Lampetra fluviatilis*). *Proc. R. Soc. Edinburgh* B64:235-252.

Rondelet, G. 1554. *Liber de piscibus marinis, in quibus verae piscium effigies expressae sunt.* Lyons: Bonhomme.

Rosen, M. W. 1959. Water flow about a swimming fish. U.S. Naval Ordnance Test Station. Technical Publication 2298.

Satchell, G.H. 1960. The reflex co-ordination of the heart beat with respiration in the dogfish. *J. Exp. Biol.* 37:719–731.

Satchell, G.H. 1971. *Circulation in Fishes.* Cambridge: Cambridge University Press.

Satchell, G.H., and Jones, M.P. 1967. The function of the conus arteriosus in the Port Jackson shark, *Heterodontus portusjacksoni. J. Exp. Biol.* 46:373–382.

Schoenlein, C., and Willem, V. 1895. Observations sur la circulation du sang chez quelques poissons. *Bull. Sci. Fr. Belg.* 26:442–468.

Science Museum, South Kensington 1876. *Catalogue of the special loan collection of scientific apparatus at the South Kensington Museum,* 2nd ed. London: Eyre & Spottiswoode.

Shoulejkin, W. 1929. Airdynamics of the flying fish. *Internat. Rev. Ges. Hydrobiol. Hydrogeogr.* 22:102–110.

Stasko, A.B., and Pincock, D.G. 1977. Review of underwater biotelemetry, with emphasis on ultrasonic techniques. *J. Fish. Res. Board Canada* 34:1261–1285.

Steno, N. 1667. *Elementorum myologiae specimen, seu musculi descriptio geometrica* Florence. (Reprinted in V. Maar. 1910. *Nicolai Stenonis opera philosophica.* Copenhagen: Tryde.)

Taylor, G.I. 1952. Analysis of the swimming of long and narrow animals. *Proc. R. Soc.* A214:158–183.

Videler, J.J., and Wardle, C.S. 1978. New kinematic data from high speed cine film recordings of swimming cod (*Gadus morhua*). *Neth. J. Zool.* 28:465–484.

Wardle, C.S., and Reid, A. 1977. The application of large amplitude elongated body theory to measure swimming power in fish. In *Fisheries Mathematics,* edited by J.H. Steele, 171–191. London: Academic Press.

Webb, P.W. 1971a. The swimming energetics of trout. I. Thrust and power output at cruising speeds. *J. Exp. Biol.* 55:489–520.

Webb, P.W. 1971b. The swimming energetics of trout II. Oxygen consumption and swimming efficiency. *J. Exp. Biol.* 55:521–540.

Webb, P.W. 1976. The effect of size on the fast-start performance of rainbow trout *Salmo gairdneri,* and a consideration of piscivorous predator-prey interactions. *J. Exp. Biol.* 65:157–177.

Weber, E.H. 1820. *De aure et auditu hominis et animalium. Pars. I. De aure animalium aquatilium.* Leipzig: Fleischer.

Weihs, D. 1972. A hydrodynamical analysis of fish turning manoeuvres. *Proc. R. Soc. (London)* B182:59–72.

Weihs, D. 1973a. The mechanisms of rapid starting of slender fish. *Biorheology* 10:343–350.

Weihs, D. 1973b. Hydromechanics of fish schooling. *Nature (London)* 241:290–291.

Weihs, D. 1974. Energetic advantages of burst swimming of fish. *J. Theor. Biol.* 48: 215–229.

Wainwright, S.A., Biggs, W.D., Currey, J.D., and Gosline, J.M. 1976. *Mechanical Design in Organisms.* London: Arnold.

Wu, T.Y. 1977. Introduction to the scaling of aquatic animal locomotion. In *Scale Effects in Animal Locomotion,* edited by T.J. Pedley, 203–232. London: Academic Press.

Wu, T.Y.-T., Brokaw, C.J., and Brennen, C. 1975. *Swimming and Flying in Nature.* New York: Plenum.

Young, T. 1809. On the functions of the heart and arteries. *Phil. Trans. R. Soc.* 1809:1–31.

Chapter 2
DYNAMIC PROPERTIES OF FISH MUSCLE
Ian A. Johnston

CONTENTS

ORGANIZATION OF MUSCLE FIBERS

Locomotion in fish is achieved using a combination of the paired and unpaired fins and segmentally arranged myotomal muscles. Red muscle fibers constitute a major proportion of the fin muscles and a relatively minor component of the trunk muscles. The proportion of red fibers in the myotomes of different species is correlated positively with sustained swimming performance and negatively with the involvement of pectoral fins during swimming at low and intermediate speeds (Greer–Walker and Pull, 1975). For example, red fibers constitute around 29.8% of the trunk muscle of *Scomber colias* (active pelagic swimmer), 7.2% in the angler fish *Lophius piscatorius* (sedentary bottom dweller), and 5.5% in *Notothenia rossii,* which primarily uses enlarged pectoral fins for sustained swimming (Greer–Walker and Pull, 1975; Walesby and Johnston, 1980).

36

Few studies have examined the organization of muscle fibers in the fins. In some species with enlarged pectoral fins (*e.g.,* nototheniids and *chimera*), individual fibers often run in a parallel fashion within the muscles, while in other fish the fin muscles are pinnate (Kryvi and Totland, 1978; Walesby and Johnston, 1980). Different fiber types are often mixed together, as in the limb muscles of terrestrial animals rather than anatomically separated, as in the myotomal muscles (Fig. 2-1; Kryvi and Totland, 1978; Walesby and Johnston, 1980; Akster, 1981).

In the case of myotomal muscles, individual fibers insert by way of small tendons into connective tissue sheets called *myosepta,* which delimit each myomere. The shape of the myomeres is complex and varies somewhat between different fish orders and during ontogeny. In general, the myomeres resemble a series of W-shaped overlapping cones (see Bone, 1978). The functional significance of this complex geometry is that it is thought to allow each muscle fiber to insert at a similar angle with the myosepta. The organization of fibers within the myomeres is also very complex. On the basis of a histologic analysis and mathematical modeling, Alexander (1969) has described two basic patterns, one in selachians and primitive bony fishes such as *Anguilla* and *Salmo* and the other in the more advanced teleost orders (see Chapter 3).

Superficial fibers run more or less parallel to the longitudinal axis of the body; however, in both primitive and advanced teleosts, deeper white fibers

Figure 2-1
Diagrammatic representation of the distribution of muscle fiber types in (*A*) dogfish (*Scyliorhinus canicula*) and (*B*) crucian carp (*Carassius carassius*). Upper drawings show a steak through the trunk taken at the point of maximum body flexure. Red muscle is indicated by the shaded area. The horizontal lines illustrated in the lower drawings indicate the segment of muscle oriented with the skin at the top. S, superficial; OR, outer red; IR, inner red; OW, outer white; IW, inner white; R, red; P, pink; and W, white muscle fibers. (Based on the observations of Bone and Chubb, 1978, and Johnston *et al.,* 1974)

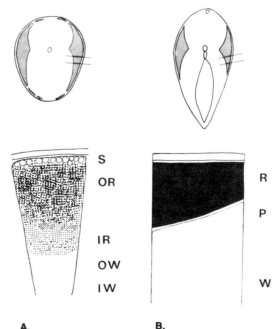

(Fig. 2-2) are arranged in complex three-dimensional patterns with some fibers making angles of 30 degrees or more with the longitudinal plane of the fish. In the more advanced teleost fish, the trajectories made by fibers in adjacent myotomes form segments of a helix. Alexander (1969) reached several important conclusions about the function of this arrangement: first, both patterns result in all white fibers contracting to a similar extent for a given body flexure; second, bending of the body is achieved with very little sarcomere shortening. For example, he calculated that the longitudinally arranged red fibers would have to shorten by about 10% of their resting lengths during swimming compared to 7% to 9% for white fibers organized on the selchian pattern and only 2% to 3% for the helically arranged white fibers of acanthopterygians (Alexander, 1969). Indirect evidence for the isometric nature of contraction of myotomal muscle is provided by endurance exercise

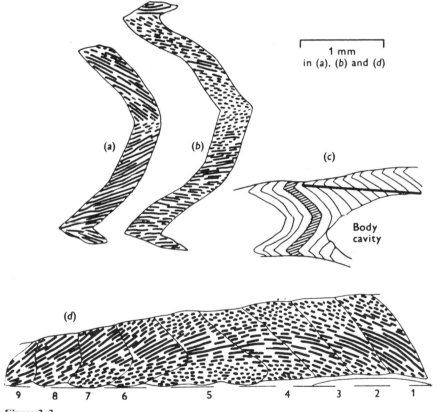

Figure 2-2
Diagrammatic representation of the shape of myomeres and organization of muscle fibers in *Xiphophorus maculatus* (teleostei). (a and b) Longitudinal vertical sections of myomere (hatched in c). Approximately horizontal section of myomeres cut in the plane indicated by the thick line at right angles to the median plane. (Reproduced by kind permission of Alexander, 1969)

training experiments. In saithe (*Pollachius virens*) and brook trout (*Salvelinus fontinalis*), enforced swimming for several weeks in a flume or respirometer produces hypertrophy of both red and white muscle fibers with very little change in their aerobic capacity (Greer–Walker and Pull, 1975; Johnston and Moon, 1980a and b). This type of response is characteristic of training regimes for athletes that are designed to contain a high component of isometric exercise (*e.g.*, weight lifting; Holloszy and Booth, 1976; Goldspink *et al.*, 1976).

Alexander (1969) also suggested that the helical teleost arrangement would result in a faster body flexion for the same rate of contraction of muscle fibers than would the selachian pattern, but at the expense of a weaker bending moment. This correlates with the somewhat higher swimming speeds of teleosts than of sharks. It is interesting to note that the selachian pattern is probably retained in the caudal penduncle of teleosts where the stronger bending moments are more able to transmit the forces to the caudal fin.

FIBER TYPES

Classifications of fiber types based on color followed the original description of red and white muscles in the elasmobranch *Torpedo* by Lorenzini in 1678. During the last 20 to 30 years, such terminologies have been largely discarded as unsatisfactory by workers on amphibian, avian, and mammalian muscle. For example, Revel (1962) found that some apparently red fibers in the bat cricothyroid muscle were able to contract more quickly than could some white fibers. In these animals, terms such as *red* and *white* have been replaced by classifications based on innervation, contraction speed, and metabolic characteristics. For example in mammals, muscle fibers are usually divided into two broad categories, twitch and tonic, according to their type of innervation and response to electrical stimulation. Twitch fibers are then further subdivided into three broad groups: slow oxidative (SO), fast oxidative glycolytic (FOG), and fast glycolytic (FG). Among the vertebrates, classifications based on muscle color have only been retained by workers on fish muscle. This is largely because physiological information on muscle contraction speed has been lacking until the last year or so and partly because innervation is not a suitable character for classification in this group of animals. For example, both red and white muscles are multiply innervated in the majority of teleosts (Barets, 1961; Bone, 1964). The relationship between classifications of fish muscle based on color and their physiological and metabolic characteristics together with a suggested terminology is given in Table 2-1.

Figure 2-1 shows the distribution of fiber types in the segmental muscles of dogfish (*Scyliorhinus canicula*) and carp (*Carassius carassius*) based on histochemical criteria. The usual procedure is to stain serial frozen sections for an aerobic enzyme (*e.g.*, succinic dehydrogenase or nitroblue tetrazolium reductase), a glycolytic enzyme (*e.g.*, phosphorylase), and myofibrillar adeno-

Table 2.1

RELATIONSHIP BETWEEN CLASSIFICATIONS OF FISH MUSCLE FIBER TYPES BASED ON COLOR AND PHYSIOLOGICAL CHARACTERS

COLOR CLASSIFICATION	PHYSIOLOGICAL CHARACTERS
Dogfish (Scyliorhinus canicula L.)[a]	
Superficial (S)	Unknown
Outer red (OR)	Slow, highly aerobic non-action potential generating
Inner red (IR)	fibers. OR fibres distinguished histochemically by their higher staining for succinic dehydrogenase activity and less alkaline-stable myofibrillar ATPase
Outer white (OW)	Fast twitch, intermediate aerobic and highly developed glycolytic capacity.
Inner white (IW)	Fast twitch glycolytic, low aerobic capacity.
Common carp (Cyprinus carpio L.)[b]	
Red (R)	Slow, highly aerobic, non-action potential generating fibers.
Pink (P)	Fast twitch high aerobic and glycolytic capacities
White (W)	Fast twitch glycolytic, low/intermediate aerobic capacity. Although both carp pink and white fibers are twitch fibers they differ from the corresponding fibers of dogfish in that they are multiply innervated.

[a]Data from Bone and Chubb, 1978.
[b]Data from Johnston et al., 1974, 1977.

sine triphosphatase (ATPase) activity (Fig. 2-3). Because glycogen storage levels are usually significantly higher in slow fibers than fast fibers, staining with periodic acid-Schift (PAS) also provides a convenient way of distinguishing between fiber types.

Bárány (1967) has shown a good correlation between the unloaded speeds of shortening of different muscles and their Mg^{2+} Ca^{2+} myofibrillar ATPase activity measured biochemically. The histochemical technique for demonstrating myofibrillar ATPase activity has two serious drawbacks that make it an unreliable indicator of muscle speed (Johnston et al., 1974): first, the staining procedure demonstrates Ca^2-activated myofibrillar ATPase rather than the physiologically relevant Mg^{2+} Ca^{2+}-activated ATPase. Studies with glycerinated fibers have shown that although myosin will hydrolyse CaATP at high rates (in the absence of Mg^{2+}), this is not associated with either tension generation or shortening (Bendall, 1969). Second, in order to differentiate between fiber types it is usually necessary to preincubate the sections at either high (10.2 to 10.4) or low (4.2 to 4.3) pH before incubation for ATPase activity (Guth and Samaha, 1969; Johnston et al., 1974, 1975; Raamsdonk et al., 1980; Carpene et al., 1982). The incubation itself must also be carried out at unphysiologic high pHs (pH 9 to 9.4) in order to precipitate the reaction products. Thus the histochemical stain for myofibrillar ATPase distinguishes fibers on the basis of their relative pH stabilities rather than according to their absolute enzyme activities. Unfortunately, these are not usually correlated. For example for common carp the relative ease of inactivation of Ca^{2+}-activated myofibrillar ATPase activity at pH 10.4 (histochemical procedure) is red > white > pink fibers compared to biochemical measurements of $Mg^{2+} Ca^{2+}$ ATPase activity, which increase in the order red > pink > white (Johnston et al., 1974, 1977).

Similarly, in perch (Perca fluviatilis), jaw and axial muscle contain certain red fibers that show the most alkaline-stable ATPase activity and yet have ultrastructural characteristics typical of slow fibers and do not show any reaction with antisera raised against fast muscle proteins (Akster and Osse, 1978; Akster, 1981). Thus considerable caution should be exercised in the histochemical classification of fish fiber types and where possible collaborative physiological, immunologic, or structural evidence is sought.

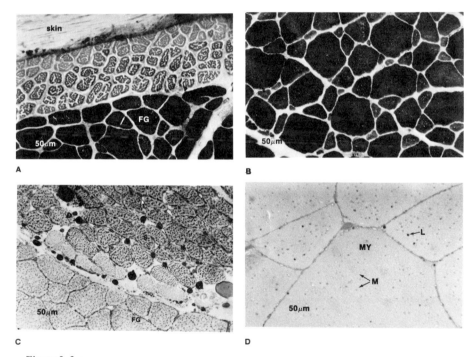

Figure 2-3
Histochemical sections (10 μ) of brook trout muscle stained for myofibrillar ATPase (A and B) and succinic dehydrogenase (C). A shows unstained slow fibers (S) inactivated by exposure to alkaline pH and darkly stained 'fast' fibers, (FG). B, Fast muscle illustrating the wide variation in fiber size yet uniform ATPase staining pattern. C, Section taken at the boundary between heavily stained slow (S) and lightly stained fast fibers (FG). Section D shows a semithin (1 μ) plastic embedded section of fast muscle stained with p-phenylene diamine. Note the relative abundance of mitochondria (M), the isolated lipid droplet (L) and regular packing of myofibrils (MY). (After Johnston and Moon, 1980a)

At least five major fiber types can be distinguished in the dogfish, four in the perch, three in the carp, and only two in the brook trout (Akster, 1981; Bone, 1978; Johnston *et al.*, 1977; Johnston and Moon, 1980a). In general, multiply innervated slow fibers are arranged in a superficial wedge adjacent to the lateral line canal system (Figs. 2-1 and 2-3); however, in scrombroid fishes the slow muscle is internalized and associated with a vascular countercurrent heat exchanger, the rete mirabile (see Sharp and Pirages, 1978). In all fish the bulk of the musculature is composed of fast glycolytic fibers that show a variety of patterns of innervation and metabolic characteristics (Bone, 1970; Johnston and Moon, 1980a). Fibers that generally show an alkaline-stable myofibrillar ATPase activity sometimes occur as an intermediate band of muscle between the slow and fast glycolytic (FG) regions (Fig. 2-1). These so-called pink or fast oxidative glycolytic (FOG) fibers generally merge somewhat with the underlying FG fibers giving the transition zone a mosaic appearance (Johnston *et al.*, 1974). In carp, FOG fibers have activities of key glycolytic enzymes that are higher than that of FG fishes, and they possess a myosin light chain composition characteristic of vertebrate fast muscles (Johnston *et al.*, 1977). In perch, a layer of FOG fibers is found adjacent to the skin, superficial, and interspersed with slow fibers as well as intermediate between the S and FG zones (Akster, 1981).

MUSCLE CONTRACTION SPEED

Recently, Altringham and Johnston (1982a) have investigated the force-velocity relationship of single-skinned muscle fibers isolated from the myotomes of cod (*Gadus morhua*) and dogfish (*Scyliorhinus cannicula*). In skinned fiber preparations, the sarcolemma is removed either by dissection or detergent treatment enabling the mechanical properties of the contractile proteins to be studied in isolation of nerve and membrane effects. Fibers are usually activated by addition of Ca^{2+} to an ethylene glycol bis (beta-aminoethylether) N N' tetra-acetic acid (EGTA) buffer system, and ATP supply is provided by an ATP regenerating system (ATP, phosphocreatine, and creatine kinase). As with other vertebrate muscle fibers, the threshold for tension generation occurs at a free Ca^{2+} concentration of around 0.6 μM (pCa 7.2), and maximum tensions are produced at around 3 to 7 μM (pCa 5.52 to 5.18); Altringham and Johnston, 1982b). Maximum isometric tensions (Table 2-2) are comparable to values found for other vertebrate skinned muscle fiber preparations (Hellam and Podolsky, 1969).

In both cod and dogfish, the pCa-tension relationship of slow fibers is shifted to lower free Ca^{2+} concentrations than that for fast fibers (Fig. 2-4). A similar finding has been reported for rabbit fast and slow muscle fibers (Kerrick, 1976). This indicates a lower Michaelis constant (K_m) for Ca^{2+} in fast fibers and means that for a given rate of removal of Ca^{2+} by the sarcoplasmic reticulum, fast muscle will relax more rapidly.

Altringham and Johnston (1982a) used isotonic step tension releases to measure contraction velocity of maximally activated (pCa 5.52) fibers under

Table 2.2
CONTRACTION PROPERTIES OF FISH MUSCLE FIBERS

SPECIES	FIBER TYPE	T°C	V_MAX (muscle lengths/s)	P_O (kg · cm^{-2})	PREPARATION
Dogfish[a]					
(*Scyliorhinus canicula*)	slow	8°C	0.67	0.84	Single skinned myotomal fiber
	fast	8°C	2.34	1.87	"
Cod[a]					
(*Gadus morhua*)	slow	8°C	0.53	0.85	"
	fast	8°C	1.01	1.90	"
Tilapia mossambica[b]	slow	18°C	1.5	0.2	Small intact fiber bundles from adductor opperculi muscle
	fast	18°C	2.6	0.4	

Data from Altringham and Johnston, 1982b[a], and Flitney and Johnston, 1979[b], V$_{max}$, unloaded speed shortening; P$_O$, maximum isometric tension.

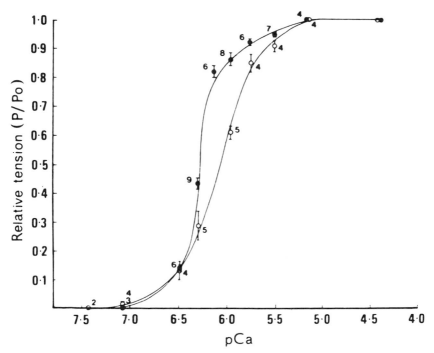

Figure 2–4
pCa-tension relationship for fast (*open circle*) and slow (*closed circles*) muscle fibers isolated from cod myotomes. Values represent mean ± SE of 5 to 8 experiments at 8°C. (From Altringham and Johnston, 1982b)

different loads. Unloaded speeds of shortening of fast fibers are two to three times greater than in slow fibers. A similar approximately two-fold difference in V_{max} between fast and slow fibers has been reported for *Tilapia mossambica* using live fiber preparations isolated from the adductor operculi muscle (Flitney and Johnston, 1979). In both cases, the relative difference in shortening speed was much less than the six- to tenfold difference reported between amphibian fast and slow fibers (Constantin *et al.,* 1967; Lannergren, 1978). This is perhaps not surprising because whereas slow fibers in frog are tonic and have a role in maintaining posture, those in fish are actively involved in locomotion. In this respect, the multiply innervated, nonaction-potential generating fibers in fish have a role more analogous to the slow twitch fibers of mammalian limb muscles. Interestingly, unloaded contraction speeds of mouse and rat fast fibers are also only around two or three times greater than that of slow fibers (Close, 1964; Luff, 1981).

The force-velocity relationship of single fibers isolated from dogfish myotomes is shown in Figure 2-5. Points below 0.6 (P_O) of the maximum isometric force (Po) on the curve can be fitted to a linear form of the Hill equation, and values for Hill's constants (a/Po, b) calculated. Hill (1938)

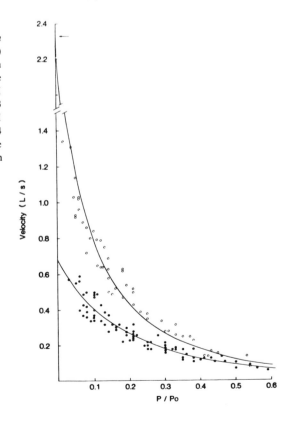

Figure 2-5
Force-velocity curves for fast (*open circles*) and slow (*closed circles*) skinned muscle fibers isolated from dogfish myotomes. Fibers were maximally activated in 10 mM imidazole, pH 7.0; 2.5 mM ATP; 3 mM $MgCl_2$; 5 mM EGTA; 10 mM phosphocreatine; 110 mM KCl; 4 mM $CaCl_2$ (pCa 5.52); creatine kinase 20 U · ml^{-1} (8°C). (From Altringham and Johnston, 1982a)

suggested that the exact shape of the force-velocity curve is related to the heat production such that as the relationship becomes more curved (a/P_O decreases) then the ratio of work rate/work + heat increases, and the muscle becomes more efficient. Support for this concept was obtained by Woledge (1968) from experiments on the thermal and mechanical properties of tortoise rectus femoris muscle at $0°C$. Compared to frog twitch fibers (a/P_O-0.26), tortoise slow fibers (a/P_O-0.07) had a work rate/work + heat ratio that was some 70% higher. Although the exact quantitative relations are unknown, Woledge suggested that a more curved force-velocity relationship is associated with a more efficient conversion of free energy into work (*i.e.,* a greater amount of work per mole of high energy phosphate).

Values for a/P_O are 0.21 and 0.28 for cod fast and slow fibers respectively (Altringham and Johnston, 1982a). These values are toward the upper range reported for comparable fiber types (Hill, 1938; Lanergrens, 1978; Woledge, 1968). A much lower value of a/P_O of 0.06 was obtained for dogfish fast fibers (Altringham and Johnston, 1982a). In interpreting the significance of such data for studies of locomotion, it is important to consider the mechanical constraints under which the muscles are operating.

Alexander (1969) calculated that fish fast myotomal muscles operate almost isometrically (*i.e.,* the overall length changes are largely caused by extension and recoil of the tendons). A similar situation may occur in certain limb muscles during running. In some muscles, activity results primarily in the storage of elastic strain energy in the tendons and is subsequently released by recoil during each stride (Goldspink, 1977). Theoretically, for an isometric contraction there is no work done because there is no shortening (actually some work done is a result of the shortening of the series elastic components). Comparative studies of the energetics of isometric contractions often make use of the term *economy*. For example, Goldspink (1975) has shown that for a 1-min isometric contraction, chicken slow muscle is 15 to 18 times more economic than is fast muscle expressed as $g.s^{-1}$ work/mM of high energy phosphate utilization. It may be that a requirement for a high isometric economy may have been a major factor in the evolution of certain fish muscles.

INNERVATION AND ELECTROPHYSIOLOGIC PROPERTIES

Focally Innervated Fast Muscles

Despite a wide range of body forms and locomotor habits, the basic arrangement of muscle fiber types in the myotomes of different fishes is remarkably constant; however, this similarity belies major differences in the pattern of motor innervation between the fast muscles of different fish groups

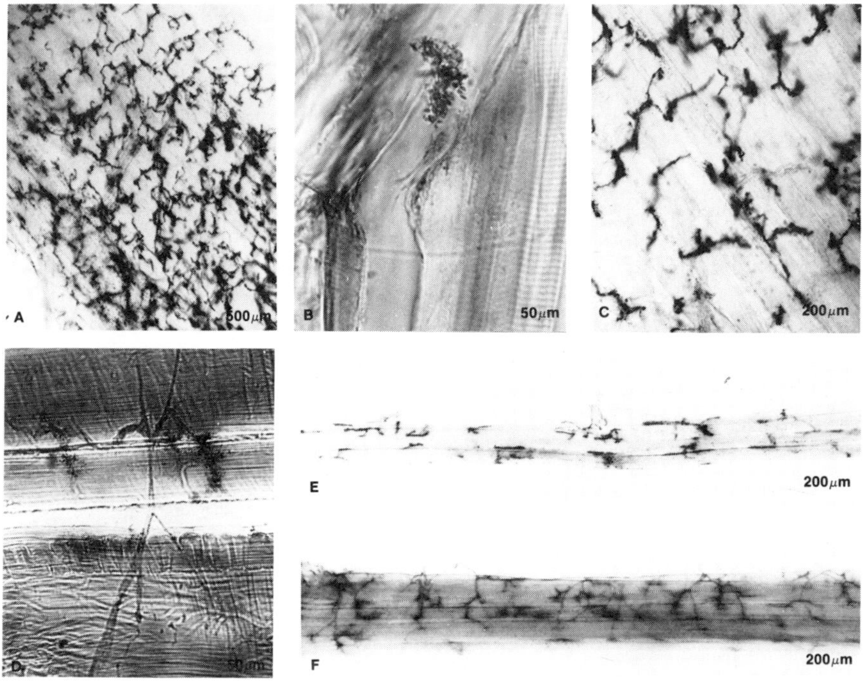

Figure 2-6
Muscle end-plates and preterminal motor axons stained for acetylcholinesterase activity. All these presentations are from teleost myotomal muscle. *A*, Slow fibers from tench (*Tinca tinca*); note the dense innervation and extensive preterminal branching. *B*, Fast fibers from eel (*Anguilla anguilla*) showing a single end-plaque type ending. *C*, Fast fibers from tench showing a complex distributed innervation. *D*, Preterminal branching in the multiply innervated fast fibers of cod (*Gadus morhua*). *E* and *F*, A small bundle of fast fibers from tench (*E*) and cod (*F*) showing the large number of individual end-plates of variable structure. (From Altringham and Johnston, 1981; Johnston and Bernard, 1982a; Egginton and Johnston, 1982a; and unpublished material)

(Fig. 2-6). In elasmobranchs, chondrosteans, dipnoans, and a few teleosts, fast fibers are focally innervated at one myoseptal end (Barets, 1961, Bone, 1964, 1970). Single motor end-plates represent the usual pattern of innervation found among vertebrate twitch fibers; however, elasmobranch fast fibers show an interesting deviation from this plan (Bone, 1972). In *Scyliorhinus*, *Squalus*, *Raja*, *Torpedo*, and *Rhina*, each fiber is innervated by two separate axons of different sizes that fuse to form a single end-plate. Furthermore, there are two types of motor terminal, each containing vesicles of different size ranges, 50 nm and 100 nm (Bone, 1972; Best and Bone, 1973). Because only acetylcholinesterase has so far been demonstrated in the subsynaptic folds of the end-plates, the function of this "dual innervation" remains a mystery. It is also unclear whether a similar arrangement is found among other groups that have focally innervated fast fibers. For example, fast fibers of the European eel *Anguilla anguilla* appear to be innervated by only a single motor axon (Fig. 2-6).

Only a few studies have examined the electrophysiologic properties of isolated, focally innervated fish fast muscles (Barets, 1961; Hagiwara and Takahashi, 1967). These muscles respond to supramaximal depolarizing pulses with a propagated action potential overshooting zero potential by about 20 mV (Hagiwara and Takahashi, 1967). In response to a single stimulus of sufficient strength, elasmobranch white fibers produce a fast twitch (Johnston, 1980a). On multiple stimulation they give fused tetani at stimulation frequencies of around 5 to 8 Hz and produce maximum isometric tensions at 10 to 20 Hz (Johnston 1980a).

Multiply Innervated Fast Muscles

Among the teleost fishes only those considered to have relatively primitive taxonomic features have fast fibers with single end-plates (Bone, 1964, 1970, 1978). In the majority of teleosts, including all the acanthopterygian orders, the fast fibers are multiply innervated (Barets, 1964; Bone, 1970). This type of fast muscle innervation is not common among vertebrates and has only been reported in a few isolated cases (*e.g., Xenopus* iliofibularis muscle; see Lannergren, 1978). In the case of myotomal muscles, each fiber receives a complex distributed innervation. Typically there are a large number of end-plates and several innervating motor axons (Bone, 1964; Hudson, 1969; Altringham and Johnston, 1981). For example in the short-horned sculpin (*Myoxocephalus scorpius*) each abdominal fast fiber is innervated by at least two to five axons derived from each of four spinal nerves (Hudson, 1969). In this species the number of terminations ranges from 8 to 22, with an average of 14.5 per fiber (Hudson, 1969).

Hudson (1969) considered that each end-plate was derived from a separate axon with only a small amount of multiterminal branching. A broadly similar pattern of innervation was observed for cod myotomal fibers (Altringham and Johnston, 1981). The number of end-plates per white fiber was found to be somewhat higher adjacent to the slow muscle zone (20 per fiber) than toward the vertebral column (15 per fibres).

Although white muscle contains fibers with a wide range of different sizes, this was not found to be correlated with the number of end-plates per fiber (Altringham and Johnston, 1981). Furthermore a given axon was found to exhibit preterminal and terminal branching giving rise to end-plates on fibers with a wide range of different sizes (Fig. 2-6). It was relatively uncommon for branches of an axon to terminate on the same fiber (Altringham and Johnston, 1981). In his analyses Hudson (1969) considered these regions of preterminal branching to represent one end-plate; however, because the distance between two such terminations can be as great as that between two end-plates from different axons, such fibers should be considered multiterminally innervated. This difference in interpretation illustrates the difficulties in making quantitative analyses of such a complex and diffuse network of innervation. It seems highly likely that within the basic framework of multiply innervated, fast motor systems, there will exist many individual differences and variations between different species both in relation to mode of life and phylogeny. It would be a mistake to view all multiply innervated fast fibers as equivalent because even small differences in the extent of polyneuronal innervation and preterminal branching might have important functional implications to fiber recruitment and the energetics of locomotion in a particular species.

Even fewer electrophysiologic studies have examined multiply inner-vated fast fibers. Hudson (1969) studied a nerve muscle preparation from the abdominal myotomes of *Myoxocephalus scorpius*. He found stimulation of spinal nerves produces two distinct electrical responses; either local junction potentials leading to a graded contraction or propagated action potentials resulting in a fast twitch (Hudson 1969). In general, supramaximal stimuli gave rise to typical all-or-none spike potentials, while submaximal stimuli resulted in junction potentials of which the amplitude could be quantitized in discrete steps providing evidence for innervation by several different motor axons (Fig. 2-7).

Simultaneous measurements of tension and membrane potential have not so far been attempted but are crucial to understanding the activation of these fibers. If fish fast fibers can be activated *in vivo* in the absence of a spike potential, then this would have important implications for locomotion. For example, it may require the activation of several different motor neurons to elicit a spike potential. If this is the case, subthreshold junction potentials would allow a graded response within the fast muscle system. Full activation of the fibers might well require the simultaneous and perhaps asynchronous activity of a number of different motor neurons allowing some added flexibility to power development by the swimming muscles. Evidence from electromyographical studies suggests that the pattern of fiber recruitment differs in relation to swimming speed according to whether the fast fibers are focally or multiply innervated (see below).

The stimulation characteristics of multiply innervated fast fibers differ from those described above for elasmobranchs (Johnston, 1980b). For example, Flitney and Johnston (1979) investigated the properties of fast and slow fiber bundles (5 to 20 fibers) isolated from the adductor operculi muscles of *Tilapia mossambica*. Fast fibers were found to respond to a single supramaximal stimulus with a small twitch; twitch tension was usually only around 5% of maximum tetanic tension (Fig. 2-8). On multiple stimulation, fast fibers produce graded, fused tetani reaching a maximum at 250 to 300 Hz. It therefore requires much higher stimulation frequencies to elicit maximum isometric tensions from multiply than from focally innervated fast muscles

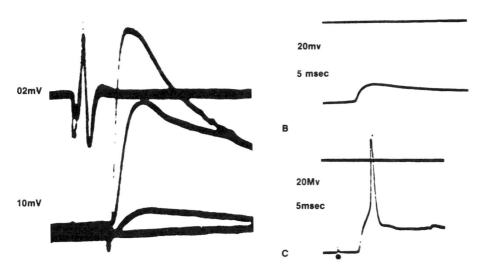

20mv

5 msec

02mV

B

20Mv

5msec

10mV

C

A

Figure 2-7
Electrophysiologic recording from the abdominal myotomes of the short-horned sculpin (*Myoxocephalus scorpius*). *A,* Simultaneous recordings of compound action potential of the nerve (*upper trace*) and concomittant response from a single muscle fiber (*lower trace*) to variations in stimulus intensity. *B,* Intracellular recording from a fast muscle fiber showing a junction potential recorded in the absence of a spike potential. *C,* Typical over-shooting spike potential. (From Hudson, 1969)

(Fig. 2-8). Similar results were obtained for somewhat larger fiber bundles isolated from cod myotomes (Johnston, 1980a).

Slow Muscles

In contrast to fast muscles, it appears that slow fibers receive a broadly similar type of innervation in all fishes (Barets, 1961; Bone, 1964). Typically, each fiber receives a number of terminations of the *engrappe* type and may be innervated by one or more different axons (Fig. 2-6). In general, slow fibers produce only local junction potentials in response to depolarizing pulses (Stanfield, 1972). In this they resemble the tonic fibers of terrestrial vertebrates although they differ in other important respects (*e.g.,* their high mitochondrial contents and relatively well-developed sarcotubular system; Johnston, 1980b, 1981a).

Tilapia slow fibers do not produce a mechanical response at stimulation frequencies below about 10 Hz (Flitney and Johnston, 1979). In contrast, dogfish and cod slow myotomal fibers respond to a supramaximal stimulus with a small twitch around 5% of Po (Johnston, 1982a). In this connection it is interesting to note that Stanfield (1972) found that 8 out of 27 dogfish slow

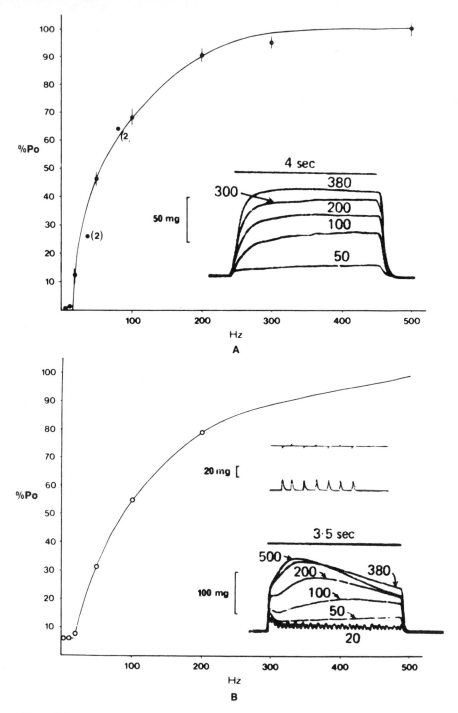

Figure 2-8
Effect of stimulation frequency (Hz) on the tension development (Po) of small fiber bundles isolated from the *adductor operculi* muscles of *Tilapia mossambica* (18°C). Slow fibers (above); fast fibers (below). Insets show original records of 4s isometric tetani. (From Flitney and Johnston, 1979)

fibers examined showed a significantly large inward sodium current on depolarization, suggesting that they might be capable of propagating an action potential, although one was never observed. Clearly, further electrophysiologic studies are needed on fish slow fibers to resolve this point.

Rates of rise of isometric tensions (dP/dT) at optimal stimulation frequency are around 7 and 10 times faster in fast than in slow fibers from *Tilapia* adductor operculi and cod myotomal muscle, respectively (Flitney and Johnston, 1979; Johnston, 1982a). This relative difference in dP/dT between fiber types is far greater than the two-to threefold difference between unloaded shortening speeds reported for these muscles (Flitney and Johnston, 1979; Altringham and Johnston, 1982a). In view of the relatively isometric nature of contraction in fish myotomes, this suggests that at least in multiply innervated fibers the muscle membrane properties are the major factor in determining contraction times *in vivo*.

ULTRASTRUCTURAL CHARACTERISTICS

In recent years a growing number of papers have reported on quantitative measurements of fish muscle ultrastructure. A number of factors should be considered in appraising the usefulness of such studies. First is the problem of heterogeneity and nonuniform distribution of fiber populations. For example, although slow myotomal fibers have been reported to comprise a fairly homogenous population in brook trout (Johnston and Moon, 1980a), eel (Egginton and Johnston, 1981a and b), and anchovy (Johnston, 1982b), this is not the case for tench (*Tinca tinca* L.) and presumably many other species (Johnston and Bernard, 1982a and b). Tench slow fibers adjacent to the skin have significantly higher fractional volumes of subsarcolemmal mitochondria than do deeper fibers (Johnston and Bernard, 1982b).

An even more marked heterogeneity is often observed with fast fiber populations, not only with respect to size (Johnston and Moon, 1981) but also according to regional distribution within the myotome (Egginton and Johnston, 1981b). The elver stage of the European eel (*Anguilla anguilla*) is sufficiently small (~ 6 mm^2 cross-sectional area) to allow individual fibers within the myotome to be located using a coordinate mapping system with morphologic features as reference points. It was found that superficial fast fibers near the skin have significantly higher mitochondrial contents and are smaller than those fibers toward the vertebral column (Fig. 2-9).

In many cases the large size of the fish under study makes regional sampling techniques unpracticable; however, in such cases it is essential to make measurements from a sufficiently large number of fibers to avoid a bias. Around 60 to 120 fibers selected at random from a total of five or six individual animals is usually sufficient for this purpose. It is often helpful to express ultrastructural data in terms of a frequency distribution rather than simply giving the average values of the character under study. In

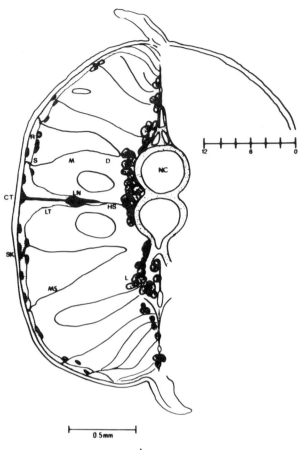

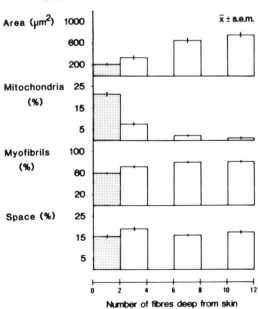

Figure 2-9
(*Upper*) Diagrammatic representation of a steak through the trunk muscle of the elver stage of the European eel (*Anguilla anguilla*) showing the anatomic details used as reference point for fiber sampling. R, red muscle; S, superficial white; M, mid-white muscle; D, deep white muscle; NC, nerve chord; LT, lateral line triangle; LN, lateral line nerve; HS, horizontal septum; L, lipid; MS, myosepta; SK, skin. (The numbers along the transect refer to the number of fibers deep from the skin.) (*Lower*) Histograms illustrating the relative changes in muscle components along the transect from skin to vertebral column. (From Egginton and Johnston, 1982a and b)

52

addition, recent studies have shown that factors such as endurance exercise training (Johnston and Moon, 1980a), oxygen availability (Johnston and Bernard, 1982a and b), starvation (Patterson and Goldspink, 1973; Johnston, 1981b and c), and environmental temperature (Johnston and Maitland, 1980; Johnston, 1982c) can markedly affect muscle ultrastructure. For example, the mitochondrial volume of slow fibers from the myotomes of Crucian carp (*Carassius carassius*) is 25% in fish acclimated to 2°C and only 14% in fish acclimated to 28°C (Johnston and Maitland, 1980).

In view of the plasticity of fish muscle, quantitative investigations of ultrastructure are best carried out either on individuals acclimated to carefully controlled laboratory conditions or by sampling defined stocks of wild populations and recording as many environmental variables as possible.

Table 2-3 summarizes a selection of the available data on the ultrastructure of fish slow and fast glycolytic muscle fibers. In general, the characteristics of fast aerobic fibers are intermediate between those of S and FG fibers (see Kryvi, 1977; Johnston and Maitland, 1980; Akster, 1981). Myosin filament lengths ($\sim 1.6\ \mu$) are similar in all fiber types (Akster, 1981); however, actin filament lengths increase in the order: slow > fast aerobic > fast glycolytic (Akster, 1981). This reflects the relative contraction velocities of

Table 2.3
ULTRASTRUCTURE OF FISH MYOTOMAL MUSCLES

PARAMETER	MUSCLE FIBER TYPE	
	Slow fibers (S)	Fast Fibers (FG)
Z-disc	'thick'	'thin'
M-line	present	present
Myofibrillar volume (%)	61.0 Eel[a]	80.4 Eel[a]
	63.0 Perch[b]	78.0 Perch[b]
	43.1 Tench[c]	73.1 Tench[c]
	46.0 Brook trout[d]	
Mitochondria fraction (%)	21.4 Eel[a]	1.2 Eel[a]
	22.0 Perch[b]	6.0 Perch[b]
	22.9 Tench[c]	4.5 Tench[c]
	31.3 Brook trout[e]	9.3 Brook trout[e]
Sarcoplasmic reticulum percent muscle fiber volume	2.1 Eel[a]	6.0 Eel[a]
	4.4 Tench[c]	3.2 Tench[b]
	5.1 Rainbow trout[f]	13.7 Rainbow trout[f]
T-system percent myofibrillar volume	0.31 Eel[a]	0.38 Eel[a]
	0.18 Perch[b]	0.27 Perch[b]
	0.29 Tench[c]	0.40 Tench[c]
	0.10 Rainbow trout[f]	0.40 Rainbow trout[f]

[a]Egginton and Johnston, 1981b.
[b]Akster, 1981.
[c]Johnston and Bernard, 1982b.
[d]Johnston and Moon, 1980a.
[e]Johnston and Moon, 1981.
[f]Nag, 1972.

these fiber types because a larger actin filament means fewer sarcomeres in series per unit fiber length and a slower speed of shortening.

Fish slow fibers differ from multiply innervated slow fibers in amphibia with respect to their high mitochondrial contents, abundant capillary supply, and extensively developed sarcotubular system (see Johnston, 1980b, 1981a for comparative data and Table 2-3). Mitochondrial fractions (MF) in fish slow fibers are considerably higher than for mammalian slow twitch fibers (Eisenburg et al., 1974) and are comparable to that of mouse (38%) and finch (34%) ventricle (Bossen et al., 1978). For most fish, the vascularization and mitochondrial volume of slow fibers correlates well with their predicted scopes for aerobic activity. For example, mitochondria occupy 18% to 24% of slow fiber volume in *Scyliorhinus canicula* (Totland et al., 1981) and 34% in *Etmopterus spinax* (Kryvi, 1977), sedentary bottom-living and active mid-water elasmobranchs, respectively.

An interesting exception to this general correlation is that of the skipjack tuna (*Katsuwonus pelamis*). This species maintains elevated brain and slow muscle temperatures by means of a countercurrent vascular heat exchanger (Carey and Teal, 1969; Stevens and Neill, 1978; see also Chap. 8). Both field observations of swimming behavior and morphologic physiological data on the respiratory and cardiovascular systems of this species point to one of the highest aerobic scopes for activity of any fish (Stevens and Neill, 1978); however, slow muscles of the skipjack tuna have a mitochondrial fraction (MF) that is only half ($\sim16\%$) that of another scombroid, the Atlantic mackerel (*Scomber scomber*), which does not operate muscle temperatures much above ambient temperature (Bone, 1978). It seems possible that an elevated body temperature allows mitochondria to operate somewhat more efficiently such that a higher scope for aerobic activity can be achieved at the same time as reducing the proportion of muscle fiber volume given over to mitochondria.

Mitochondria occupy around 46% of the cell volume of slow fibers of the European anchovy (*Engraulis encrasicolus;* Johnston, 1982b). Anchovies are active pelagic species that during filter feeding expand the gape of their mouths, increasing the body cross-section by a factor of around four times. The continuous activity and high drag forces associated with this method of feeding require a high and sustained power output from the slow muscle. Mitochondria in anchovy slow fibers are not only numerous but also have a highly developed cristae structure (Fig. 2-10). In cross-section, each muscle fiber is highly flattened such that compared to a cylindrical fibre of the same area, anchovy fibers have more than twice the surface-to-volume ratio (Greer–Walker et al., 1980). The average number of capillaries per fiber is 13, such that about 50% of the external surface of the fiber is vascularized. The extreme aerobic nature of the tissue is illustrated by the fact that no myofibril is more than 8 μ from the nearest capillary and more than 95% of myofibrils are adjacent to mitochondria (Johnston, 1982b; Fig. 2-10). In contrast, mitochondrial volume in the slow fibers of the juvenile eel is only 20%, and around 66% of fibers have no direct capillary contact (Egginton and Johnston, 1982a and b). Compared to anchovy, eel muscle mitochondria also have a relatively simple cristae structure (Egginton and Johnston, 1982b). These observations are compatible with a limited and rather inflexible aerobic scope for activity in the eel.

A large number of factors other than capillary density affect tissue perfusion and oxygenation, including blood flow, perfusion distribution, myoglobin concentrations, and factors affecting the hemoglobin-oxygen equilibrium. Nevertheless, there is good correlation between certain parameters of vascularization such as the capillary surface supplying 1 μ^3 of fiber volume and mitochondrial volume (Fig. 2-11A). In cases where mitochondrial volume is subject to modification in relation to temperature or

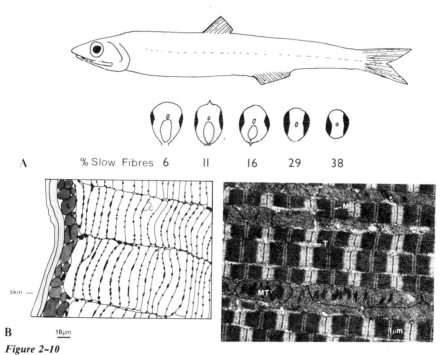

Figure 2-10
Slow muscle fibers from the myotomes of the European anchovy (*Engraulis encrasicolus*). *A,* Lateral view of the fish showing the relative proportions of slow muscle fibers at different points along its length. *B, (Left)* A camera lucida drawing of a transverse section through anchovy slow muscle stained with p-phenylene diamine (L, lipid droplets; C, capillaries). Note the highly flattened muscle cells and numerous capillaries. (*Right*) Electron micrograph (longitudinal section) of an anchovy slow fiber showing the high mitochondrial density and complex cristae structure. Note also the prominent M-line and well-developed T-system (MT, mitochondria; T, T-system; and M, M-line)

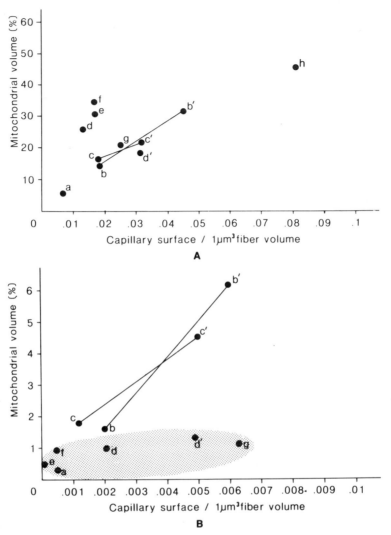

Figure 2-11

A, The relationship between mitochondrial fractional volume (%) and the capillary surface supplying 1 μ^3 of fiber volume for slow muscles. Data from the following species: (a) *Chimaera* (Kryvi and Totland, 1978); (b) Crucian carp acclimated to 28°C; (b[1]) Crucian carp acclimated to 2°C (Johnston and Maitland, 1980); (c) tench acclimated to low oxygen 1.7 kPa PO₂; (c[1]) tench acclimated to air-saturated water (Johnston and Bernard, 1982a); (d) dogfish (*Scyliorhinus canicula;* Totland *et al.,* 1981); (e) shark (*Etmopterus spinax;* Kryvi, 1977); (f) (*Galeus melastomus;* Kryvi, 1977); (g) juvenile eel (*Anguilla anguilla;* Egginton and Johnston, 1981); (h) European anchovy (*Engraulis encrasicolus;* Johnston, 1981b). *B,* The relationship between mitochondrial fractional volume (%) and the capillary surface supplying 1 μ^3 of fiber volume for fast muscles. Data from the following species of fish: (a) Chimaera (Kryvi and Totland, 1978); (b) Crucian carp acclimated to 28°C; (b[1]) Crucian carp acclimated to 2°C (Johnston and Maitland, 1980); (c) tench acclimated to low oxygen 1.7 KPa Po₂; (c[1]) tench acclimated to air-saturated water (Johnston and Bernard, 1982a); (d) and (d[1]) dogfish (*Scyliorhinus canicula;* Totland *et al.,* 1980); (e) shark (*Etmopterus spinax;* Kryvi, 1977); (f) shark (*Galeus melastomus;* Kryvi, 1977); (g) juvenile eel (*Anguilla anguilla;* Egginton and Johnston, 1981a). The shaded area represents data from species with focally innervated fast muscle fibers.

oxygen availability, changes in capillary supply occur in parallel, suggesting that the area available for diffusion of oxygen or nutrients is a limiting factor in fixing the maximum aerobic capacity of the muscle (Johnston, 1982c).

Compared to slow fibers, there is even greater interspecific variation in the capillary supply and mitochondrial volume of fast glycolytic fibers. It seems likely that this reflects the different extents to which FG fibers are involved in sustained activity. The relationship between mitochondrial volume and capillary surface supplying 1 μ^3 of fiber volume for FG fibers is shown in Figure 2-11B. The shaded area represents species that are only thought to recruit FG fibers for burst swimming activity; in such species (*e.g.,* dogfish, *Scyliorhinus canicula*), mitochondrial volumes are generally less than 1% (Totland *et al.,* 1981). Such low mitochondrial densities are likely to be sufficient only for resting metabolism (*e.g.,* maintenance of ion gradients, protein turnover, etc.).

Somewhat higher mitochondrial volumes have been found in teleosts that recruit their FG fibers for sustained activity (Johnston and Moon, 1981). For example, the mean MF of brook trout, carp, and tench are 9.3%, 4.6%, and 1.8–4.5%, respectively (Johnston and Moon, 1981; Johnston and Bernard, 1982b). There is considerable heterogenity in the MF of fast fiber populations (Fig. 2-12). In general, smaller fibers tend to have somewhat greater MFs than do larger ones (Fig. 2-12). It seems likely that for at least some species, the aerobic capacity of FG fibers might be sufficient to support slow-speed swimming activity.

Myofibril packing is more regular and dense in fast glycolytic fibers than slow fibers, reflecting the requirement of this fiber type to develop tension extremely rapidly during burst swimming (Table 2-3).

Figure 2-12
Relationship between fiber size (μ^2) and mitochondrial fractional volume (%) for tench fast muscle. (From Johnston and Bernard, 1982b)

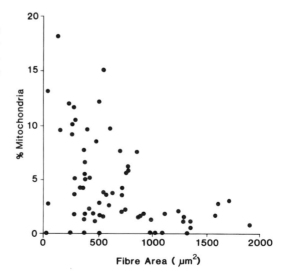

In general, the volume of sarcoplasmic reticulum (SR) is somewhat higher in fish S and FG fibers than it is in analogous amphibian and mammalian muscles. For example, SR occupies 4.6% of fiber volume in guinea pig white vastus muscle (Eisenberg and Kuda, 1975) compared to 7% and 13.7% in the FG myotomal fibers of shark (*Galeus melastomus*) and rainbow trout, respectively (Kryvi, 1977; Nag, 1972). This is in part related to the higher frequency of contraction-relaxation cycles found in fish swimming compared to most types of terrestrial locomotion, necessitating a high rate of Ca^{2+} uptake from the myoplasm. A diagrammatic representation of the sarco-tubular system of S and FG fibers of the perch (*Perca fluviatilis*) is shown in Figure 2-13. In most myotomal muscle fibers, the T-tubules are located at the Z-disc. This is the case for both S and FG fibers of perch (Akster, 1981), trout (Nag, 1972), coalfish (Patterson and Goldspink, 1972), carp (Johnston and Maitland, 1980), and numerous other fishes; however, red fibers in perch musculus levator operculi have T-tubules located at either the Z-disc or A/I band junction (Akster, 1981). A similar location of T-tubules at the A/I band junction is found in certain fast-acting, sound-producing muscles (Eichelberg, 1976), suggesting that the location of the T-system is not particularly correlated with either actin filament length or muscle speed.

RECRUITMENT OF MUSCLE FIBERS DURING SWIMMING

The now classic paper by Bone (1966) was the first to investigate the recruitment of fast and slow muscles directly using electromyographic

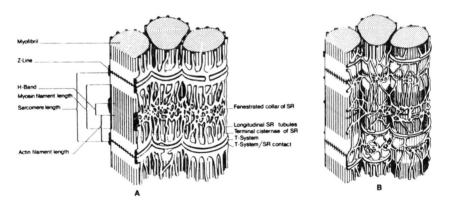

Figure 2-13
Diagrammatic representation of the sarcomere components and membrane systems of (*A*) fast and (*B*) slow fibers from the perch (*Perca fluviatilis* L.). (Produced by kind permission of Dr. Hendrica Akster, from Akster, 1981)

recording techniques. This study chiefly used dogfish (*Scyliorhinus canicula*), but some observations were also made on smooth hounds (*Mustelus vulgaris*), tope (*Galeorhinus galeus*), and spur dogs (*Squalus acanthius*). The fish were pithed, the spinal chord destroyed to the level of the rear pectoral fins, and the gills ventilated with a seawater circulation. With the snout attached to a board, the body made steady "swimming movements" corresponding to around 35 to 40 tail beats per minute (Bone, 1966). Under these conditions electromyograms (EMGs) could only be recorded from the superficial red muscle layer, the white fibers remaining electrically silent; however, on pinching the tail the fish altered from a slow rate of "swimming" to a more active one, and electrical activity could be recorded from electrodes placed in the white muscle (Bone, 1966).

From these experiments and on the basis of histologic and biochemical disimilarities between the red and white muscles, Bone concluded that there was a distinct division of labor between the slow and fast motor systems. Red fatigue-resistant fibers were considered to be able to provide all the power necessary for sustained swimming speeds using aerobic metabolic pathways and both lipid and carbohydrates as fuels. In contrast, the white fibers were thought to be entirely dependent on anaerobic glycogenolysis for their energy supply and to contain sufficient glycogen for only around 1 to 2 minutes of vigorous swimming (Bone, 1966).

Indirect evidence that this simple division of labor between red and white muscles did not apply to all fish soon began to accumulate. For example, Greer–Walker (1971) found that in saithe (*Pollachius virens*), endurance exercise training at quite moderate swimming speeds ($\leq$ two body lengths per second) resulted in hypertrophy of both red and white muscles. Various biochemical studies also provided evidence for glycogen depletion and lactate accumulation in fast fibers during sustained swimming (Pritchard *et al.*, 1971; Johnston and Goldspink, 1973a and b). Electromyographic evidence for the recruitment of FG fibers at intermediate speeds was soon forthcoming (Hudson, 1973; Johnston *et al.*, 1977). The threshold speed for recruitment of fast glycolytic fibers was found to be around 1.4 body lengths per second in rainbow trout (Hudson, 1973); 2 to 2.5 body lengths per second in mirror carp (Johnston *et al.*, 1977), 0.8 to 2.0 body lengths per second in saithe (Johnston and Moon, 1980b), and 1.8 body lengths per second in brook trout (*Salvelinus fontinalis*) (Johnston and Moon, 1980a). These are all speeds that can be maintained almost indefinitely. Evidence for an orderly recruitment of fiber types (slow → fast aerobic → glycolytic) has been obtained for large carp in which the fast aerobic fiber layer is sufficiently extensive to allow placement of EMG electrodes (Johnston *et al.*, 1977).

The fast fibers of all the above teleost species are multiply innervated (Bone, 1964, 1970). Because multiply innervated FG fibers have distinct electrophysiologic (Stanfield 1972; Hudson 1969) and contractile properties (Johnston 1980a; 1982a) to those of elasmobranchs (Stanfield, 1972; Hudson, 1969; Johnston, 1980a; 1982a), it is tempting to relate these differences in the pattern of recruitment to differences in motor innervation. Support for such a concept was found by Bone and colleagues (1978) from electromyographic experiments on the Pacific herring (*Clupea harengus pallasi*). Herring belong to a primitive group of teleosts that in common with elasmobranchs have FG fibers that are innervated by a single engrappe type end-plate (Bone, 1978). In herring, only slow fibers are recruited at low speeds (≤4 body lengths per second). Higher speeds (≥5 body lengths per second) result in the recruitment of FG fibers and fatigue of the fish within another 1 to 2 minutes swimming (Bone *et al.*, 1978). Thus compared to fish that recruit their fast fibers at low speeds, there is a very sharp transition between levels of effort that can be maintained almost indefinitely and those leading to fatigue.

The two extreme patterns of fiber recruitment found in herring (type A) and mirror carp (type B) are illustrated in Figure 2-14; however, in view of the diversity of multiply innervated fast muscles, it seems highly unlikely that a sharp division can be drawn between these two types of behavior. For example, many fish with multiply innervated fast fibers may have reverted to the type A pattern of fiber recruitment. Evidence for this comes from EMG studies with striped bass (*Morone saxtilis*) and bluefish (*Pomatomus sultatrix*) in which the threshold speeds for recruitment of fast fibers are 3.2 and 4.5 body lengths per second respectively (Freadman, 1979). Many more such studies are required before the extent of the correlation between mode of swimming, fast muscle innervation, and fiber recruitment can be firmly established.

SPECIAL ADAPTATIONS FOR RAPID TAIL-BEAT FREQUENCIES

From videorecordings of free-swimming fish it is known that the top speed of a 100 cm cod is around 5 to 6 body lengths per second, requiring a tail-beat frequency of around 9 Hz (Wardle, 1975). Small fish can only swim at around half this absolute speed but achieve much greater relative speeds (~20 lengths per second) and higher tail-beat frequencies (~ 30 Hz). For example, during burst swimming, the myotomes on either side of a 10-cm sprat are required to activate, contract, and relax in only 30 msec (Wardle, 1975). This impressive performance appears to be associated with a number of special adaptations to promote rapid relaxation in the fast muscle (Johnston, 1981a).

The cytoplasm of vertebrate fast muscles contains a series of homologous Ca^{2+}-binding proteins (components I through V) called *parvalbumins* (Hamoir and Distéche, 1972). These low molecular-weight, acidic proteins bind

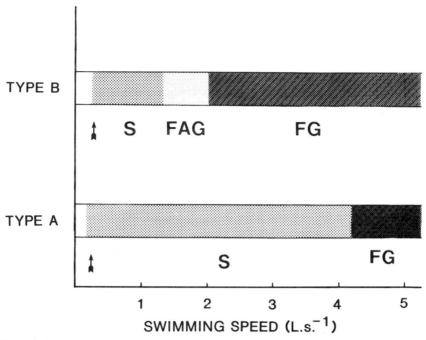

Figure 2-14
The relationship between swimming speed and the thresholds for recruitment of different fiber types in the herring (type A) and common carp (type B). S, slow fibers; FAG, fast aerobic glycolytic fibers; and FG, fast glycolytic fibres. The arrow shows the swimming speed below which the pectoral fins provide the main propulsive effort. (Based on the experimental data of Johnston *et al.,* 1977 for carp; and Bone *et al.,* 1978 for herring.

2-g atoms Ca^{2+} per mole with a similar affinity to that of troponin C (Benzonana, Capony, and Perchere, 1972); they occur in particularly high concentrations in the fast muscles of fish and other aquatic vertebrates. For example, the concentration of parvalbumin in hake fast muscle is around 1 mM compared to around 30 μM for mammalian fast muscles (Baron *et al.,* 1975; Hamoir *et al.,* 1980).

Although the role of parvalbumins has not been conclusively established, considerable evidence suggests their participation in relaxation (Pechere *et al.,* 1977; Gillis and Gerday, 1977; Gillis and Lefevre, 1982). According to this hypothesis, parvalbumins function as a shuttle mechanism between Ca^{2+}-binding proteins on the myofibril, troponin C (TNC), and the saroplasmic reticulum. It is envisaged that Ca^{2+} released from the SR is exchanged from TNC and rapidly becomes bound to the parvalbumins causing only a transient activation of crossbridges. Subsequently active Ca^{2+}-pumping by the sarcoplasmic reticulum is able to re-accumulate the Ca^{2+} by exchange from the parvalbumins (*e.g.,* see Gillis and Gerday, 1977). Using a computer simulation of the kinetics of Ca^{2+} movements in the muscle cell and by choosing appropriate values for parvalbumin concentration, binding affinities and the maximum rate of calcium pumping of Ca^{2+}-pumping, Gillis and Leferrer (1982) have calculated that the parvalbumins are unlikely to become saturated *in vivo*, an essential prerequisite for their participation in relaxation.

In addition to the high concentration of parvalbumin, the SR of fish muscle is also highly developed. McArdle and Johnston (1981) found that the rate of Ca^{2+}-uptake into frozen tissue sections (10 μM) of trout fast muscle was 2.8 times higher at 10°C than that of rat fast muscle at 37°C.

The glycolytic pathway in fish fast muscles also shows a number of adaptations for high ATP turnover (see Driedzic and Hochachka, 1978; Johnston, 1981a). An interesting feature in elasmobranchs is the lack of hormonal activation of glycogen b and phosphorylase in elasmobranchs (Fischer, Blum *et al.*, 1975). While rabbit fast muscle phosphorylase kinase is activated or inhibited by cyclic adenosine monophosphate (cAMP)-dependent protein kinases or specific phosphatases acting in response to circulating catecholamines, the dogfish enzyme depends only on Ca^{2+}-binding for its activity (Fischer *et al.*, 1975; Fischer, Alaba *et al.*, 1978); thus, in the case of dogfish fast muscle, glycogen breakdown depends entirely on nervous activity and proceeds rapidly and essentially independent of the circulation.

Acknowledgments

The author is grateful to both the Science & Engineering Research Council and the Natural Environment Research Council of the United Kingdom for support.

REFERENCES

Akster, H.A. 1981. Ultrastructure of muscle fibres in head axial muscles of the perch, (*Perca fluviatilis* L.) A quantitative study. *Cell Tissue Res.* 219:111–131.

Akster, H.A., and Osse, J.W.M. 1978. Muscle fibre types in head muscles of the perch, *Perca fluvitalis* L. Teleostei. A histochemical and electromyographical study. *Neth. J. Zool.* 28:44–110.

Alexander, C. McN. 1969. The orientation of muscle fibres in the myomeres of fishes. *J. Marine Biol. Assoc. UK* 49:263–290.

Altringham, J.D., and Johnston, I.A. 1981. Quantitative histochemical studies of the peripheral innervation of cod (*Gadus morhua*) fast myotomal muscle fibres. *J. Comp. Physiol.* 143:123–127.

Altringham, J.D., and Johnston, I.A. 1982. The pCa-tension and force-velocity characteristics of skinned fibres isolated from fish fast and slow muscles. *J. Physiol.* 333:421–449.

Altringham, J.D., and Johnston, I.A. 1982b. The isometric tension properties of skinned fast and slow fibres isolated from cod and dogfish myotomal muscles. *J. Physiol. (Lond.).* In press.

Bárány, M. 1967. ATPase activity of myosin correlated with speed of muscle shortening. *J. Gen. Physiol.* 51:197–216.

Barets, A. 1961. Contribution a l'etude des systemes moteur lent et rapide du muscle lateral des teleosteens. *Arch. Anat. Morphol. Exp.* 50(suppl):91–187.

Baron, G., Demaille, J., and Detruge, E. 1975. The distribution of parvalbumins in muscle and other tissues. *FEBS Lett.* 56:156–160.

Bendall, J.R. 1969. *Muscles, Molecules and Movement.* London: Heinemann Press.

Benzonana, G., Capony, J.-P., and Pechere, J.F. 1972. The binding of calcium to muscular parvalbumins. *Biochim. Biophys. Acta* 278:110–116.

Best, A.C.G., and Bone, Q. 1973. The terminal neuromuscular junctions of lower chordates. *Z. Zellforsch. Mikrosk. Anat.* 143:495–504.

Bone, Q. 1964. Patterns of muscular innervation in the lower chordates. *Int. Rev. Neurobiol.* 6:99–147.

Bone, Q. 1966. On the function of the two types of myotomal muscle fibres in elasmobranch fish. *J. Marine Biol. Assoc. UK* 46:321–349.

Bone, Q. 1970. Muscular innervation and fish classification. *Symp. Int. Zoofil.* 1st Univ. Salamanca, 1970, pp. 369–377.

Bone, Q. 1972. The dogfish neuromuscular junction: Dual innervation of vertebrate striated muscle fibres. *J. Cell Sci.* 10:657–665.

Bone, Q. 1978. Locomotor muscle. In *Fish Physiology,* edited by W.S. Hoar, and D.J. Randall, vol. 7, 361–424. New York and London: Academic Press.

Bone, Q., and Chubb, A.D. 1978. The histochemical demonstration of myofibrillar ATPase in elasmobranch muscle. *Histochem. J.* 10:489–494.

Bone, Q., Kicenuik, J., Jones, D.R. 1978: On the role of the different fibre types in fish myotomes at intermediate swimming speeds. *Fish. Bull.* 76:691–699.

Bossen, E.H., Sommer, J.R., and Waugh, R.A. 1978. Comparative stereology of the mouse and finch left ventricle. *Tissue Cell* 10:773–784.

Carey, F.G., and Teal, J.M. 1969. Regulation of body temperature by the blue fin tuna. *Comp. Biochem. Physiol.* 28:205–213.

Carpene, E., Vegetti, A., Mascarello, F., and Scapolo, P. 1982. Histochemical pattern in the red and white muscle of fishes and some biochemical data on myofibrillar ATPase. *J. Muscle Res. Cell Motility.* In press.

Constantin, L.L., Podolsky, R.J., and Tice, L.W. 1967. Calcium activation of frog muscle fibres. *J. Physiol.* 188:261–271.

Close, R. 1964. Dynamic properties of fast and slow skeletal muscles of the rat during development. *J. Physiol.* 173:74–95.

Driedzic, W.R., and Hochachka, P.W. 1978. Metabolism of fish during exercise. In *Fish Physiology,* edited by W.S. Hoar, and D.J. Randall, vol 7, 503–543. New York, San Francisco, London: Academic Press.

Egginton, S., and Johnston, I.A. 1982a. Muscle fibre differentiation and vascularisation in the juvenile European eel (*Anguilla anguilla* L.). *Cell Tissue Res.* In press.

Egginton, S., and Johnston, I.A. 1982b. A morphometric analysis of regional differences in myotomal muscle ultrastructure in the juvenile eel (*Anguilla anguilla* L.). *Cell Tissue Res.* In press.

Eichelberg, H. 1976. The fine structure of the drum muscles of the trigger fish, *Therapon jarbua*, as compared with the trunk musculature. *Cell Tissue Res.* 174:453–463.

Eisenberg, B.R., Kuda, A.M. 1975. Stereological analysis of mammalian skeletal muscle 11. White vastus muscle of the adult guinea pig. *J. Ultrastruct. Res.* 51:176–187.

Fischer, E.H., et al. 1975. Concerted regulation of glycogen metabolism and muscle contraction. In *Metabolic Interconversion of Enzymes,* edited by S. Shaltiel, 1–8. Heidelberg: Springer Verlag.

Fischer, E.J., et al. 1978. In *Versatility of Proteins,* edited by Hao Li Choh, 133–149. London: Academic Press.

Flitney, F.W., and Johnston, I.A. 1979: Mechanical properties of isolated fish red and white muscle fibres. *J. Physiol.* 295:49–50.

Freadman, M.A. 1979. Role of partitioning of swimming musculature of striped bass, *Morone saxatalis* Walbaum and bluefish, *Pomatomus saltatrix* L. *J. Fish Biol.* 15:417–423.

Gillis, J.M., and Gerday, C. 1977. Calcium movement between myofibrils, parvalbumins and sarcoplasmic reticulum in muscle. In *Calcium Binding Proteins and Calcium Function,* edited by R.H. Wasserman et al. Amsterdam: Elsevier, North Holland.

Gillis, J.M., and Lefevre, J. 1982. A stimulation study of the distribution of Ca and Mg between troponin, parvalbumins and the sarcoplasmic reticulum, at rest and during contraction. *J. Muscle Res. Cell Motility.* 3:120.

Goldspink, G. 1975. Biochemical energetics for fast and slow muscles. In *Comparative Physiology—Functional Aspects of Structural Materials,* edited by L. Bolis, H.P. Maddrell, and K. Schmidt-Nielsen, 173–185. Amsterdam: Elsevier-North Holland.

Goldspink, G., Howell, K.F., and Ward, P.S. 1976. Effects of exercise on muscle fibre size. In *Medicine Sport,* Vol. 9. *Advances in Exercise Physiology,* edited by E. Jokl, 103–113. Basel: Karger.

Goldspink, G. 1977. Muscle energetics and animal locomotion. In *Mechanics and Energetics of Animal Locomotion,* edited by R. McN. Alexander and G. Goldspink, 57–79. London: Chapman & Hall.

Gray, J. 1933. Studies in animal locomotion. *J. Exp. Biol.* 10:88–104.

Greer–Walker, M. 1971. The effects of starvation and exercise on the skeletal muscle fibres of the cod (*Gadus morhua* L.) and coalfish (*Gadus virens* L.) respectively. *J. Cons. Int. Explor. Mer.* 33:421–427.

Greer–Walker, M., and Pull, G.A. 1975. A survey of red and white muscle in marine fish. *J. Fish Biol.* 7:295–300.

Greer–Walker, M., Horwood, J., and Emerson, L. 1980. On the morphology and function of red and white skeletal muscle in the anchovies *Engraulis encrasicolus* L. and *E. Mordax* Girard. *J. Marine Biol. Assoc. UK* 60:31–37.

Guth, L., and Samaha, F.J. 1969. Qualitative differences between actomyosin ATPase of slow and fast mammalian muscle. *Exp. Neurol.* 25:138–152.

Hagiwara, S., and Takahashi, K. 1967. Resting and spike potentials of skeletal muscle fibers in salt-water elasmobranch and teleost fish. *J. Physiol. (Lond.)* 190:499–518.

Hamoir, G., Focant, B., Distéche, M. 1972. Proteinic criteria of differentiation of white cardiac and various red muscles in carp. *Comp. Biochem. Physiol.* 41B: 665–674.

Hamoir, G., Gerardin-Outhiers, N., Focant, B. 1980. Protein differentiation of the superfast swimbladder muscle of the toadfish *Opsanus tau. J. Mol. Biol.* 143:155–160.

Hellam, D.C., and Podolsky, R.J. 1969. Force measurements in skinned muscle fibres. *J. Physiol (Lond.)* 200:807–819.

Hill, A.V. 1938: The heat of shortening and the dynamic constants of muscle. *Proc. R. Soc.* 126B:136–195.

Holloszy, J.O., and Booth, F.W. 1976. Biochemical adaptations to endurance exercise in muscle. *Ann. Rev. Physiol.* 38:273–291.

Hudson, R.C.L. 1969. Polyneuronal innervation of the fast muscles of the marine teleost *Cottus scorpius* L. *J. Exp. Biol.* 50:47–67.

Hudson, R.C.L. 1973. On the function of the white muscles in teleosts at intermediate swimming speeds. *J. Exp. Biol.* 58:509–522.

Johnston, I.A. 1980a. Contractile properties of fish fast muscle fibres. *Marine Biol. Lett.* 1:323–328.

Johnston, I.A. 1980b. Specialisation of fish muscle. In *Development and Specialization of Muscle,* edited by D. F. Goldspink. *Soc. Exp. Biol.* Seminar Series 7:123–148. Cambridge: Cambridge University Press.

Johnston, I.A. 1981a. Structure and function of fish muscles. *Symp. Zool. Soc. Lond.* 48:71–113.

Johnston, I.A. 1981b. Physiology of muscle in hatchery raised fish. In *Physiology of salmonid cultivation,* edited by C. Cowey. *Comp. Biochem. Physiol* Suppl. B. 73B: 103–124.

Johnston, I.A. 1981c. Quantitative analysis of muscle breakdown during starvation in the marine Flatfish *Pleuronectes platessa. Cell Tissue Res.* 214:369–386.

Johnston, I.A. 1982a. Biochemistry of fish myosins and contractile properties of fish skeletal muscle. *J. Mol. Physiol.* 2:15–29.

Johnston, I.A. 1982b. Quantitative analyses of ultrastructure and vascularization of the slow muscle fibres of the European Anchovy *Engraulis encrasicolus. Tissue Cell.* 14:319–328.

Johnston, I.A. 1982c. Capillarisation, oxygen diffusion distances and mitochondrial content of carp muscles following acclimation to summer and winter temperatures. *Cell Tissue Res.* 222:325–337.

Johnston, I.A., and Bernard, L.M. 1982a. Muscle fibre differentiation and vascularization of tench skeletal muscles. The effects of long-term acclimation to hypoxia. *Cell Tissue Res.* 227:161–177.

Johnston, I.A., and Bernard, L.M. 1982b. Quantitative analyses of the effects of long-term hypoxia on the ultrastructure of tench (*Tinca tinca* L.) skeletal muscles. *Cell Tissue Res.* 227:179–199.

Johnston, I.A., Davison, W., and Goldspink, G. 1977. Energy metabolism of carp swimming muscles. *J. Comp. Physiol.* 114:203–216.

Johnston, I.A., and Goldspink, G. 1973a. A study of the swimming performance of the crucian carp *Carassius carassius* L. in relation to the effects of exercise and recovery on biochemical changes in the myotomal muscles and liver. *J. Fish Biol.* 5:249–260.

Johnston, I.A., and Goldspink, G. 1973b. A study of glycogen and lactate in the myotomal muscles and liver of the codfish (*Gadus virens* L.) during sustained swimming. *J. Marine Biol. Assoc. UK* 53:17–26.

Johnston, I.A., and Maitland, B. 1980. Temperature acclimation in crucian carp: A morphometric analyses of muscle fibre ultrastructure. *J. Fish Biol.* 17:113–125.

Johnston, I.A., Moon, T.W. 1980a. Exercise training in skeletal muscle of brook trout (*Salvelinus fontinalis*). *J. Exp. Biol.* 87:177–194.

Johnston, I.A., Moon, T.W. 1980b. Endurance exercise training in the fast and slow muscles of a teleost fish (*Pollachius virens*). *J. Comp. Physiol.* 135B:147–156.

Johnston, I.A., and Moon, T.W. 1981. Fine structure and metabolism of multiply innervated fast muscle fibres in teleost fish. *Cell Tissue Res.* 219:93–109.

Johnston, I.A., Patterson, S., Ward, P.S., and Goldspink, G. 1974. The histochemical demonstration of myofibrillar adenosine triphosphatase activity in fish muscle. *Can. J. Zool.* 52:871–877.

Johnston, I.A., Ward, P.S., and Goldspink, G. 1975. Studies on the swimming musculature of the rainbow trout. I. Fibre types. *J. Fish Biol.* 7:451–458.

Kerrick, W.G.L. 1976. Development of differences between red and white muscles in sensitivity to Ca^{2+} in the rabbit from embryo to adult. *Nature (London)* 260:440–441.

Kryvi, H. 1977. Ultrastructure of the different fibre types in axial muscles of the sharks *Etmopterus spinax*, and *Galeus melastomus*. *Cell Tissue Res.* 184:287–300.

Kryvi, H., and Totland, G.K. 1978. Fibre types in locomotory muscles of the cartilaginous fish *Chimaera monstrosa*. *J. Fish. Biol.* 12:257–265.

Lannergren, J. 1978. The force-velocity relation of isolated twitch and slow muscle fibres of *Xenopus laevis*. *J. Physiol.* 283:501–521.

Lorenzini, S. 1678. *Observazioni intorno alle Torpedini*, Florence: Onofori.

Luff, A.R. 1981. Dynamic properties of the inferior rectus extensor digitorum longus, diaphragm and soleus muscles of the mouse. *J. Physiol.* 313:161–172.

McArdle, H.J., Johnston, I.A. 1981. Ca^{2+}-uptake by tissue sections and biochemical characteristics of sarcoplasmic reticulum isolated from fish fast and slow muscles. *Eur. J. Cell Biol.* 25:103–107.

Nag, A.C. 1972. Ultrastructure and adenosine triphosphatase activity of red and white muscle fibers of the caudal region of a fish, *Salmo gairdneri*. *J. Cell Biol.* 55:42–57.

Patterson, S., and Goldspink, G. 1972. The fine structure of red and white myotomal muscle fibres of the coalfish (*Gadus virens*). *Z. Zellforsch. Mikrosk. Anat.* 133:463–474.

Patterson, S., and Goldspink, G. 1973. The effect of starvation on the ultrastructure of the red and white myotomal muscles of the Crucian carp (*Carassius carassius*) *Z. Zellforsch. Mikrosk. Anat.* 146:375–384.

Pechére, J.F., Derancourt, J., and Jarech, J. 1977. The participation of parvalbumins in the activation–relaxation cycle of vertebrate fast skeletal muscle. *FEBS Lett.* 75:111–114.

Pritchard, A.W., Hunter, J.R., and Lasker, R. 1971. The relation between exercise and biochemical changes in red and white muscles and liver in the jack mackeral *Trachurus symmetricus*. *U.S. Fish Wildlife Service Fish. Bull.* 69:379–386.

Raamsdonk, W. Van., Te Kronnie, G., Pool, C.W., and van de Laarsse, W. 1980.

Muscle fibre types in the myotomal muscle of the teleost *Brachydanio rerio. Acta Histochem* (Jena) 67:200–216.

Revel, J.P. 1962. The sarcoplasmic reticulum of the bat cricothyroid muscle. *J. Cell Biol.* 12:571–588.

Sharp, G.D., and Pirages, S. 1978. The distribution of red and white swimming muscles, their biochemistry, and the biochemistry phylogeny of selected scombrid fishes. In *The Physiological Ecology of Tunas,* edited by G.D. Sharp and A.E. Dizon, 41–78. New York, San Francisco, London: Academic Press.

Stanfield, P.R. 1972. Electrical properties of white and red muscle fibres of the elasmobranch fish (*Scyliorhinus canicula*). *J. Physiol.* 222:161–186.

Stevens, E.D., Neill, W.H. 1978. Body temperature relations of tunas, especially skipjack. In *Fish Physiology,* edited by W.S. Hoar and D.J. Randall, vol. 7, 315–359. New York: Academic Press.

Totland, G.K., Kryvi, H., Bone, Q., and Flood, P.R. 1981. Vascularization of the lateral muscle of some elasmobranchiomorph fishes. *J. Fish Biol.* 18:223–234.

Walesby, N.J., and Johnston, I.A. 1980. Fibre types in the locomotory muscle of an Antarctic teleost, *Notothenia rossii.* A histochemical, ultrastructural and biochemical study. *Cell. Tissue Res.* 208:143–164.

Wardle, C.S. 1975. Limit of fish swimming speed. *Nature (London)* 255:725–727.

Webb, P.W. 1978. Hydrodynamics: Nonscrombroid fish. In *Fish Physiology* edited by W.S. Hoar, and D.J. Randall, 189–237. New York: Academic Press.

Woledge, R.C. 1968. The energetics of tortoise muscle. *J Physiol* 197:685–707.

ABBREVIATIONS

EGTA	Ethylene glycol bis (β-aminoethylether) N N' tetraacetic acid.	**PAS**	Periodic acid-Schiff.
FG	Fast glycolytical muscle fibers.	**Po**	Maximum isometric tension.
FOG	Fast oxidative (aerobic glycolytic) muscle fibers.	**S**	Slow muscle fibers.
MF	Mitochondrial fraction.	**SR**	Sarcoplasmic reticulum.
		Vmax	Maximum (unloaded) speed of muscle shortening.

Chapter 3
TO BEND A FISH
Stephen A. Wainwright

CONTENTS

THE CENTRAL QUESTIONS

Fishes of most species swim by producing undulatory movements that cause their flanks and median fins to push backward against the surrounding water; this generates the thrust for swimming. Bending of the fish body is seen in a first approximation as the result of the contraction of longitudinal body musculature alternately on the right and left sides of the nonshortening backbone. In this ideal view, the locomotor muscle on each side is a unit, and like a human sartorius muscle, each muscle cell runs the length of the muscle and attaches to bones by a tendon at each end. When a muscle cell contracts, it does so all at once.

Two conditions in fishes indicate that this view is inaccurate and that further explanation is necessary to understand how contraction of the body musculature causes locomotor body bending in fishes. First, a fish locomotor muscle is made of a series of muscle cells; each cell attaches to thin, collagen-fiber reinforced myosepta that in turn attach to horizontal septa, skin, or backbone and median septum. There is apparently no straight line of tensile

68

force along the muscle, through a tendon, to a bone. Second, electromyographic data show that muscle contraction spreads backward along one side of the fish body: contracting muscle apparently pulls against inactive, presumably relaxed muscle posterior to it (Grillner, 1974). It seems improbable that force is transmitted by relaxed, compliant muscle.

The following statements and questions arise from these conditions and will guide views of the literature and future research. Any analysis of undulatory swimming in fishes must account for muscle cells, their innervation and attachments, the array and properties of connective tissues and backbone, and the design of the entire locomotor system. When a muscle cell contracts, what does it pull on? What is the trajectory of its force and shortening that ultimately bends the backbone? What structural features of muscle, septa, skin, and backbone permit and limit their role in locomotor bending? Does the release of elastic energy from a deformed skeletal structure aid in any phase of body bending? With the fish's engine (bulk of the locomotor muscle) situated forward and the propeller (caudal fin) aft, where is the drive shaft?

This chapter discusses the locomotor structures of selachian and teleost fishes that swim by undulation of the body; from principles of mechanics and morphology, it predicts kinds of changes in these structures during swimming and mentions mechanical properties that permit, control, and limit the function of structural features in swimming. A hypothetical explanation of the locomotor body bending in fishes is stated, and the means to achieve it and the chances of success in this endeavor are considered.

THE BASIC SYSTEM

Skeleton

The set of all supportive and protective structures in an animal's body is its skeleton. The skeleton provides the tensile integrity of the body, and it functions by reacting to mechanical forces. The following, oversimplified summary describes the postcoelomic skeleton of most squaloids and teleosts from outside inwards.

The multilayered, collagenous dermis forms a cylindrical tube (Fig. 3-1A) that surrounds the body; the tube is bisected from dorsal to ventral side by the median septum. This septum is a flexible collagen-fabric membrane that suspends the backbone (Fig. 3-1A and B). The backbone is a longitudinal series of spool-shaped vertebral centra joined end-to-end by collagenous intervertebral ligaments. Cartilaginous or bony arches attached to the centra protect the spinal cord dorsally and the dorsal aorta ventrally (Fig. 3-1A). In teleosts, long bony spines arise from these arches and reinforce the median septum (Fig. 3-1A and B). The tube is further divided longitudinally by three

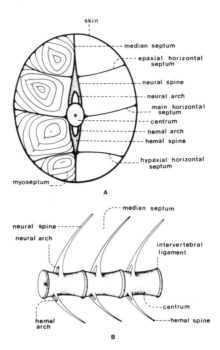

Figure 3-1
Diagrams of the teleost postcoelomic skeletal system. *A,* Cross-section showing the cylindrical tube of skin partitioned into channels filled with muscle; bone is stippled. *B,* Lateral view of the backbone, anterior at left.

horizontal septa that are roughly perpendicular to the median septum. The main horizontal septum intersects the median septum along the backbone (Fig. 3-1*A*), and the other two lie dorsal and ventral to the main one. Intermuscular bones, when present, reinforce septa.

Because the skin, the intervertebral ligaments, and the four septa are made of fibrous collagen in a gel matrix, the entire skeleton is flexible. Vertebral centra are rigid, and the backbone confers axial stiffness on the skeleton. Intervertebral ligaments ensure limited and frictionless flexibility but prohibit torsion and lateral shearing of the backbone. Rigid neural and hemal arches attached to the centra limit the magnitude of dorsoventral flexure to a small fraction of lateral flexure.

Thus the skeleton is seen as a membranous tube divided longitudinally by membranous septa and stiffened locally by vertebral structures that limit the directions and magnitude of bending. The skeletal tube is a cluster of eight channels that run the length of the body, four on each side. The number of channels varies: squaloids have five on a side, and some bony fishes have three. These channels are filled with longitudinal musculature that supplies the force for undulatory locomotion.

Musculature

Seen from the side with the skin removed, fish locomotor musculature is organized into a series of short segments called *myomeres* that fill the channels in the skeleton from the head to the tail. There are two myomeres per vertebra. All the muscle cells in a myomere are oriented roughly longitudinally, and they attach, fore and aft, to myosepta, yet another set of flexible, collagen-fabric membranes that span the body transversely. Each myomere on one side of most bony fish has the form of a dorsoventral stack of three or four cones: the dorsal-most and ventral-most cones point backward, and the larger middle cones(s) point forward (Fig. 3-2). Myomeres and myosepta have the same shape and their cones lie nested in one another. A single myomere may span from 3 to 12 intervertebral joints between the tips of its anterior and posterior cones depending on the species and the position of the myomere in the body.

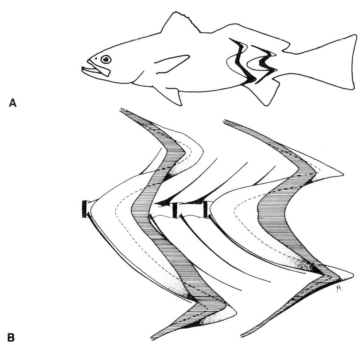

A

B

Figure 3-2
Myomeres and myosepta in the sea trout *Cynoscinon regalis nebulosis. A,* Lateral view showing the position of the two myomeres shown in *B. B,* Myomeres and their position with regard to the backbone. Hatched area is next to the skin; dashed lines indicate the hidden margin of myomere where it attaches to the backbone. Anterior and posterior surfaces of myomeres are covered by myosepta.

The Focus

The musculature fits into the skeleton as follows: each of the longitudinal sets of nested cones fits into one of the skeletal channels bounded by skin and median and horizontal septa. The open ends of myoseptal cones merge with the fabric of the skin and horizontal septa (Figs. 3-1*A* and 3-3). Myoseptal cone tips do not attach directly to other skeletal elements but muscle cells attach to them, fan out, and attach to the next myoseptum or to the median septum. In fact, horizontal septa appear to be formed by the merger of myosepta, and herein lies the focus of this account of the skeletomuscular system. Evidence from carcharhinid sharks, sea trout (*Cynoscinon regalis nebulosis*), and white marlin (*Tetrapturus albidus*) suggests that muscle cells anchored to the median septum pull on the tip of the myoseptal cone that in turn transmits the force to the skin and thence inward by means of the horizontal septa to the median septum and the backbone, which bends in response to the transmitted force.

PRINCIPLES OF SKELETAL MECHANICS

It is necessary to identify force trajectories in fish; this is easier if the following structures are recognizable:

> those that transmit tensil forces in a straight line without decrement
> those that convert circumferential tensile forces into longitudinal forces
> those that resist bending, compression, or torsion
> those that disperse forces
> those that accept and transmit either point forces or distributed forces
> those that permit bending, especially without kinking
> those that generate or accommodate hydrostatic forces

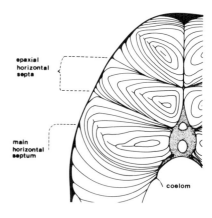

Figure 3-3
Cross-section of a blacktip shark (*Carcharhinus limbatus*, 109 cm long) through the coelom. Note the thickness of myosepta as they attach to the skin, merging of myosepta into three horizontal septa, and stout attachment of horizontal septum to the backbone. Bone is stippled.

Stiff and Pliant Materials

From the liquid in the intervertebral capsule of a shark through cartilage, septa, skin, and bone, there is a continuous series of materials of increasing stiffness. Fluids do not resist deformation, but by their viscosity they resist the rate of deformation (Vogel, 1981). Because all structural materials are hydrated, all can be expected to have some viscous component to their otherwise elastic behavior. Elasticity or stiffness is the property of solids that measures how forcefully a solid resists deformation and returns to its undeformed shape.

When a tensile force (F) is applied to a fiber of cross-sectional area (A), a stress ($\sigma = F/A$) is induced in the fiber, and its change of length (ΔL) is reported as strain ($\epsilon = \Delta L/L_0$). The stiffness of the fiber is the stress per unit strain (σ/ϵ) and is called E, the elastic modulus.

The stiffest material in fishes is made up of bone or calcified cartilage; the stiffness is caused by the presence of submicroscopic crystals of calcium salts bound by a hydrated matrix of collagen, glycoproteins, and proteoglycans. Crystallinity and high degrees of preferred molecular orientation are sources of stiffness, and collagen, the most abundant component of skeletal materials in vertebrates, is a highly oriented, crystallizable fibrous protein. Preferred molecular orientation in plant and animal tissues can most easily be seen in thin specimens with a polarized light microscope (Bennet, 1961). This microscope shows such order in skin, septa, vertebrae, spines, ribs, and cartilage of fishes; it also allows the direction of molecular orientation to be determined, which is also found to be the direction of greatest stiffness in these materials.

The directions of preferred orientation and greatest stiffness in soft tissues can also be determined by teasing them apart with fine tools under a stereomicroscope. For example, septa have regions where fibers are large, densely arrayed, and aligned parallel to one direction (Fig. 3-4A). Other regions of the same septum may show two sets of parallel fibers that are set at some angle to each other (Fig. 3-4B); in still other regions, fibers will have random orientation in the plane of the septum (Fig. 3-4C). If the numbers of fibers per unit area of the septum is the same in each case, the greatest stiffness will be in the parallel-fibered, tendonlike case (Fig. 3-4A), the next greatest will be parallel to either set of fibers (Fig. 3-4B), and the next stiffest will be in any direction (Fig. 3-4C). A low stiffness but a high extensibility will occur in Figure 3-4C and in the directions between fibers in Figure 3-4B. The tendonlike material depicted in Figure 3-4A may have no structural integrity at all normal to its fibers.

Notice that pulling on fibers in all the examples in Figure 3-4 would give a linear response as shown in the stress-strain curve in Figure 3-5A. This means that stress and strain are proportional to one another by a constant value that tells the slope of the line and the stiffness of the sample:

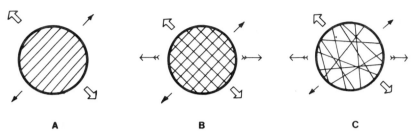

A   **B**   **C**

Figure 3–4
Diagrams of membranes reinforced with stiff fibers. *A*, Parallel fibers: stiff along solid arrows; virtually no strength along hollow arrows. *B*, Orthogonal array with two directions of parallel fibers: stiff along solid and open arrows; stiffness increases along feathered arrows. *C*, Random array of fibers; equal stiffness in all directions.

$$\sigma = E\epsilon \tag{1}$$

This is the kind of response obtained from a tendon if all fiber kinks have been pulled out before the test.

Of more general interest is the response obtained from pulling on an orthogonal array in the bias direction (Fig. 3-4*B*; *feathered arrows*); the curve is shown in Figure 3-5*B*. An example of this stress response is the extension of skin on the extending side of a swimming shark. The graph says that the first unit of stress produces a large amount of strain; the skin stiffness is very low. The next units of stress produce progressively less strain until a very high stiffness is observed. The general applicability of this stress response for soft tissues in nature was given us by Gordon (1978) in an account that should be required reading; it means that the amount of deformation varies with the amount of stress applied. Because a muscle contracts progressively, any such tissue pulled by a muscle will stretch according to both the force and the time—or loading rate—since the contraction began. Recall that because all biomaterials contain water, they are all viscous. Interactions between the viscous and elastic components of material behavior in living systems are at

Figure 3–5
Stress-strain curves for fiber-reinforced membranes. Curve A is typical for tensile tests parallel to fibers; curve B is typical for tests not parallel to oriented fibers. Note that while breaking stress (end of the curve) may be the same in both cases, breaking strain can be an order of magnitude greater at high angles to the fibers.

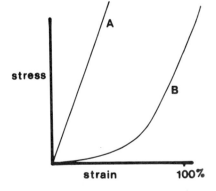

once fascinating, important, and incredibly complex and difficult to analyze.

Fibers of various sizes tell a lot about what to expect from pliant materials. The fiber can be oversimplified as a linear series of atoms held together by their interatomic bonds. Such a structure resists tensile forces but bends readily, and because it is impossible to load axially in compression because of its tendency to buckle, it is useless in such a function. Applying these principles to observations of the distribution of f bers in nature, a rule of thumb arises: *arrays of parallel fibers function by transmitting tensile forces.* One should look for fibers, measure their angular relation to major morphologic axes, and follow this orientation direction to seek the source and insertion or site of action of the forces they transmit.

Liquid or gel materials resist compression if they are tightly contained; they can also permit and even facilitate shearing motions. Permission of motion is just as important as resistance to it, but it can be overlooked if organisms are viewed only in terms of the "problems" they face.

Skeletal Elements

Rigid bony elements can accept point forces where a tendon attaches, and the force is then transmitted throughout the bone. Because this is true, huge muscles can apply large forces to one point, and the lengths of the bones allow for lever systems and their attendant mechanical, speed, and deformation advantages (Alexander, 1968). Blocks of bone such as vertebral centra allow the great locomotor muscles to apply their force to the backbone.

Ribs and spines will not change length appreciably and may act as levers; they may also bend. If two rods of bone of equal length have radii r and $2r$, there is an interesting difference in the amount of force it takes to bend them both by the same amount. The flexural stiffness of a rod is given by

$$\text{flexural stiffness} = E \cdot I \tag{2}$$

where E is the stiffness of the material, and I is the second moment of area of the cross section.

I depends on the shape and dimensions of the rod's section; it is an expression of the distribution of material in the section according to its ability to resist bending.

$$I = \int_0^r y^2 dA \tag{3}$$

where dA is each increment of the area of the section that is distance y from the centroid of the section.

For a rod of circular section

$$I = \frac{\pi r^4}{4} \tag{4}$$

so a rod of radius $2r$ will be stiffer than one of radius r by a factor of 16.

Equation 3 also tells how the shape of the rod's section controls flexural stiffness. For a beam with a rectangular section,

$$I = \frac{ab^3}{12} \tag{5}$$

where b is the dimension lying in the plane of bending. A bone with a rectangular section 1 mm $\times$ 12 mm would have I of 1 mm^4 when bent the easy way and I of 144 mm^4 when bent the hard way. Obviously, the shapes of rigid elements that are bent in swimming must be carefully examined.

Tendons and ligaments are the easiest of the pliant materials to recognize, and their functions are the easiest to guess. They transmit tensile forces from end to end, and they permit deformation in all other directions. It is interesting that except as they appear in tuna (Kishinouye, 1923; Fierstine and Walters, 1968) and in the caudal peduncle of most fishes (Alexander, 1969), tendons have not been widely recognized in fish locomotor systems.

Membranous structures dominate the morphology of fishes. One could assume that the original notochord was a fluid-filled membrane with axial stiffness caused by hydrostatic pressure. This function may remain in the intervertebral capsule, as will be discussed later. Fish skin is known to be a fabric of layers of parallel collagen fibers that wind in right and left-handed helices around fish bodies (Marshall, 1965). Myosepta are known to have more complex arrays of collagen fibers (Willemse, 1972) and so is the median septum (M. LaBarbera, personal communication). The orientation of collagen fibers in horizontal septa of teleosts remains to be described.

The Locomotor System

In analyzing the postcoelomic body of fishes, bone, cartilage, gel, fluid, and fibers may occur in their infinite arrays. They may be attached to muscle, organized into cords, membranes, chunks or rods, and all are subject to the contraction of muscle and the bending of the body.

The contraction of locomotor muscle bends the backbone and appears also to compress it axially. This focuses attention on the rigid vertebrae that can accept point forces but cannot deform and the intervertebral joints that must sustain the axial compression and permit bending. In addition, tracts of parallel collagen fibers in septa are recognized and assumed to transmit forces in septa and skin. Fabrics of skin and septa resist motion along their fibers and permit motion in other directions.

A muscle that contracts also exerts a force normal to its contraction axis: as it shortens, it gets fatter, applying a distributed force, much like a hydrostatic force, to any membranous structures that enclose it. These matters and the principles controlling them are deferred to the section on internal pressure.

MORPHOLOGICAL CHANGES DURING BODY BENDING

The morphologic features known or suspected to be involved in bending the fish body and their possible changes in shape are shown in Figure 3-6. Movies of swimming fish taken from above show changes in body shape (Fig. 3-6*A* and *B*) and skin dimensions during swimming, but no record of such information is accompanied by changes in myomeric dimensions, cross-sectional areas of muscle, skin thickness or fiber angles, length of vertebral centra, or length of intervertebral ligaments.

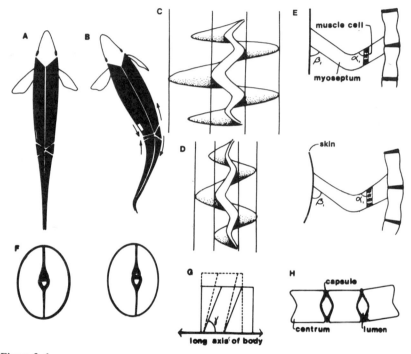

Figure 3-6

Morphologic changes occurring during locomotor bending in fishes. *A,* and *B,* Skin elongates on the convex, extending side and shortens on the concave, contracting side. *C,* A myomere when body is straight. *D,* The same but on the concave side of bent body; the dorsoventral dimensions does not change. *E,* (below) Horizontal section through backbone, a muscle cell, two myosepta, and skin when body is straight; (above) Structures from E when muscle is contracted and body is bent. (α, angle between the muscle cell and myoseptum; β, angle between the myoseptum and skin.) Note that the distance from backbone to skin increases. *F,* Cross-sections of fish body (body straight at left, bent to the left at right) showing increase of cross sectional area of muscle on contracting side S and decrease on extending side X. *G,* The solid-lined square represents a patch of midlateral skin at rest, and the dashed line rectangle represents the same skin patch on the shortened side of a bent fish. Diagonal lines are dermal collagen fibers (γ, fiber angle). *H,* Horizontal section through two vertebral centra of a shark with body straight (left) and body bent (right).

Muscle Trajectories

Willemse (1966) has shown on graphic models that the myomeres become shorter during muscle contraction, and their conical angles increase (β in Fig. 3-6E increases). It appears that there can be no change in the dorsoventral dimension, so the thickness (distance from the axial skeleton to the lateral skin) must increase during contraction if muscle volume is to remain constant. The complete lack of morphometric data on change in myomeric shape in a swimming fish is a severe impediment to our understanding of the mechanisms underlying fish swimming.

Alexander (1969) has described the patterns of orientation of muscle fibers in fishes; he defined an imaginary line he called the *muscle fiber trajectory* that is determined by following the course of a muscle cell through a myotome, across a myoseptum, through a muscle cell in the next myotome, and so on. He revealed two patterns of muscle cell trajectories corresponding to two swimming modes: he found the selachian pattern in dogfish, eel, sturgeon, and *Amia* and in the caudal peduncles of most teleosts. He found the teleost pattern in *Ciliata, Xiphophorous, Pterophyllum, Clupea, Perca, Gonichthyes, Hyphessobrycon, Sebastes,* and *Scomber.*

In the selachian pattern, the muscle cell trajectories lie in nested cones that have the same dimensions as myotomal cones but that are pointed in the opposite direction (Fig. 3-7). The lateral-most cells lie at angles less than 10 degrees to the long axis of the body, while more medial cells lie at large angles, up to 37 degrees to the body axis. The tendons extending from the tips of myomeric cones lie some distance from the axial skeleton. Myosepta thicken as they approach attachments with skin and horizontal septa (Fig. 3-3, Willemse, 1972). The stout attachment of myosepta to the skin is responsible for the difficulty in cleanly skinning a shark or dogfish.

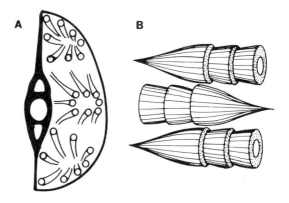

Figure 3-7
Features of the selachian muscle fiber trajectories. *A,* Cross-section showing convergence of muscle cells in cones (anterior is into the page). (Redrawn from Alexander, 1969.) *B,* Lateral view of muscle cell trajectory cones (anterior at left).

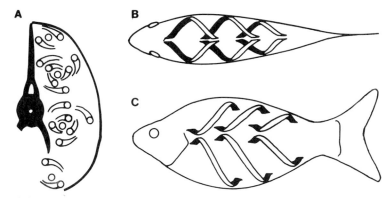

Figure 3-8
Features of the teleost muscle cell trajectories. *A,* Cross-section showing helical array of muscle cells (anterior is into the page). *B,* Dorsal and *C,* lateral see-through views of the helices. (Redrawn from Alexander, 1969).

In the teleost pattern, the muscle fiber trajectories are helices, the axes of which lie less than half the distance from the axial skeleton to the skin (Fig. 3-8). Muscle cells near the axes of the helices lie in horizontal planes, while medial and lateral cells lie at pitch angles up to 32 degrees to the body axis. Tendons occur at cone tips, but they are relatively thinner than those in the selachian pattern. Myosepta are thin throughout, and although they attach to the medial septum and the skin, they are not particularly stout at these junctions (Willemse, 1972; Hebrank, personal communication).

In order to understand Alexander's (1969) proposed functional significance of the selachian and teleost patterns of muscle cell trajectories, it must be recalled that for each muscle there is a rate of contraction at which the efficiency of generating tension is maximum (Hill, 1950). Alexander suggests that red muscles operate at a rate of contraction that promotes efficiency, while white muscle operates at rates that promote the highest power output. He calculates that a fish with the selachian pattern shortens its muscle cells by 7% to 9% to effect a body bend that a teleost can produce with a contraction of 2% to 3%. Another way to put this is that if all fish swimming muscle has the optimum rate of contraction, those with helical muscle cell trajectories will reach this optimum contraction rate at higher swimming speeds than will those with conical muscle cell trajectories. Bainbridge (1958) has reported that teleosts appear to swim faster than selachians of the same size. Still another comparison of the two patterns is that the selachian one maximizes the production of muscular force, while the teleost one maximizes speed.

Alexander (1969) also noted that the selachian pattern is found in the caudal peduncle of most teleosts. He examined this design feature for a functional advantage for the fish and found that if the peduncle were designed as a cantilever based on the body and supporting the forces that are applied to the tail during swimming, the best shape for the peduncle would be one in which the linear dimensions of any cross-section are proportional to the cube of the distance from the section to the center of loading (solid line in Fig. 3-9). Because caudal peduncles of fishes have much thinner shapes (dashed line in Fig. 3-9), it is clear that tensile stresses in muscles in the peduncle will be much higher than those in muscles anterior to it. Alexander pointed out that muscle in the selachian pattern produce more force per unit sectional area than will muscle in the teleost pattern. To provide for higher tensile stresses in the caudal peduncle in the tunas, which are not only the fastest swimmers for their size but whose caudal peduncles are also proportionately thinner than those of other fishes, there are great tendons made of nested myoseptal tendons from many anterior myotomes running through the peduncle to the caudal fin. In the caudal peduncle of squaloids, regions of myosepta near the skin are greatly thickened and look like tendons. Following the rule of thumb, these will be found to transmit tensile stresses.

Force Trajectories and Horizontal Septa

While muscle cells are arranged in trajectories, cones, and myomeres, they also attach to myosepta. Because myosepta have tracts of collagen fibers (illustrated by Willemse, 1972, for *Squalus*) and because the main function of oriented fibers in animals is to sustain tensile loads, some portion of the force of muscle contraction can be expected to be transmitted by myosepta. Most of the force may be transmitted by the tracts of collagen fibers in the directions of the highest degree of orientation.

A force trajectory is defined here as an imaginary line or family of lines beginning in a muscle cell and running through the series of connected tissues that transmit the force of muscle cell contraction to the axial skeleton. When a force trajectory reaches a myoseptum, part of it will be transmitted straight through to the next muscle cell and part will be transmitted in the myoseptum along the collagen tracts. In myosepta of *Squalus,* Willemse (1972) shows such

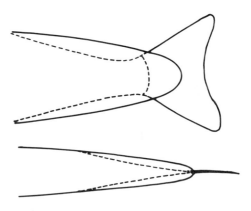

Figure 3-9
Lateral and top views of fish tails. Explanation is given in the text. (From Alexander, 1969).

a tract running in an arch from anterior to posterior end of a myoseptum and ending in the tendinous extension of the myoseptal cone tips. He shows another tract nearly at right angles to this that surrounds the myomeric cones and is continuous with tracts in the horizontal septum.

A clear picture of force trajectories is coming from studies of white marlin (*Tetrapturus albidus*) and blue marlin (*Makaira nigricans*) (S. A. Wainwright, unpublished observations). In fishes it is particularly dangerous to generalize from observations made on a single species, especially when the species is as highly specialized for fast swimming as are marlin; nevertheless, the basic structure of the marlin is similar enough to that of other fish that it is worth describing as a guide for hypotheses and future observations. The major unique features of the marlin are in the backbone; first, neural and hemal spines are expanded into broad plates that make the backbone a great lath of bone that extends two-thirds of the body length; second a pair of anterior zygapophyses from each centrum extend forward across the intervertebral joint and overlap the backward extended neural spine of the next anterior vertebra (Cuvier and Valenciennes, 1831).

The marlin force trajectory is as follows. Muscle cells originating on the backbone converge and insert on each of the two anterior-pointing myoseptal cones. Myoseptal fibers lie in tracts (Fig 3-10) that begin at the cone tip as diffuse tracts facing the backbone, becoming denser as the fibers enlarge and converge into a broad, thick longitudinal tract on the skin side of the cone. Where this tract and its myoseptal cone merge with the skin, the myoseptum is thick and its attachment to the skin is stout and strong. The line of attachment of the myoseptum to the skin is a V-shaped line with the V pointing forward. At the posterior, open end of the myoseptum, the dense tract of collagen fibers follows the cone surface from the skin backward and inward as stout tendinous tracts in the horizontal septum on one side of the cone and on the other side of the cone in the epaxial or hypaxial horizontal septum (Fig. 3-10). The tendinous tract in the horizontal septum attaches to the midlateral crest of each centrum. The tracts in the epaxial and hypaxial horizontal septa attach to the median septum along the distal ends of the neural and hemal spines, respectively. The tendinous tracts in the main horizontal septum of the marlin are probably homologous to the similarly placed and oriented array of highly discrete tendons in this position in tuna (Kishinouye, 1923). The epaxial and hypaxial horizontal septa have not been previously described as such. Data and photos of dissections of black tip shark (*Carcharhinus Limbatus*) and sea trout (*Cynoscinon regalis nebulosis*) show that there is a thick septal structure lying between adjacent rows of nested cones. This septum is formed by the merging of myosepta in all these fish (Fig. 3-10). It is at the points of fusion of skin and horizontal septa that myosepta are thickest and their fibers are largest, most densely packed, and oriented longitudinally. The presence of tendinous tracts in horizontal septa of fishes other than tuna and marlin has been neither sought nor yet reported but it is likely that they will be found.

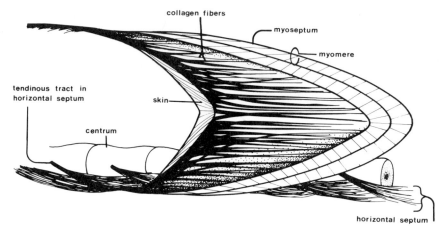

Figure 3-10

Some of the elements in the force trajectory system of the epaxial muscle cone in a marlin. Anterior to right. Muscle cells in the myomere (shown hatched in vertical section) originate anteriorly on the greatly expanded vertebral neural spines (not shown) or on a myoseptum. It is assumed that all muscle anterior to this is in tension. When the cells contract, they pull on their insertion: the next posterior myoseptum. The array of collagen fibers in the myoseptal cone transmits the force and displacement outward and backward on the cone's surface to the myoseptal junction with the skin. Collagen fibers in the skin transmit the work backward and dorsad and ventrad to the junction of skin with horizontal septa. Then the work is transmitted inward and backward in the tendinous tracts of the horizontal septa to the vertebrae.

The information gained so far leads to the following hypothetical force trajectory for muscles made of anterior-pointing cones in fishes that swim by undulation: muscle cells have their origin on backbone and median septum, and they converge and insert on myoseptal cones (Alexander, 1969; Willemse, 1972). Collagen-fiber tracts in the cones transmit forces backward and outward in the myoseptum to its attachment with the skin, thence backward along the skin and then backward and inward in tendinous tracts in epaxial, main, and hypaxial horizontal septa to the median septum and the backbone. This account does not include the backward-pointing cones that are here predicted to have a similar arrangement: tendinous tracts in horizontal septa may exist that cross the tracts for the forward-pointing cones. This hypothesis has the advantage that anterior muscle pulls mainly on oriented collagen tracts rather than on muscle posterior to it. Posterior muscle in backward-pointing cones will similarly pull on collagen tracts rather than on muscle only.

Assuming that force is transmitted across obtuse angles where membranous structures meet, circumferential forces in the myoseptum generated by the thickening of contracting muscle are transmitted by the horizontal septum to the axial skeleton. Longitudinal forces are transmitted along myosepta such that successive myosepta slide past one another, causing the angle between the muscle cell and myosepta to increase, as is shown in Figure 3-6E. Myosepta may transmit forces to the axial skeleton and through their thickened peripheral tracts to the skin. Depending on the internal hydrostatic pressure of the fish's body, the skin should be stiff enough to transmit forces longitudinally to its attachment with axial skeleton at head and tail.

Muscle contraction brings myosepta closer together (Fig. 3-6E), causing myomeric cones to shorten longitudinally and to expand laterally (Fig. 3-6C, D, E, and F); meanwhile, muscle cells and myomeres on the opposite side of the fish are being passively extended. The distance between myosepta is increasing, and the angles between muscle cells and myosepta (α in Fig. 3-6E), between myosepta and skin (β in Fig. 3-6E), and between skin collagen fibers and the long axis of the fish (γ in Fig. 3-6G) are decreasing.

The Backbone

The structure of teleost backbones was not described in detail until Symmons' (1979) comparative study. Figure 3-11 is redrawn from her diagram, showing the features common to most of the species she studied. The bony centrum is hollow and shaped like an hourglass in her diagrams of the juvenile fish she studied; it is full of fluid and has a notochordal strand running the entire length of the backbone. At each intervertebral joint there is a notochordal disc lying in the plane of the joint and attaching at its perimeter to the inner intervertebral ligament (IIL) that lies like an O-ring between the edges of the centra. Her interpretation is that the IIL undergoes longitudinal compression and prevents centra from touching one another. Just outside the IIL is the external intervertebral ligament (EIL), which attaches to the outermost edge of the centra. Because it bows outward and is thin, it appears suited to resist tension between centra; it will buckle further outward if it is compressed longitudinally.

There are no published accounts of intervertebral structures in selachians, and the following account is based on unpublished observations. Centra of carcharhinid sharks of roughly 1 m in length have no continuous

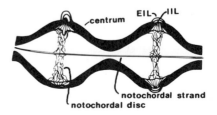

Figure 3-11
Horizontal section through the backbone of a juvenile teleost showing bony centrum (solid black) and pliant structures and the fluid continuity throughout the backbone. Joint at left is bent. (Redrawn from Symmons, 1979.)

Figure 3–12
Horizontal section through intervertebral structures on one side of a
bent blacktip shark, 109 cm long. *A,*
Convex, extended side. *B,* Concave,
contracted side. A and B are camera
lucida drawings of a 20-μ thick
section of a plastic embedded backbone.

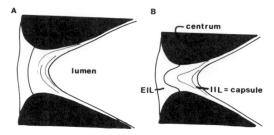

central cavity; instead, there is a closed intervertebral capsule of laminar
cartilage attached firmly to the concave ends of two calcified centra. Figure
3-12 shows that the capsular material is thickest at the equator, where it bulges
out between the edges of the centra. It is certainly analogous to the IIL of
teleosts, but it is in these sharks only a part of the much larger capsule. While
the IIL may undergo longitudinal compression, J.H. Hebrank (personal communication) has noted that hydrostatic pressure in the capsule may be high
enough to keep the IIL in tension at all times! If the capsule is helically wound
with collagen as are mammalian intervertebral discs and the notochord of
amphioxus, it would be yet another example of a hydrostatic structure
wherein the stress on the internal fluid is ultimately taken as tensile stress by
fibers in the capsular wall.

A capsule full of fluid under pressure makes a fine frictionless joint. An
aqueous fluid will not change volume under muscle-driven forces, and it
transmits forces across the joint evenly to all surfaces it touches. If a pin is
stuck into a capsule of a freshly killed shark, a drop of fluid squirts out as the
pin is withdrawn. This indicates that the fluid in the capsule is under pressure
when the fish is at rest. Capsular pressure can be measured in the backbone of
a living dogfish (*Mustelus canis*) after the adjacent capsules have been
punctured, indicating that there is not fluid continuity between capsules in the
dogfish. There is a structure in 1-m long carcharhinids that overlies the
capsule and connects the edges of the centra as does the EIL in teleosts. No
systematic study has yet been made of intervertebral pressures in any fish, and
in fact, no bending tests have been carried out on isolated backbones in
compression. This comment assumes that fish backbones are always compressed in life.

Symmons (1979) described the expansion of isolated backbones as she
cut the dorsal longitudinal ligament, indicating that this ligament holds the
living backbone in compression. Symmons also tested the axial strand and the
notochordal tissues nonquantitatively and concluded that they prevent
"short, sharp movements" from dislocating vertebrae and that they are
responsible for most of the resilience of the backbone. Hebrank (1982b)
observed considerable hysteresis in these structures and concluded that
because they lie on the neural axis (down the center of the backbone), they will
never experience tensile stresses as high as those experienced by the much
stronger, more lateral EIL. She also found no difference in flexural stiffness

between backbones where dorsal longitudinal ligament had been cut and whole ones. While the mechanical functions of these axial structures remain unclear, there is no indication that they contribute to the properties of the backbone in bending.

Isolated backbones of eel (*Anguilla rostrata*) and spot (*Leiostomus xanthurus*) are stiff in compression but compliant in tension, while that of skipjack tuna (*Katsuwonus pelamis*) is stiff in tension and compliant in compression (Hebrank, 1982a). Structural studies may show that the intervertebral ligaments in the tuna buckle on the concave side to permit bending, but at this time no biologically interesting interpretation of the difference in bending mechanisms of spot and tuna is offered.

Backbones isolated from eel, spot, and coho salmon (*Oncorhynchus kisutch*) have low flexural stiffness over the range of lateral curvature that exceeds those seen in movies of swimming fish (Hebrank, 1982; M. LaBarbera, personal communication on salmon). Calculations from data of flexural stiffness for eel and spot indicate that elastic energy stored and released by the isolated backbone in physiological body bends may be as much as 50% of the metabolic energy expended in swimming (Hebrank, 1982b).

The medial septum is rigidly supported by neural and hemal spines that overlap the centrum posterior to their centrum of origin. Connecting the spines is a membrane consisting of collagen fibers in arrays of preferred orientation as shown in Figure 3-13. M. LaBarbera and J. Schmitz (personal communication) have noted that this fibrous array would be put into tension if the backbone were axially compressed or bent. Complex systems of struts and ties that take a substantial portion of compressive or bending loads as tensile stresses have been called *tensegrity structures* by Buckminster Fuller (Marks, 1960). Tensegrity structures usually have their compression members isolated from each other by tension elements; until the stresses are known in intervertebral structures during swimming, it cannot be decided whether the

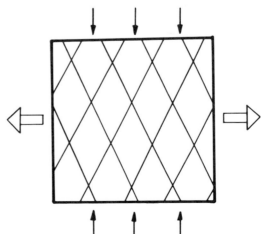

Figure 3-13
Sample from midlateral skin of a lemon shark *Negaprion breviros- tris* used for uniaxial and biaxial testing. Diagonal lines show the orientation of dermal collagen fibers; hollow arrows indicate the longitudinal axis of the fish and the direction of the applied force; solid arrows show the direction of dorso- ventral shortening that occurs when no force is applied to oppose.

fish backbone is a tensegrity system. Hebrank and LaBarbera have recorded no significant difference between the compressive properties of whole backbones and ones whose median septa have been removed implying they are not.

THE SKIN

Force transmitted by way of myosepta to the axial skeleton applies a bending moment to it, but what happens to the force transmitted to the skin? In order to answer this, something must be known about the stiffness of the skin and any changes in stiffness that may occur during swimming.

Body shape changes are easily seen, and if the skin has been suitably marked, changes in length and height of the skin can be measured from movies (Fig. 3-6G). When a half-meter long eel swims, a marked rectangle on the midlateral skin stretches and contracts ±10% to ±15% longitudinally while contracting and stretching ±6% to ±8% circumferentially (Hebrank, 1980). Similar measurements made on a lemon shark (*Negaprion brevirostris*) 87 cm long cruising slowly, showed that skin length changed ±10% and skin height changed ±3% while the body was bent into a 38-cm minimum radius of curvature. During fast swimming, changes in skin length were ±15%, while the body bent into tighter curves of 20-cm radius (Wainwright *et al.*, 1978). These dimensional changes in shark skin are those expected from a material reinforced by rigid fibers in right and lefthand helical arrays at 60 to 65 degrees to the long axis. This is, in fact, the range of fiber angles in the skin over most of the body at rest. Eel skin is stiffer circumferentially (tensile elastic modulus is 14.6 MPa) than longitudinally (3.5 MPa), but here the collagen fiber angle is 45 degrees. This fiber angle should ensure identical stiffness and extensibility in longitudinal and circumferential directions; clearly some as yet undescribed structures besides fiber angle govern skin mechanisms in the eel (Hebrank, 1980).

Internal Pressure and Skin Properties

The connections among the structural features of shark skin and its mechanical properties to be reviewed here lead to the hypothesis that in sharks and eels, the skin functions as a whole body tendon, transmitting the work of muscle contraction to the caudal fin. Principles of fiber-wound pressurized cylinders and biaxial stresses in membranes support the argument.

The first principle is that the stress in the wall of any thin-walled pressurized cylinder is given by

$$\sigma = pr/t \tag{6}$$

where p is the internal pressure, r is the radius of the cylinder, and t is the thickness of the cylinder wall (skin) (Wainwright *et al.*, 1976). The second principle arises from the geometry of the cylinder: in the wall of a pressurized cylinder, the circumferential stress is twice the longitudinal stress (Wainwright *et al.,* 1976). If a pressurized cylinder is reinforced by a helical wrapping of stiff fibers, the balance of circumferential and longitudinal stresses can be controlled to produce any combination of radial and longitudinal shape changes in the cylinder. The single design feature that controls shape change of the cylinder is the fiber angle in the cylinder wall that makes the wall into a bias-cut fabric (Fig. 3-13). From these connected principles it becomes clear that the wall material is subjected to biaxial forces: circumferential and longitudinal ones. A bias-cut fabric subjected to biaxial stresses in directions that bisect the angles made by the fibers behaves differently than does one subjected to a uniaxial stress. Figures 3-14 and 3-15 show this behavior in an isolated sample of lemon shark skin (Hebrank and Vosburg, personal communication).

These principles have been applied to the 87-cm long lemon shark wherein a pressure was measured under the skin of 7 to 14 kPa above ambient at rest, 20 to 35 kPa while cruising, and 200 kPa during a sprint (Wainwright *et al.,* 1978). The shark body is nearly cylindrical, and the fiber angle at rest is 62 degrees. Skin stresses were estimated to be 0.3 MPa in the cruising shark and 2.8 MPa in the sprinting one. When the longitudinal muscle contracts, its radius increases faster than does the radius of the half cylinder of skin that wraps it; thus, a distributed force is applied over the skin. This force is analogous to a hydrostatic pressure, but it will only be present in the skin directly overlying the contracting muscle. Relaxed muscle will damp the transmission of this force to other areas.

Because the principles show that the internal pressure sets the dominating circumferential stress, isolated skin samples were tested biaxially by holding the circumferential stress constant and then pulling in the longitudinal direction. Figure 3-15 shows the results for longitudinal tests on skin samples held at circumferential stresses like those recorded during slow (0.3 MPa) and fast (2.8 MPa) swimming. Over the range of elongations measured from movies of swimming fish, the stress in the skin increases 13-fold from slow to fast swimming, and skin stiffness increases 3.76-fold (from 0.8 to 3.0 MPa).

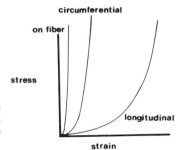

Figure 3–14
Stress-strain curves for uniaxial tests on the lemon shark skin sample in Figure 3-13. The amount of deformation at low stress depends heavily on the angle between the force axis and the fiber orientation.

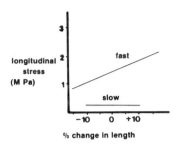

Figure 3–15
Longitudinal stress-strain curves from a biaxial test on the lemon shark skin restrained at constant stress in the circumferential direction: 0.3 MPa for the slow swimming curve and 2.8 MPa for the fast swimming one.

These experiments show that shark skin has the extensibility necessary for the tight bends the body makes in fast swimming. The stiffness of the skin will be controlled by the internal pressure of the shark. Greater skin stresses require greater stiffness if the skin is to transmit the force of muscle contraction. That this can happen in shark skin, keeping it stiff while it shortens in parallel with the underlying muscle, shows a tendon function quite unlike the familiar tendons, in which lengths and stiffness remain constant where they function in series with muscles.

The degree to which any of these conditions applies in other fishes is not known, with the exception that eel skin biaxial properties are similar to those of shark skin (Hebrank, 1980). Skin of spot and skipjack tuna have the crossed-helical collagen-fiber array, but the skin is very thin and does not contract circumferentially when it is pulled longitudinally. Clearly, the collagen fibers are not tightly interlinked and may shear past one another in these skins. In these fishes, the biased collagen-fiber array may serve only to inhibit wrinkling of the skin that would spoil the fish's surface for the best hydrodynamic performance (Hebrank, 1982b).

Transverse Work of Muscles

Most muscles that have been studied do their useful work longitudinally; the increase in diameter that accompanies shortening is also forceful but is not used by most animals. In the shark and the eel, the radial expansion of contracting muscle creates a large circumferential stress in the skin that because the fiber angle is greater than 55 degrees, is shed diagonally along the fibers and contributes to the shortening of the skin. This is an advantage of the crossed-fiber reinforcement of the skin; it allows the transverse work of muscle contraction to help shorten the skin. The contracting locomotor muscle of a shark or eel directly shortens its overlying skin, indirectly shortens the skin by its transverse work, and transmits its force via the skin to the backbone at the head and tail. It is noteworthy that these fish have the selachian pattern of muscle cell trajectories that maximize force output. Because skin stiffness during swimming has not been measured, it is not certain that all the pieces of the preceding argument, drawn from isolated skin samples, are true for the swimming fish; neither is it known whether elastic energy stored in the skin at the extreme position in bending is released to contribute to the acceleration of unbending.

THE MISSING LINK

Most important to testing these and other related hypotheses connecting the contraction of muscle to the bending of the fish body in locomotion are the time course of force generation and shortening in successive muscle cells in muscle trajectories down the body of a swimming fish. Electromyographs illustrate only the electrical activity and say nothing about muscle tension or length changes. X-ray opaque beads can be surgically implanted on myosepta, and x-ray movies made of swimming fish might provide data on dimensional changes. If the surrounding water destroys image contrast, x-ray movies can be taken of a fish struggling in air. The measurement of tension in a muscle cell in a myoseptum or in a horizontal septum *in vivo* are of paramount importance but of abiding difficulty.

CONCLUSION

The great slabs of muscle on the sides of fishes must certainly be the power source for undulatory swimming. They are connected by myosepta to horizontal septa, skin, and the median septum containing the backbone. Because all of these skeletal elements contain tracts of oriented collagen fibers, they may all transmit force and deformation from the muscle to the caudal fin, and they must all be part of the explanation of how fish muscle bends the body. While the most important information yet to be gathered is also the most difficult to get, simple observations, measurements, and experiments continue to provide startling new insights. This subject is a perfect example of the interconnectedness of the universe, whose nature we are discovering in parallel with the rest of our advancing knowledge. Anyone who is impatient with our progress or in doubt of its outcome should read Jacob Bronowski's Silliman Lectures (1978) and then enjoy the pursuit of progress.

REFERENCES

Alexander, R.M. 1968. *Animal Mechanics.* Seattle: University of Washington Press.

Alexander, R.M. 1969. Orientation of muscle fibres in the myomeres of fishes. *J. Marine Biol. Assoc. UK* 49:263–290.

Bainbridge, R. 1958. The speed of a swimming fish as related to size. *J. Exp. Biol.* 35:109–123.

Bennet, H.S. 1961. Polarized light microscopy. In *McClung's Handbook of Microscopical Technique,* edited by R.M. Jones. New York: Hafner Publishing.

Bronowski, J. 1978. *The Origins of Knowledge and Imagination.* Cambridge, MA: Yale University Press.

Cuvier, G., and Valenciennes, A. 1831. *Histoire Naturelle des Poissons,* vol. 8. Paris. (Reprinted by A. Asher, Amsterdam, 1969.)

Fierstine, H.L., and Walters, V. 1968. Studies in locomotion and anatomy of scombroid fishes. *Mem. South Calif. Acad. Sci.* 6:1–31.

Gordon, J.E. 1978. *Structures.* Harmondsworth, U.K.: Penguin Books.

Grillner, S. 1974. On the generation of locomotion in the spinal dogfish. *Exp. Brain Res.* 20:459–470.

Hebrank, M.R. 1980. Mechanical properties and locomotion function of eel skin. *Biol. Bull.* 158:58–68.

Hebrank, M.R. 1982a. Mechanical properties of fish backbones in lateral bending and in tension. *J. Biomech.* 15:85–89.

Hebrank, M.R. 1982b. Roles of the backbone and skin in fish locomotion. Ph.d. dissertation, Duke University.

Hill, A.V. 1950. The dimensions of animals and their muscular dynamics. *Sci. Progr.* 38:209–230.

Kishinouye, K. 1923. Contributions to the comparative study of the so-called scombroid fishes. *J. Coll. Agric., Imp. Univ. Tokyo* 8:293–475.

Marks, R.W. 1960. *The Dymaxion World of Buckminster Fuller.* Carbondale, IL: Southern Illinois University Press.

Marshall, N.B. 1965. *Life of Fishes.* London: Weidenfeld and Nicholson.

Symmons, S. 1979. Notochordal and elastic components of the axial skeleton of fishes and their functions in locomotion. *J. Zool. (London)* 189:157–206.

Vogel, S. 1981. *Life in Moving Fluids.* Boston: Willard Grant Press.

Wainwright, S.A., Biggs, N.D., Currey, J.D., and Gosline, J.M. 1976. Mechanical Design in Organisms. New York: John Wiley & Sons.

Wainwright, S.A., Vosburgh, F., and Hebrank, J.H. 1978. Shark skin: Function in locomotion. *Science* 202:747–749.

Willemse, J.J. 1966. Functional anatomy of the myosepta in fishes. *Proc. Akad. Wetensch. Kon. Nederl.* 69C:58–63.

Willemse, J.J. 1972. Arrangement of connective tissue fibers in the musculus lateralis of the spiny dogfish, *Squalus acanthias. Z. Morph. Tiere.* 72:221–244.

SYMBOLS

A	cross-sectional area	**p**	pressure
E	elastic modulus	**r**	radius
EIL	external intervertebral ligament	**t**	thickness
F	tensile force	α	angle between a muscle cell and myoseptum
I	second moment of area of cross-section	β	angle between myosepta and skin
IIL	internal intervertebral ligament	γ	fiber angle
		ϵ	strain
L_0	initial length	σ	stress
ΔL	change in length		

Chapter 4
CARDIOVASCULAR AND RESPIRATORY FLOW DYNAMICS

B. Lowell Langille
E. Don Stevens
A. Anantaraman

CONTENTS

INTRODUCTION

In all but the simplest life forms, diffusion alone cannot satisfy the transport requirements associated with nutrient supply and removal of metabolic wastes. The development of larger, more sophisticated organisms, particularly the vertebrates, thus gave rise to convective transport systems. In almost all fishes a clearly defined vertebrate pattern is apparent; within this pattern, respiratory, gastrointestinal, and excretory systems exchange nutrients and wastes with the external environment, while a cardiovascular system transports these internally to and from the tissues. Evolutionary adaptation of these transport systems has been subjected to two primary constraints that often conflict. The first is the need to keep diffusion distances minimal. This

92

usually necessitates the proliferation of narrow flow channels within the transport systems. Narrow channels, however, lead to high flow resistances, and this runs counter to the second constraint, which is minimizing the energy costs of transport. It is therefore not surprising that highly sophisticated flow systems have evolved.

As Lighthill (1975, Chap. 10) points out, understanding the dynamics and energetics of moving fluids in physiological systems has involved more than the application of standard mechanical principles; instead, problems of physiological flows have frequently defined new areas of engineering research. This observation undoubtedly reflects the wealth of flow conditions encountered within living systems. Within circulatory systems, for example, pulsatile flow passes through a system of elastic tubes in which flow conditions can vary from transient turbulence to the creeping flow associated with very low Reynolds numbers in the microcirculation. Flow in large vessels is further complicated because entry lengths may be comparable to distances between successive branch sites, such that fully developed flow is not achieved. Water flow across the gills of fishes presents a different spectrum of problems because of the complexity of the flow channels and the variability in respiratory patterns (Holeton and Jones, 1975). Finally, excretory mechanisms are associated with peristaltic propulsion of fluids, a mode of flow that is characterized by continually changing vascular dimensions and a pumping mechanism that cannot be dissociated from the conduits carrying flow.

The above considerations have led to a wealth of studies on physiological fluid mechanics, quantitative experiments dating back at least to Hales' work on the circulation (Hales, 1733). Not surprisingly, most studies have concentrated on flow situations encountered in mammals, whereas other vertebrate transport systems are frequently analyzed in terms of these studies. This is often the only available approach considering the paucity of data on lower vertebrate systems, but the superficial nature of resemblances among vertebrate classes underscores the need for caution.

This chapter concentrates on flows through the cardiovascular and respiratory systems of fishes. Current understanding of these systems is far from comprehensive, but in some areas it is possible to draw definitive conclusions. In other areas some speculation is included in the hope that this will provide some stimulus for future research.

CARDIOVASCULAR DYNAMICS

Circulations of most fishes follow a typically vertebrate pattern: blood is driven by a central pump around a closed vascular system in which exchange takes place in microscopic capillary beds. Nonetheless, the organization of these circulatory systems displays uniquely piscine features in that blood from an undivided heart perfuses the gas exchanger (gill) and systemic circulation *in series,* with no intervening pump. Thus the entire cardiac outflow enters the ventral aorta, which divides into the arterial arches supplying the gills, and efferent vessels from the gills fuse to supply the systemic circulation, largely by means of a dorsal aorta (Fig. 4-1). Although series couplings of distinct vascular beds (*e.g.,* portal systems) are found throughout the vertebrates, two important features distinguish the coupling of gill and systemic beds in fishes and these are of major importance when considering circulatory dynamics. First, all of the cardiac output usually perfuses both systems in a single circulation; second, the vascular flow resistances of the two beds are comparable, and a large pressure drop occurs across both systems. The result is a system in which each of the two beds influences the perfusion and hemodynamics of the other and also influences the nature of cardiovascular coupling.

THE HEART

A four-chambered heart perfuses the circulation of fishes with the sinus venosus, atrium, ventricle, and conus arteriosus arranged in tandem (Fig. 4-2) to deliver blood from the veins to the ventral aorta by sequential contractions that reflect a peristaltic origin. The conus has fused with the ventricular outflow tract in most teleosts (Fig. 4-2), although exceptions exist (Smith, 1918). The cardiac chambers are separated by valves from each other and from the ventral aorta so that flow does not reverse after entering the atrium.

The mechanics of cardiac pumping has been most extensively studied in elasmobranchs (Sudak, 1965; Satchell and Jones, 1967; Satchell, 1970, 1971). In these species, the heart is encased in a rigid pericardium that limits changes in the volume of the complete heart; the volume changes associated with

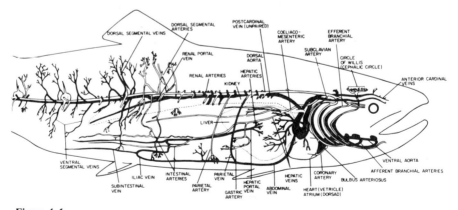

Figure 4-1
Diagram of the heart and major blood vessels of the Pacific salmon. Darkened vessels (veins, ventral aorta, and afferent branchial arteries) carry venous blood from the tissues to the gills. (After Smith and Bell, 1976)

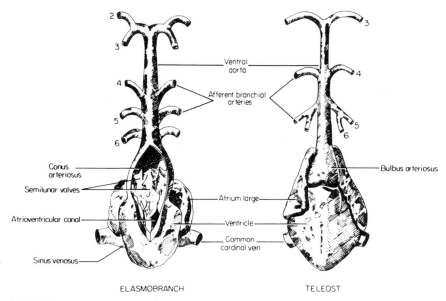

Figure 4-2
The hearts and major afferent arteries of an elasmobranch (*left*) and a teleost (*right*). (After Hildebrand, 1974)

ventricular ejection are largely offset by coincident filling of the sinus and atrium. This mechanical coupling of ejection and filling results because ventricular ejection produces negative intrapericardial pressures that draw the atrial wall outward. Negative pressures are therefore transmitted to the atrial and sinus cavities and contribute to the pressure gradients (venous to cardiac) that fill them (Fig. 4-3). Filling of the heart through suction forces may also depend on the relatively rigid structure of veins of elasmobranchs that prevents their collapse. Veins often consist only of an endothelium that lines contiguous structures, or when a venous wall is well defined, it is often fused with the surrounding tissues (Satchell, 1978). In contrast, Guyton and associates (1957) have shown that negative right atrial pressures cannot significantly increase cardiac filling in mammals because the veins collapse and thereby limit venous return.

Ventricular outflow in elasmobranchs passes through the conus arteriosus enroute to the ventral aorta. The conus contracts after the ventricle, but its volume is so low that it contributes little to cardiac ejection; thus ventral aortic flows are near zero once the ventricle relaxes (Fig. 4-3). Conus contraction is probably more important in preventing backflow from the ventral aorta (Satchell and Jones, 1967) than in propelling blood. The conus is lined with several tiers of valves, but often only one of these can span the lumen of the relaxed conus (Satchell, 1971).

In teleosts, both the pericardium and veins tend to be more collapsible,

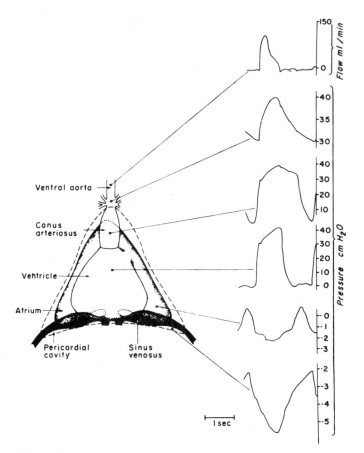

Figure 4–3

Pressures and flows recorded in the cardiac chambers and outflow tract of the heart of an elasmo-branch (*Heterodontus portusjacksoni*). (From Satchell (1970), by permission)

and filling of the heart by suction forces must be less significant than in elasmobranchs. The few available data show positive venous pressures in teleosts (Stevens and Randall, 1967; Randall, 1968). Differences in the dynamics of cardiac ejection can also be inferred because ventricular outflow enters an elastic bulbus rather than the muscular conus arteriosus of elasmobranchs. Although ventricular and ventral aortic pressures resemble those of elasmobranchs (Fig. 4-4), the flow pulse recorded just distal to the bulbus is much different from that downstream of the elasmobranch conus. Outflow from the bulbus persists throughout the cardiac cycle with over 30% of outflow occurring during ventricular diastole (Stevens, et al., 1972). This diastolic flow reflects large storage of blood in the bulbus during systole and subsequent delivery during diastolic recoil. This "windkessel" function is the result of a high distensibility of the bulbus, which is 30 times that of the mammalian aorta (Licht and Harris, 1973). Clearly this contributes much to the smoothing of gill perfusion. In some species the large volume changes of the bulbus during the cardiac cycle apparently necessitate special adaptations to prevent aortic regurgitation into the ventricle during diastole. Trout (*Salmo gairdneri*) have developed papillae (nodular projections of elastic tissue from the bulbus wall) to which the aortic valves attach, thus preventing

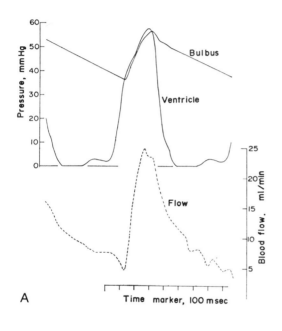

A

Figure 4-4

A, Pressures and flows recorded in the cardiac chambers and outflow tract of the heart of a teleost (*Ophiodon elongatus*). (From Stevens et al., 1972, by permission) *B*, Dorsal aortic pressure and inflow in *Gadus morhua*. (From Jones et al., 1974, by permission)

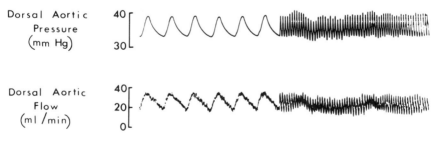

Dorsal Aortic Pressure (mm Hg)

Dorsal Aortic Flow (ml/min)

5 seconds   50 seconds

B   Time

their eversion in the same way that papillary muscles ensure competence of the atrioventricular valves of mammals.

FLOWS IN THE VASCULAR SYSTEM

The cylindrical geometry of the blood vessels would suggest that rigorous analysis of pressure-flow relations should be possible; in reality, pulsatile flow through these branching, distensible tubes is complex, and several generations of models of vascular function have been presented. This is not just the result of a desire for ever increasing accuracy and sophistication; instead, earlier models suffered from fundamental drawbacks, and that precluded understanding of basic features of physiological pressures and flows. For example early "windkessel" or "elastic reservoir" models of arterial function pictured the arterial tree as expanding and recoiling in synchrony during the cardiac cycle, whereas it takes about one-quarter of a cycle for the pulse to traverse most mammalian arterial systems. Consequent wave propagation phenomena give rise to arterial pressures and flows that cannot be described in terms of this simple model.

Similarly, earliest attempts at understanding flow in single straight segments of arteries assumed parabolic (Poiseuille type) velocity profiles. In large arteries of mammals the continual starting and stopping of flow gives rise to inertial effects that produce different velocity profiles. It will be shown that flow conditions in piscine circulations can be quite different from those in mammals and that this influences the choice of the most appropriate vascular models. Indeed, strong arguments can be presented that the most suitable hemodynamic approach depends on the species of fish being examined and, in some cases, even on its physiological state. Flows in isolated segments of large blood vessels are considered first. This is followed by a discussion of factors influencing pressure-flow relations in the complete vascular system.

Local Blood Flow Patterns in Single Vessels

It is frequently pointed out that Poiseuille was primarily interested in problems of blood flow when he developed what has become the fundamental relationship between flow in pipes and the pressure gradients that drive them

$$\frac{\delta p}{\delta z} = \frac{4\mu U(r)}{R^2 - r^2} = \frac{8\mu}{\pi R^4} \cdot Q \qquad (1)$$

where z is the coordinate along the axis of the pipe, $\frac{\delta p}{\delta z}$ is the pressure gradient, μ is fluid viscosity, r is radial position, R is the pipe radius, U is fluid velocity and Q is volume flow rate through the pipe. In reality, Poiseuille's law

finds little applicability in the (mammalian) circulation. In the microcirculation, the size of blood cells becomes significant when compared with vessel
size so the assumption of a Newtonian fluid (implicit in assigning an invariant
viscosity to blood) becomes intractable. In large mammalian vessels. Poiseuille-type flow does not occur because the flow is highly pulsatile and
because inertial effects give rise to secondary flows at bends and branch sites.
In other species, however, the nature of flow in large arteries is variable, and a
range of flow regimes is encountered.

Considering first steady (time-averaged) flows in cylindrical vessels, three
different flow regimes can be identified with three ranges of the Reynolds
number, $Re = \dfrac{\rho U R}{\mu}$. For $Re < 1$, inertial effects are negligible, thus flow follows vessel geometry even at bends and branch sites ("creeping flow"). For Re
between 1 and 500 to 1000, such geometric irregularities produce secondary
(nonaxial) flows; boundary layer separation, vortex formation, and helical
flows near branches are examples of secondary flows. Thus disturbances are
produced at the origins of arteries, and these disrupt downstream flows. The
distance that disturbances are propagated downstream defines the "entrance
length" of the vessel, which is usually arbitrarily defined as the distance before
velocity profiles no longer deviate from Poiseuille flow by more than 1%.
When measured in vessel radii, the entrance length is about 1/6 Re. The third
flow regime corresponds to $Re > 1000$; when inertial effects totally destabilize
flow and large, randomly varying, nonaxial velocities are produced (*i.e.*, the
flow is turbulent).

Turbulence is probably a rare event in the arterial systems of resting
fishes, even the largest species. Evidence for this is found in available data on
blood flows and velocities in the large vessels. For example, Johansen and
colleagues (1966) measured flow velocities in the ventral aorta of a 20-kg skate
(*Raja binoculata*) and found that peak velocities were below 20 cm/sec. This
yields Re of 300, assuming that blood viscosity is 3 cP (3 times that of water), a
typical value for vertebrate blood, and that ventral aortic radius is 1 cm. On
the other hand, cardiovascular adjustments of fishes to exercise include up to
tenfold increases in cardiac output. Because these increases in cardiac output
are often largely caused by increased stroke volume as opposed to heart rate
(Jones and Randall, 1978), it is likely that parallel increases in peak Re result,
and thus systolic turbulence in the ventral and dorsal aortae of large species
during exercise is likely.

Laminar flow probably characterizes all physiological situations for the
smaller species (1 to 3 kg) that are more commonly studied. In a resting, 2.5-kg
cod (*Gadus morhua*) for example, a cardiac output of 40 ml/min (Jones et al.,
1974) flows through a ventral aorta that has a radius of about 0.25 cm. This
yields a $Re \simeq 30$ and turbulence is unlikely even at the much elevated flows
associated with stress or exercise. Nonetheless, flow in large arteries must be

characterized by secondary flow phenomena, and disturbances at the origins of large arteries in these species generate entrance lengths that are of the order of one to ten vessel diameters. The nature of such disturbances at branch sites for intermediate Reynolds numbers has now been well studied (Ferguson and Roach, 1972; O'Brien and Ehrlich, 1977, Langille and Adamson, 1981) Side branches of arteries tend to trap the slowly moving (low inertia) fluid near the walls of the parent vessel while the more rapidly flowing fluid in the mainstream is simply deflected toward but not into the daughter branch (Fig. 4-5A). Fluid inertia also causes flow to impinge on the downstream lip of the branch ostia, and then flow is deflected around the wall of the branch. In the mainstream of the daughter branch, flow is forced into a double helical pattern, but trapped vortices are not seen in any branches that approximate anatomic geometry. In Y-type bifurcations, the mainstream flow impinges on the carina of the branch before generating the double helical pattern of flow described above, in the daughter vessels. These patterns are based on models of steady flow through rigid vessels, but there is now evidence that time-averaged flows in blood vessels are similar. Vascular endothelial cells align themselves with time-averaged flow (Langille and Adamson, 1981), and this alignment gives a clear indication of secondary flows in large arterial branches (Fig. 4-5B). A simple axial alignment of cells is seen near smaller branches where Reynolds number is low.

Although very small species of fish have not been the subject of detailed hemodynamic study, it is clear that secondary flow phenomena must be of decreasing importance. Thus, in a 5-g goldfish, it is probable that secondary flows exist only in the aortae, and in even smaller species creeping flow must characterize the complete vascular system.

Pulsatile Flow

The above considerations characterize steady (time-averaged) flow but ignore the pulsatile nature of blood flow. While nonsteady flows introduce many problems, some sophisticated analyses have now shed light on such flows in arteries. One of the most successful approaches has been that of Womersley (1957), who linearized the Navier–Stokes equations to derive analytical descriptions of sinusoidal flow. The more complex (nonsinusoidal) flows that occur physiologically can then be synthesized from Womersley's analysis by using Fourier analysis techniques, again assuming linearity. Some of the assumptions required for linearization (notably, neglecting convective accelerations) have been questioned, but most features of arterial flows can be accounted for using this approach. For a lucid description of nonlinear methods of analyses and the additional accuracy they provide, the reader is referred to Atabek (1980).

A second assumption that simplifies analysis of pulsatile flow is that local

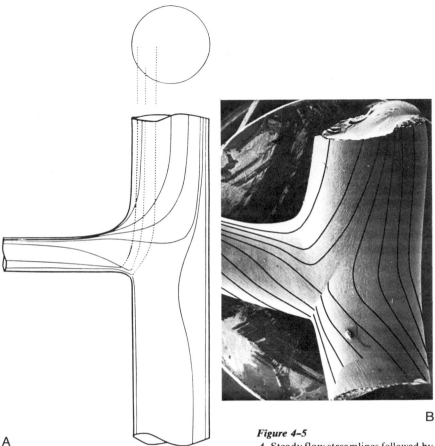

A

B

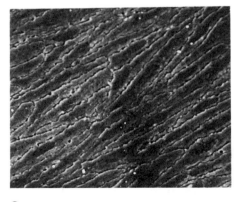

C

Figure 4-5

A, Steady flow streamlines followed by dye injections into a model arterial branch site. Reynolds number in the upstream parent vessel is 500, and 20% of the total flow enters the branch. Solid lines indicate streamlines near the walls of the vessels. *B,* Plastic injection cast of an arterial junction. Black lines illustrate time-averaged direction of flow near the wall of the branch. Flow direction is derived from the orientation of endothelial cells, which are aligned by flow. Cell orientation is measured from the impressions they leave in the casts (see *C*); markers are 100 μ. *C,* High-power view of the cast shown in *B,* illustrating impressions of endothelial cells and their protruding nuclei in the cast.

pressure-flow relations can be analyzed by considering the arteries to be rigid vessels. Arterial compliance has a major effect on overall arterial function, but the local distension of most individual arteries is small. Systemic arterial radii change by less than 5% during the cardiac cycle of mammals (see Patel and Vaishnav, 1980), and because available data indicate that fish arteries are not more compliant (Learoyd, 1963, cited in Satchell, 1971), large variations in diameters are not anticipated. In addition, most blood vessels are well "tethered" to surrounding tissues, so it is safe to assume that longitudinal excursions of the vessel wall are very small (Patel and Vaishnav, 1980). Womersley (1957) has shown that at the level of approximation involved in linearization, *local* pressure-flow relations are not affected by the assumption of a rigid wall.

Linearization and symmetry considerations reduce the three-dimensional Navier–Stokes equation to the single scalar equation

$$P \cdot \frac{\delta w}{\delta t} = -\frac{\delta P}{\delta z} + \mu \frac{\delta^2 w}{\delta r^2} + \frac{l}{r} \frac{\delta w}{\delta r} \tag{2}$$

where w is the axial (z) component of the fluid velocity vector, and r is radial position. Assuming that temporal variations in the pressure gradient are sinusoidal, one can write

$$-\frac{\delta P}{\delta z} = Pe^{\mathrm{int}} \qquad w = w_1 e^{\mathrm{int}} \tag{3}$$

and substitution into equation 2 yields Bessel's equation (zero order)

$$\frac{\delta^2 w_1}{\delta r^2} + \frac{l}{r} \frac{\delta w_1}{\delta r} - \frac{i\, n\, \rho}{\mu} = \frac{P_1}{\mu} \tag{4}$$

Boundary conditions required to solve equation are the "no-slip condition," which indicates that fluid adjacent to the wall is at rest, $w_1\,(r = R) = 0$, and

$$\left(\frac{\delta w_1}{\delta r} \right)\bigg|_{r=0} = 0 \tag{5}$$

which follows from symmetry and the requirement that the solution be continuous. Thus the solution to equation 4 for a vessel of radius R is

$$W = \frac{P}{i\, n\, \rho} \left(1 - \frac{J_0 \left(\alpha \frac{r}{R} \iota^{3/2} \right)}{J_0 \left(\alpha \iota^{3/2} \right)} \right) e^{\mathrm{int}} \tag{6}$$

and integrating over the vessel cross-section yields the volume flow rate

$$Q = \frac{\pi R^2 P_1}{i\,n\,\rho}\left(1 - \frac{2\,J_1(\alpha\iota^{3/2})}{\alpha\iota^{3/2}\,J_0(\alpha\iota^{3/2})}\right)e^{\text{int}} \tag{7}$$

where $\alpha = R\sqrt{\frac{\eta\rho}{\mu}}$. More general (nonsinusoidal) pressure gradients can be treated by applying Fourier decomposition (McDonald, 1974). The non-dimensional parameter, α (Womersley parameter), specifies the shape of velocity profiles at any instant, although absolute velocity also depends on ρ and n. Thus α defines the effects of the oscillatory nature of flow (α^2 can be thought of as a nondimensional frequency). Figure 4-6 shows instantaneous velocity profiles predicted by equation 6 for every 15 degrees of a sinusoidal cycle and for $\alpha = 0.05$, 3.34, and 6.67. Note that the velocity of the fluid in the centreline (with the greatest peak velocity and hence most inertia) lags behind

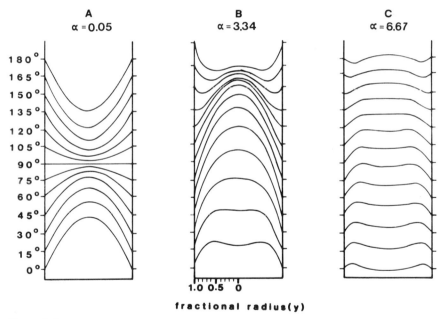

Figure 4-6
Velocity profiles in cylindrical vessels produced by a sinusoidal pressure gradient. Velocity profiles are shown for one-half of one cycle, and adjacent profiles are separated in time by one twenty-fourth of a cycle (15 degrees). Velocity profiles are similar for the second half of the cycle, but in the opposite direction. Note that as α increases velocity profiles deviate from parabolic. Velocity profiles in *B* and *C* are the result of oscillating pressure gradients that are of equal amplitudes. The pressure gradient needed to produce the profiles in *A* is one-fourth as large. (*B* and *C*, after Womersley, 1957).

that of the slower moving fluid close to the wall when α is large. Also, as α increases the profiles deviate more from the parabolic profiles of steady flow predicted by equation 1 and became more blunted, or even bimodal. These features of the velocity profile are observed *in vivo* (Nerem et al., 1974) although quantitative comparisons with Womersley's theory requires Fourier synthesis of the velocity profiles associated with nonsinusoidal pressure oscillations. At high values of α, fluid inertia results in smaller oscillation of volume flow rate for the same pressure gradient. Furthermore, a significant phase lag between pressure gradient and flow rate is observed. This phase lag approaches 90 degrees at very high values of α. If α is less than one, then instantaneous volume flow rate (Q) varies by less than 2% from that predicted by Poiseuille flow, and the phase difference between pressure gradient and flow is less than 10%. In addition, the velocity profiles at any instant are parabolic. In other words, flow is quasistatic at low values of α, and Poiseuille's law (equation 1) can be applied at any instant in time.

In mammals, α is remarkably consistent for homologous vessels from different species, and variations are within an order of magnitude (1.5 to 15) for the fundamental harmonic of flow for the aortae of mice, dogs, and humans, despite 30-fold differences in vessel radii. This is because variations in radii are largely offset by opposing changes in frequency, because heart rate tends to decrease with increasing species size (heart rates of mice are 600 to $700/min^{-1}$ whereas human heart rates are 60 to 70/min at rest). Thus there is "similarity" among pulsatile flows in homologous arteries of mammals and quasistatic flows cannot be anticipated at the values of α occurring in the major vessels. The same is not true for fishes. The heart rate of a 2-g stickleback (*Gasterosteus aculeatus*) is 60 to $100/min^{-1}$ (Clark, 1927), and this is comparable to the heart rate of a 1.5-kg salmon (Smith et al., 1967) and only four times that of a 40-kg shark (Lyon, 1927). As a result, α for the shark aorta is approximately 10 (for the first harmonic of the flow signal), whereas $\alpha \ll 1$ for the stickleback. For these smaller species, then, flows in larger arteries should be related to pressure gradients by Poiseuille's law at any instant in time (Fig. 4-6A). In larger species, oscillatory flows in larger arteries are better described in terms of equations 6 and 7, and velocity profiles will be nonparabolic.

Pressure-Flow Relations of the Complete Circulation

When considering interrelationships between pressures and flows for the complete circulation, the effects of the gill beds are of particular interest. Mean blood pressure decreases by about 25% between the ventral and dorsal aortae (Holeton and Randall, 1967; Helgason and Nilson, 1973; Short et al., 1977), that is, gill vascular resistance (R_g) is about one-third of the resistance of the systemic beds (R_s). In addition, regulatory adjustments may affect

R_g/R_s. For example, swimming at maximal speeds causes a three-fold increase in cardiac output in trout (Kiceniuk and Jones, 1977). Blood pressure changes during exercise are buffered by dilation in both the gills and systemic beds (Piiper et al., 1977), but these effects are more pronounced in the latter. Thus maximal exercise causes R_g/R_s to increase from 0.25 to 0.65 (Kiceniuk and Jones, 1977).

Perhaps the most surprising feature of arterial pressures and flows in fishes is the modest effect of the gills on the oscillatory components of these variables. The large oscillations in arterial pressure and flow produced by vertebrate hearts are effectively damped out within most microcirculatory beds, but this is not true for fish gills. Pulse pressure in the dorsal aorta is consistently more than 50% of the ventral aortic pulse, and diastolic flow in systemic vessels can fall to half the peak systolic level (Fig. 4-4*B*). The relationship between pulsatile arterial pressures and flows depends on the distribution of resistive, inertial, and elastic properties of blood vessels (*i.e.,* depends on vascular impedance). At the simplest level, a vascular system can be viewed as an arterial elastic reservoir supplying peripheral resistance vessels (a windkessel model); thus the fish circulation may be modelled as a series coupling of two such systems, one corresponding to gill perfusion by way of the ventral aorta and the other corresponding to systemic perfusion by way of the dorsal aorta. Satchell (1971) proposed an electrical analogue for such a model (Fig. 4-7), according to which voltage is the analog of pressure and current is the analog of flow. Electrical resistance therefore represents vascular resistance, and capacitance represents arterial compliance, defined as

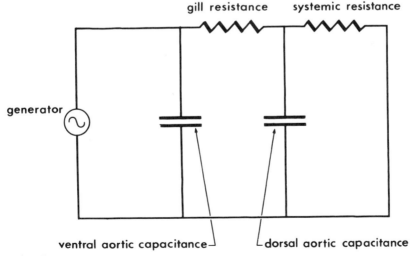

Figure 4-7
Electrical analogue of the fish circulatory system in which electrical capacitance mimics vascular compliance and electrical resistance mimics flow resistance.

the volume change of a complete arterial tree per unit change in pressure (dV/dP). Useful information from such models depends on comparisons of predictions with physiological pressures and flows. The paucity of systematic hemodynamic studies is therefore limiting, but some consistencies are apparent in the data that are available. There is evidence that arterial compliance is concentrated in the prebranchial vessels, which is to say that high compliance of vessels afferent to the gills is favored in Satchell's model. The presence of the highly elastic bulbus in teleosts and its role in depulsating flow have already been mentioned. Analogous structures are not found in elasmobranchs, but elasticity measurements indicate that the ventral aorta is some six times as distensible as the dorsal aorta (Lander, 1964).

The adaptive significance of concentrating compliance in prebranchial vessels is of obvious interest. Taylor (1964) has argued that the degree of compliance of the systemic arteries of mammals represents a balance between reducing cardiac work on the one hand and allowing for rapid regulatory adjustments of blood pressure on the other. Cardiac work is reduced when a high compliance effectively buffers pressure and flow oscillations in the system (windkessel function) because this reduces the systolic pressures the ventricle must generate and also reduces the work that must be expended to start and stop blood flow with each cardiac cycle. Low arterial compliance permits rapid adjustments of blood pressure because less blood must be transferred from veins to arteries when pressure is raised or lowered. If it is true for fish that the need for rapid regulatory adjustments imposes an upper limit on arterial compliance, it is not obvious how this compliance should be optimally distributed between the two arterial systems. Certainly, increasing ventral aortic compliance should further buffer pressures and flows through the system (and thereby reduce cardiac work) because blood stored in this vessel is distributed to the complete circulation during diastole; however, the effects of altered systemic arterial compliance are less clear. To address this question, Jones and associates (1974) constructed a hydraulic model of the cod circulation, which consisted of a pulsatile pump driving blood into an elastic reservoir (ventral aortic compliance, C_{va}) that fed a flow resistor (gill beds resistance, R_g). This resistor drained into a second elastic reservoir (systemic arterial compliance, C_{da}) that finally supplied a second flow resistor (systemic resistance, R_s). By adjusting these components, physiological pressures and flow could be mimicked, and the effects of further adjusting vascular compliances could be assessed. Figure 4-8 shows that increasing dorsal aortic compliance reduced both ventral and dorsal aortic pressure oscillations. Cardiac work, however, is primarily determined by ventral aortic pulse pressure because this pressure determines ventricular systolic pressure, a correlate of the cardiac tension-time integral. Changes in this pressure were modest; in addition, an increase in C_{da} caused greater flow oscillations in the gills (Q_{da}). A rigorous analysis of Satchell's electrical analogue indicates that for a given input flow oscillation (stroke volume), the ratio of ventral to dorsal aortic pressure oscillations is given by

$$\frac{P_{\text{va}}}{P_{\text{da}}} = \left(\left[1 + \frac{R_s}{R_g} \right]^2 + \left[2 \ R_s \cdot C_{da} \right]^2 \right)^{1/2} \tag{8}$$

thus ventral aortic pulse pressure (and cardiac work) are minimized when C_{da} is as small as possible (*i.e.,* when as much of the arterial compliance as possible resides proximal to the gills).

Although the above considerations indicate that compliance may be concentrated in prebranchial vessels, the systemic circulation cannot be viewed as a rigid, purely resistive network. Instead, it performs some windkessel function that is indicated by comparisons of pulse flow and pulse pressure at the origin of the dorsal aorta, which are equal percents of their means in a purely resistive system. Pulse flow into the dorsal aorta is over 50% of mean flow whereas pulse pressure is less than 20% of mean pressure (Jones et al., 1974), a finding consistent with a system of significant compliance.

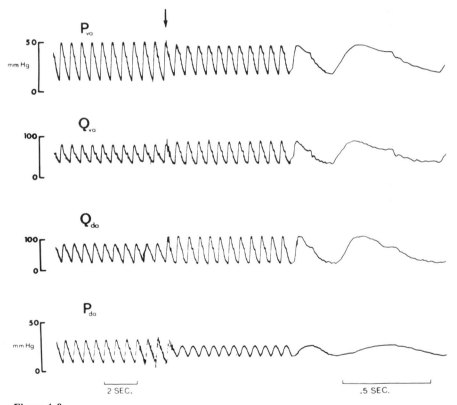

Figure 4-8
Pressures and flows before and after "gill resistance" in hydraulic model. Traces (from top to bottom): pressure proximal to "gills" in "ventral aorta" (P_{va}); flow proximal to "gills" in "ventral aorta" (Q_{va}); (arbitrary units); flow distal to "gills" in "dorsal aorta" (Q_{da}) (arbitrary units); pressure distal to "gills" in "dorsal aorta" (P_{da}). At arrow, a compliance was introduced into "dorsal aorta" distal to gills.

Significant compliance despite stiffer walls, when compared with the pre-branchial system, is not necessarily surprising because the systemic arterial tree is much the larger of the two. The compliance (dV/dP) of even a stiff-walled system can be relatively large if its absolute volume is large.

There is some evidence that arterial compliance is not invariant. Watson and Cobb (1979) describe both smooth muscle and autonomic innervation of the bulbus arteriosus and propose a contractile function. This is consistent with observations that acetycholine contracts the smooth muscle in the bulbus and that this can obliterate its elastic reservoir function in *Gadus morhua* because diastolic outflow from this chamber is eliminated (Jones et al., 1974). The functional significance of such regulation remains to be elucidated. The onset of exercise elicits intense activity of cardiac vagal fibers in some species (Stevens et al., 1972; Priede, 1976, and it may be that one manifestation of this response is a reduction in arterial compliance, which serves to speed increases in blood pressure at this time. A coincident fall in heart rate attends this vagal activity, however, so the integrated response is not easily interpreted.

Systemic arterial compliance probably also varies. Simultaneous recordings of dorsal aortic pressure and flow occasionally show an increase in pulse pressure coincident with a decreased flow oscillation at times when mean pressure and mean flow show little change (Jones et al., 1974). This finding signifies a transient increase in vascular impedance (oscillatory pressure divided by oscillatory flow) that cannot be attributed to increased resistance. Decreased arterial compliance is probably implicated. Again the functional significance of such changes is not obvious.

Wave Propagation in Fish Arteries

The analysis of pressure-flow relations in terms of windkessel models (*e.g.*, Fig. 4-7) in which elastic properties of complete arterial systems are lumped into a single compliance assumes that pressure changes occur synchronously throughout the arterial system. In homeotherms, however, it takes the pulse generated by the heart about 20% to 25% of a cardiac cycle to traverse the arterial tree (McDonald, 1974; Langille and Jones, 1975); consequently, wave transmission has a marked influence. Wave reflection occurs at peripheral arteriolar beds (McDonald, 1974), and the reflected wave interferes with the outgoing pulse. At the periphery the outgoing and reflected pressure waves are in synchrony and they interfere constructively, but near the heart the two waves are nearly 180 degrees out of phase and destructive interference results. Thus pulse pressure in the mammalian aortic root is much smaller than pulse pressure in the peripheral arteries (Fig. 4-9A), and the end result is that the heart expends less work pumping into a low impedance system. Whether such wave propagation phenomena are significant in a particular species depends on how cardiac cycle duration compares with the transit time of the pulse through the arterial system. The latter is determined by the length of the system and the pulse wave velocity (c_0), which for thin-walled vessels is given by the Moens–Korteweg equation

$$c_0 = \sqrt{\frac{Eh}{\rho}} \tag{9}$$

where E is the elastic modulus of the wall, h is the wall thickness to diameter ratio, and ρ is the density of blood. In the vertebrates that have been examined c_0 shows a surprising consistency, varying from 3 to 10 m/sec in aortas; thus, the balance between heart rate and the length of the arterial tree determines

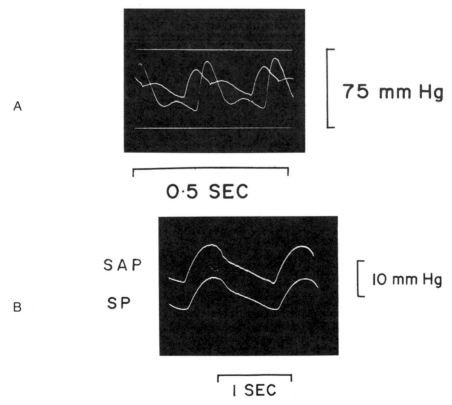

Figure 4-9

A, Pressures recorded in the aortic arch (smaller, earlier occurring pulse) and femoral artery (larger, later pulse) of the rabbit. *B*, Pressures recorded in the systemic arch (top trace) and sciatic artery (lower trace) of the frog. Mean pressures are equal for the two pressures (traces are separated for clarity). Significant wave propagation effects produce distortion of peripheral pressure pulses in all mammals (see *A*) that are not observed in the frog. Wave propagation phenomena may influence hemodynamics in large, but not very small species of fish (see text).

the magnitude of reflection effects. It might be expected that wave reflection effects would be more modest in small mammals because the time taken for the pulse to traverse the arterial system is much reduced; instead, a parallel increase in heart rate balances shorter arterial lengths, and wave transmission effects remain important (Milnor, 1979). Noordergraaf (1979) finds this pattern so consistent that he proposes a new "similarity principle" for mammalian arterial systems (*i.e.,* that resting heart rate times a characteristic length for the arterial system is species invariant).

This situation can be contrasted with that seen in small poikilotherms, the heart rates of which are much below those of mammals of similar size. Thus Langille and Jones (1975) demonstrated that pulse transit times in a number of amphibia were negligible when compared with the cardiac cycle, and wave transmission effects (*e.g.,* pressure wave amplification) were not observed (Fig. 4-9). In these species a windkessel model adequately described arterial pressure-flow relations, and it is likely that this is a general feature of small poikilotherms, including small fishes. In larger fishes the pulse wave takes longer to transverse the arterial system while heart rate variations with size are small; therefore, wave propagation effects should result. For example, it may take only 3% of a cardiac cycle for the pulse to travel the length of the dorsal aorta (about 15 cm) of a trout (assuming heart rate is 60 min^{-1}, pulse wave velocity is 5 m/sec) but 20% of a cardiac cycle to traverse the dorsal aorta (2 m) of a large shark or sturgeon (heart rate of 30/min^{-1}, pulse wave velocity of 5 m/sec). A windkessel model should apply to the former, but wave propagation phenomena must be anticipated with the latter.

Perhaps the most interesting situation is that of fishes of intermediate size because in these species it is possible that wave transmission effects come into play only during periods of regulatory adjustment when heart rate is high. Exercise, for example, causes variable heart rate responses, but a doubling is seen in some species (Jones and Randall, 1978). If arterial lengths are such that pulse transit time increases from 10% to 20% of the cardiac cycle, wave transmission effects will be of major significance at the higher rates.

Even when an appropriate balance between pulse wave transmission times and cardiac cycle duration occurs, the effects of wave transmission are difficult to predict in the absence of hard data. Amplification of the dorsal aortic pressure pulse and reduction of vascular impedance should occur, but these effects are sensitive to geometry and vasomotor tone of peripheral arteriolar beds (Langille, 1975). Furthermore, wave transmission effects in fishes must depend heavily on the branchial circulation that couples the heart and systemic beds.

It should be pointed out that the above estimates of arterial pulse wave transmission times assumes that arterial pulse wave velocities resemble those of mammals. This is probably untrue in the highly compliant bulbus arteriosus (E in equation 9 will be small), but pulse transmission times from the heart to the dorsal aorta remain brief (Taylor et al., 1977) because of the short length of this structure. If pulse wave velocities of other arteries are somewhat different in fishes than in mammals, the difference only affects the size range over which windkessel or wave transmission models apply; it is unlikely that the pulse wave velocities in the very large fish are so high that wave transmission effects are always negligible.

BLOOD FLOW IN THE SYSTEMIC MICROCIRCULATION

Satchell (1978) has reviewed many of the functional characteristics of piscine microcirculations, and differences in both structure and function, when compared with mammals, have been noted. Fenestrated capillaries with pores passing through the endothelial cells are observed in a number of beds (*e.g.,* gland cells of the pseudobranch, gas gland cells of the swimbladder, pineal gland), but capillaries of the renal tubules and glomeruli are not fenestrated in fishes. In elasmobranchs many venous capillaries exhibit openings that probably allow protein reflux, these species being devoid of lymphatics.

Generalizations concerning the actions of hormones and neurotransmitters are particularly dangerous in fishes. Most responses of systemic beds to norepinephrine and epinephrine or to sympathetic stimulation reflect alpha-constrictor mechanisms, but the gill beds dilate under this stimulus, as do the swimbladder vessels and those of the resorbant mucosa (Satchell, 1978). Vagally mediated, cholinergic vasoconstriction of the cod gas gland has been reported (Nilsson, 1972), but vagal stimulation dilates the teleost swimbladder and resorbant mucosa.

There are superficial similarities between the problems encountered in analyzing microcirculatory flow dynamics in fishes and mammals. In all vertebrate microvascular beds, Reynold's number is $\ll 1$, so the effects of fluid inertia can be neglected. Unfortunately the considerable simplification this permits is more than offset by the fact that blood cell size becomes significant when compared with vessel size such that blood no longer behaves like a continuous fluid. In addition, blood exhibits marked non-Newtonian behavior at the low velocities often encountered in the microcirculation, regardless of vessel size. As a result, the apparent viscosity (*i.e.,* the value for viscosity that is compatible with Poiseuille's law) shows great variability within the microcirculation (Lipowsky et al., 1978). Furthermore, a large temperature dependence of blood viscosity has a marked effect on physiologic function in both homeotherms and poikilotherms (Langille and Crisp, 1980). Typically, blood viscosity will more than double over a temperature range of 5° to 25°C, and such changes must be considered when interpreting the circulatory adjustments of those fishes with some capacity for thermoregulation (*e.g.,* tuna and some sharks; Carey and Teal, 1969a and b).

A number of studies have indicated that non-Newtonian behavior of mammalian blood is a product of blood cell shape and deformability and the tendency for cells to aggregate. Aggregation tends to increase apparent viscosity at low shear rates, whereas deformation and alignment of cells reduces viscosity when shear rates are high (Chien, 1976). It is likely that these factors play a role in altering viscosity in the microvasculature of fishes, but major differences between fish and mammalian blood render quantitative extrapolations pointless. Fish hematocrits are typically half those of mammals but range from 0 in icefish (Ruud, 1954) to over 40% in tuna (Becker et al., 1958). In addition, the ovoid, nucleated erythrocytes of fishes must have different deformability characteristics than those of mammals. Aggregation under low flows and its effect on viscosity have not been studied. It would appear, then, that anomalous viscosity may play an important role in determining flow in the fish microcirculation, but current data is so sparse that quantitative evaluations cannot be made. At present hemodynamics studies treat these beds simply as a source of flow resistance. While this may be adequate for analysis of central cardiovascular function, the obvious importance of the systemic exchange regions underscores the importance of future work in this area.

BLOOD FLOW THROUGH THE GILLS

The gills of most fishes are the primary sites for gas exchange with the external environment. Consequently, like the lungs of terrestrial vertebrates, they are characterized by exceptionally dense vascularization and a large surface area for gas exchange. This exchange area commonly exceeds ten times the total external body surface area. Lungs and gills are not homologous, however, and the constraints imposed on them are rarely the same; consequently, differences in adaptation of these structures can be striking. For example, unidirectional rather than tidal ventilation in fishes results in reduced energy expenditure associated with accelerating water; therefore the costs of pumping a relatively dense respiratory medium are lowered. Holeton and Jones (1975), however, have demonstrated that gill irrigation is more pulsatile than was previously thought, and there are also vascular adaptations specific to this type of ventilation. Blood flows across the exchange surface in the opposite direction to water flow (*i.e.,* the gills operate as countercurrent exchangers). Consequently, arterial oxygen tensions (Po_2) generally exceed those of expired water.

The large surface area of the gills indicates the *possibility* of a high diffusing capacity (gas exchange per unit partial pressure difference between gill capillary blood and water); on the other hand, high diffusing capacity can introduce problems in osmoregulation not faced by terrestrial vertebrates, because both ions and water can also cross the gill epithelium (Conte, 1969;

Randall et al., 1972). Even mammals exhibit submaximal diffusing capacity at rest (West, 1979); therefore observations that fish also reduce diffusing capacity at rest and increase it during times of stress are perhaps not surprising (Fisher et al., 1969). These adjustments are accomplished at least in part by redistribution of regional blood flows within the gills.

The distinct evolutionary origins and adaptive pressures imposed on gill gas exchange are reflected in a unique organization of gill vasculature. In fact, the gill beds are one of the most highly organized of all vertebrate vascular structures. The nature of this organization is associated with mechanisms for controlling local blood flow that are quite different from those controlling the randomly branching vessels seen in many beds. Most notably, the blood supply to any region of the gills depends in a unique way on controls being exercised in other regions, and an integrated response implies a complex interplay of local vascular adjustments.

Flow Distribution Within the Gills

Figure 4-10 illustrates the primary features of gill vascular structure in teleosts. Four comblike gill arches (five to seven in elasmobranchs) are each lined with two rows of filaments lined with the secondary lamellae, which are regularly spaced epithelial folds that provide the gas exchange surfaces. Blood is supplied to each gill arch by way of afferent branchial arteries that originate at the ventral aorta. These bifurcate into the afferent arch arteries from which the afferent filament arteries arise. The lamellae are perfused from these vessels by way of afferent lamellar arterioles (Fig. 4-10). Efferent lamellar, filament, arch, and branchial vessels then drain the blood from the gills into the systemic circulation, although a small component of efferent blood may enter venolymphatic sinuses.

Of particular interest is the vascularization of the secondary lamellae where exchange takes place. Here, well-defined capillaries are not observed; instead, the space is better described as a sheet of blood interrupted by an array of posts (the pillar cells; Fig. 4-10C) that prevent the lamellae from overdistending under intravascular pressure. Most of the secondary lamellae is blood space however, and a midplane section through the lamellae cuts through an area that is only 10% tissue (Farrell, 1980b). The vascular space is about 7μ thick, thus erythrocytes must deform when passing through the lamellae. The space widens slightly at the periphery of the lamellae, particularly at the apex, to form marginal channels. This sheetlike vascularization is similar to that seen in the lungs of terrestrial vertebrates (Smith and Rapson, 1977; Sobin et al., 1970), with the notable exception of birds (West et al., 1977).

Redistribution of gill blood flow to alter diffusing capacity during times of stress can theoretically occur by shunting blood to or from complete arches,

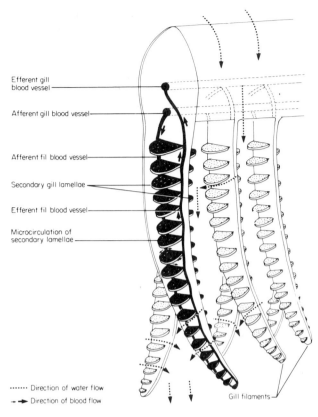

Efferent gill
blood vessel

Afferent gill blood vessel

Afferent fil blood vessel

Secondary gill lamellae

Efferent fil blood vessel

Microcirculation of
secondary lamellae

⋯⋯⋯ Direction of water flow
→—► Direction of blood flow

Gill filaments

A

B

Figure 4–10

A, Diagram of a segment of a gill arch showing an afferent arch artery supplying the filaments and
their lamellae, which ultimately drain into the efferent arch vessel. Tips of the filaments approach
those of adjacent arches so that most of the water flow must pass between the lamellae. Note the
counter current flow of water and blood at the level of the lamellae (see arrows). (After Hughes
and Morgan, 1973.) B, An injection cast of the vasculature of a segment of a gill filament (tissue has
been digested from the cast) showing the dense vascularization of the secondary lamellae (afa =
afferent filament artery, efa = efferent filament artery). C, A portion of a midplane section
through a secondary lamella showing erythrocytes (e) and pillar cells (p). (From Hughes and
Grimstone, 1965, by permission)

114

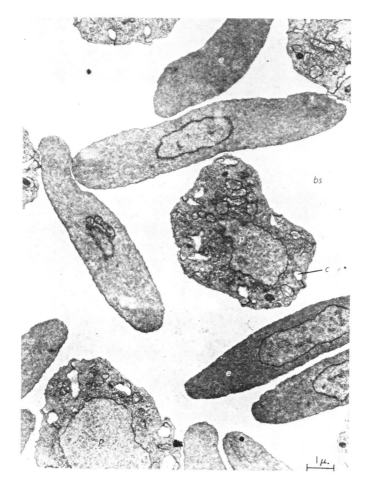

C

between different regions of a single arch, within single filaments, or within the individual lamellae. It appears, however, that resistance of vessels extrinsic to the filaments is negligible (Farrell, 1980), and thus vasomotion outside the filaments probably does not influence gill blood flow distribution.

Flow Distribution Within the Filaments

Blood flow to the lamellar units (the lamellae and their afferent and efferent arterioles) is determined by the distribution of flow resistances within the filament. Here the lamellar units provide a series of equally spaced shunts between afferent and efferent filament arteries in a manner that mimics the distribution of resistances in electric cables (Fig. 4-11). Assuming that the resistances per unit length of afferent and efferent filament arteries (Ω_a and Ω_e, respectively) and the shunt conductance per unit length of the lamellar units

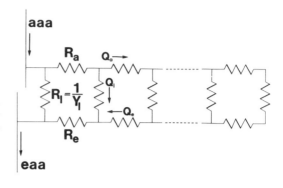

Figure 4-11
Schematic diagram of an electrical analogue of a gill filament proposed by Olson, 1979. (aaa, afferent arch artery; eaa, efferent arch artery; R_a and R_e resistance per unit length of afferent and efferent filament arteries respectively; Y_1; conductance per unit filament length of the secondary lamella; Q_a and Q_e, flow in the afferent and efferent filament arteries respectively; Q_1, lamellae blood flow per unit filament length).

(Y_1) do not vary with position along the filament, standard cable theory can be used to predict pressure and flow distribution within the filament (Olson, 1979). This assumption is not strictly valid (Farrell, 1980b), but it permits evaluation of how the different vascular units contribute to filament perfusion and its distribution. What follows is a mathematical analysis of the model Olson (1979) has proposed and some of the inferences that can be drawn from this analysis. All pressures and flows refer to time-averaged values.

First we have, by definition,

$$Y_1 = \frac{Q_1}{P_1} \qquad \Omega_a = -\frac{1}{Q_a} \cdot \frac{dP_a}{dx} \qquad \Omega_e = -\frac{1}{Q_e} \cdot \frac{dP_e}{dx} \qquad (10)$$

whereas Q_1 is lamellar flow per unit filament length, Q_a and Q_e are flows along the afferent and efferent filament arteries, and dP_a/dx and dP_e/dx are the pressure gradients along these two vessels. P_1 is the pressure driving flow through the lamellar units ($P_1 = P_a - P_e$).

At any point along the filament, flow toward the filament tip in the afferent vessel must equal flow returning in the efferent vessel ($Q_a(x) = -Q_e(x)$), therefore

$$\frac{dP_1}{dx} = \frac{dP_a}{dx} - \frac{dP_e}{dx} = -Q_a(R_a + R_e) \qquad (11)$$

In addition, all flow in the afferent filament artery must either continue along this vessel or pass through the lamellae, therefore

$$\frac{dQ_a}{dx} = Y_1 P_1 \qquad (12)$$

Combining equations 11 and 12 provides the differential equations that define pressures and flows in the filament

$$\frac{d^2 P_1}{dx^2} = (R_a + R_e)\ Y_1 P_1 \tag{13}$$

$$\frac{d_2 Q_a}{dx^2} = (R_a + R_e)\ Y_1 P_1 \tag{14}$$

These second-order differential equations are easily solved once two boundary conditions are provided: blood flow out of the filament tip (at $x = L$, the filament length) must be zero (*i.e.*, $Q_a(L) = 0$) and the pressure driving flow across the most proximal lamellae equals the pressure difference between the ventral and dorsal aortae (ΔP_g), (*i.e.*, $P_1(o) = \Delta P_g$. This condition follows directly from the fact that flow resistances of vessels extrinsic to the filaments are negligible.

Solutions of equations 13 and 14 yield the pressure drop across the secondary lamellae and the flow along the afferent filament artery

$$P_1(x) = Ae^{x/\lambda} + Be^{-x/\lambda} \tag{15}$$

$$Q_a(x) = Ce^{x/\lambda} + De^{-x/\lambda} \tag{16}$$

where

$$\lambda = [Y_1(R_a + Re)]^{-1/2} \tag{17}$$

and

$$A = \frac{\Delta P_g}{1 + e^{2L/\lambda}} \qquad B = \frac{\Delta P_g}{1 + e^{-2L/\lambda}}$$

$$C = -\frac{\Delta P_g \sqrt{Y_1/(R_a + R_e)}}{1 + e^{2L/\lambda}} \qquad D = \frac{\Delta P_g \sqrt{Y_1/(R_a + R_e)}}{1 + e^{-2L/\lambda}} \tag{18}$$

Equation 15 readily yields lamellar perfusion per unit filament length as a function of position along the filament

$$Q_l(x) = Y_1\, P_1\ (x) = Y_1(Ae^{x/\lambda} + Be^{-x/\lambda}) \tag{19}$$

Equations 15 to 19 permit estimates of the distribution of filament blood flow for any given driving pressure (ΔP_g) if gill vessel resistances are known. Farrell (1980) has determined resistances for the gill vessels in ling cod from methylmethacrylate casts of the vasculature, and these data can be used to calculate lamellar blood flow as a function of position along the filament. If the assumption is made that data from casts represents gill vasculature under resting conditions, then distal lamellae receive 60% of the perfusion of proximal lamellae at rest (Fig. 4-12). Olson (1979) used a similar approach to analyze morphometric data from the gills of the channel catfish and concluded that a greater decline (70%) in lamellar perfusion occurs along the filament in this species.

The lower rate of perfusion of distal lamellae predicted by this model reflects dissipation of lamellar perfusion pressure (P_1) as a result of resistive losses in the afferent and efferent filament arteries. Dilation of either vessel (or both) reduces these losses. Thus a nearly uniform perfusion of the lamellae of the ling cod results from a 50% increase in radius of the filament arteries (Fig. 4-12); on the other hand, a 50% decrease in the radii of these vessels reduces lamellar flow at the filament tip to 15% of that at the base of the filament. Consequently, vasomotion of the filament arteries can produce an effective "lamellar recruitment." In fact, when calculating the curves in Figure 4-12 the significant taper that occurs in the filament arteries over the distal two-thirds of their length (Farrell, 1980) was neglected; therefore, relative perfusion of distal lamellae is probably less than that predicted by the resting curve, and the potential for recruitment of distal lamellae owing to filament artery dilation is probably greater.

Recruitment or isolation of distal lamellae can also be accomplished by vasomotion of vessels within these lamellar units although this will significantly affect perfusion of other lamellae (Olson, 1979). Constriction in the distal lamellae will reduce flow in the filament arteries thereby reducing

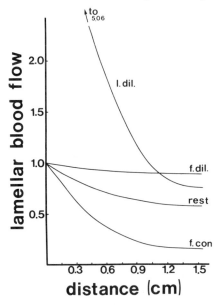

Figure 4-12
Lamellar blood flow per unit filament length (normalized to the perfusion of the most basal lamellae under resting conditions) in the ling cod predicted by the model shown in Figure 4-11. Abscissa is distance from the base of the filament; "rest" shows lamellar perfusion based on resistance measurements of Farrell (1980); "f. dil." shows the calculated results of a 50% increase in the diameters of afferent and efferent vessels and "f. con." corresponds to a 50% decrease in these diameters; "l. dil." illustrates the effects of a 50% increase in diameter of all afferent and efferent lamellar arterioles. All calculations assume that the blood pressure drop across the gills, ΔPg, does not change. Alternatively, the ordinate can be viewed as lamellar perfusion per unit pressure drop.

dissipative pressure losses in these vessels. Consequently, lamellae proximal to the constricted region will receive enhanced perfusion. Conversely, dilation of distal lamellae will 'steal' flow from proximal lamellae by redistributing pressures along the filament arteries.

A uniform dilation of all of the lamellar units also enhances flow in the filament arteries and therefore increases pressure gradients along these vessels such that the increase in filament perfusion is concentrated in the proximal lamellae (Fig. 4-12). Thus uniform lamellar dilation may be an effective mechanism for increasing gill blood flow while having minimal effects on diffusing capacity. Note, however, that generalized lamellar vasodilation does not imply that there is reduced perfusion of distal lamellae (Holbert et al., 1979), but rather that increments in flow to these structures are minimal.

The above discussion considers a number of mechanisms by which gill blood flow can be altered in an idealized situation. Techniques for quantitatively assessing mechanisms brought into play during actual regulatory adjustments are not available; nonetheless, some qualitative approaches have proved enlightening. Booth (1979) injected rainbow trout with red cells stained with acridine orange before quick-freezing the fish. The distribution of labelled cells within the gills was then assessed using fluorescence microscopy. Booth observed that some filaments received negligible perfusion in resting fish, suggesting a generalized vasoconstriction in the filament; presumably then, whole filaments can at times be recruited. He also noted that the lamellae near the base of the filament were perfused preferentially in resting fish with on average the distal 42% of the lamellae being unperfused. This is consistent with the findings of Farrell and associates (1979) that the proximal 67% of the lamellae are perfused in resting ling cod. A number of studies have demonstrated that acetylcholine, a potent constrictor of gill vasculature, can drastically reduce lamellar perfusion while epinephrine and isoproterenol open lamellar vessels even at the tip of filament. Thus adrenergic vasodilation may greatly increase diffusing capacity in times of stress. In addition, hypoxia is associated with an increase in diffusing capacity (Fisher et al., 1969) that is probably caused by recruitment of lamellae near the tips of the filament.

Blood Flow Through the Lamellae

Flow through the lamellar units depends on the flow-resistive properties of the lamellar sheet and afferent and efferent arterioles. The vasculature of the lamellae resembles the sheet-flow model previously applied to the mammalian alveoli. Fung and Sobin (1969) derived a theoretical model of alveolar sheet flow that Farrell and colleagues (1980) have now applied to the gill lamellae of ling cod. Current theory neglects the anomalous viscosity of blood and treats the pillar cells as simple cylinders, when in reality they flare at each end. If it is further assumed that the lamellar blood space is the same thickness at its afferent and efferent limits, total flow resistance, Ω, of the sheet is

$$\Omega = \frac{4\mu \ K \ L_{\text{lam}} \ m}{A_b \ h^3} \qquad (20)$$

where h = sheet thickness

A_b = area of a lamellar midplane section that passes through the blood space

μ = blood viscosity

L_{lam} = mean lamellar length

m = sheet compliance ($= \dfrac{h - h_o}{\Delta P}$ where h is sheet thickness when transmural pressure, ΔP, is zero)

K = constant characterizing sheet and pillar geometry

Recent measurements indicate that ling cod lamellae are compliant so that thickness, h, is pressure dependent, but distension of the sheet is apparently restricted to the spaces between indistensible pillars (Farrell, 1980). In the same study, lamellar resistance (calculated from a sheet flow model) was compared with resistances of afferent and efferent arterioles. It was found that resistance of the afferent lamellar arteriole was approximately six times the resistance of the lamellar sheet and 30 times the resistance of the efferent filament arteriole. Thus control of the afferent blood vessel is probably the most important intrinsic factor affecting lamellar blood flow of this species. The massive proliferation of parallel pathways within the lamellae suggests that this finding should not be surprising; therefore, arguments that distribution of flow within the lamellae can have a major effect on the pressure drop across the gills (Muir and Brown, 1971) may apply to a limited number of species. Nonetheless, vasculature within the lamellar sheet may become important when intravascular pressures are very low because this may cause the lamellae to collapse. At low pressures, ling cod lamellae thickness can fall to 5 μ (Farrell, 1980), and the rather large and relatively nondeformable fish erythrocytes may become trapped. This could account for the complete absence of perfusion of lamellae at the filament tips in resting fish (Booth, 1979), whereas the theoretical model (Figs. 4-11 and 4-12) predicts only reduced flow to this region. Data of Wood (1974) show further evidence of lamellar collapse at low pressures. He found that a differential pressure between the ventral and dorsal aorta of about 14 cm H_2O was needed just to initiate flow through isolated trout gills when pressure in efferent vessels was zero; however, when gill vascular pressures were raised by increasing efferent outflow pressures to 40 cm H_2O, a differential pressure of less than 1 cm H_2O was sufficient to initiate flow.

From the above considerations it appears that subtleties of vascular geometry within the lamellar sheet have little effect on bulk perfusion of lamellae that are sufficiently distended to pass red cells; however, the distribution of blood within intralamellar pathways may still influence gas exchange. Numerous workers have pointed out that enlarged marginal and basal channels (Fig. 4-10), uninterrupted by pillar cells, ring the lamellae (Hughes and Morgan, 1973), and these channels may distribute blood to pathways that are distant from the lamellar axis. Muir and Brown (1971) feel that the geometry of lamellar pathways in tuna, particularly marginal channels, so constrain flow that countercurrent exchange is compromised. Within the central regions of the sheet, sheet thickness decreases at sites near the basal area, which is somewhat buried in the filament tissue (Farrell et al., 1980) and therefore not optimally located for gas exchange. During times when gill intravascular pressures are high (*e.g.,* exercise), a nonuniform distension of the lamellar sheet may cause a modest redistribution of flow toward the lamellar margin. In addition there is morphologic (if not physiologic) evidence that the pillar cells are contractile (Hughes and Grimstone, 1965; Newstead, 1967). If this is so, a sensitivity to numerous agents (*e.g.,* O_2, CO_2, catecholamines) could profoundly influence flow pathways. Shunting of blood to marginal areas where water flow rates are high and diffusion distances are low could enhance diffusing capacity during periods of stress.

In summary, theoretical arguments and experimental evidence suggest that the distal lamellae are poorly perfused or unperfused under resting conditions but that these regions are well perfused during times of increased gas exchange requirements. Such recruitment of distal lamellae may result from dilation of filament arteries (afferent and/or efferent) or from dilation of the individual afferent lamellar arterioles. At present, no experimental evidence indicates whether a redistribution of gill water flow accompanies such blood flow adjustments. A major goal of the theoretical analysis of gill water flow presented in the next section is to define the determinants of gill irrigation and its distribution.

HYDRODYNAMICS OF WATER FLOW IN FISH GILL IRRIGATION

This section presents a preliminary analysis of the hydrodynamics of water flow through fish gills. The approach is more fundamental, rigorous, and quantitative than previous work and insofar as we know is original. Previous work in this area is first outlined, the biologic significance of such an analysis is discussed, and then the analysis itself is considered. A more detailed version of the analysis will be presented later (Stevens and Anantaraman, 1982).

Previous Work

G. M. Hughes has unquestionably been the driving force behind much of the work on fish gills. He provided some early models, analyzed the morphometrics of the gill and related it to fish size, and discussed some species differences. He and other measured the changes in hydrostatic pressure that occur across fish gills during the respiratory cycle. In his first analysis of water flow Hughes (1966) applied the Poiseuille equation for rectangular tubes. His equation is

$$Q = \frac{5}{24} \cdot \frac{P_1 - P_2}{\mu} \cdot \frac{d^3 b}{L_{lam}} \tag{21}$$

where P_1 and P_2 are pressures (dynes/cm^2) on either side of the sieve, μ is bulk viscosity (poise), d is pore width, L_{lam}, pore length, b, pore height (cm), and Q is volume flow. Total flow for the gill is calculated by multiplying Q by the number of pores. Total flow calculated in this way is about one order of magnitude higher than measured flow rates, and some reasons for this are discussed in detail by Steen (1971).

Hills and Hughes (1970) provided a dimensional analysis of oxygen transfer in the fish gill. Using the morphometric data of Price (1931) on the dimensions of fish gills from small mouth bass (*Micropterus dolomieu*) ranging in mass from 0.5 g to almost 1000 g, they showed how these variables scale with fish size. All variables were scaled on log-log plots. The exponents as power functions of mass are gill exchange area, 0.78; interlamellar distance, 0.09; length of secondary lamellae, 0.24; number of secondary lamellae, 0.28; and water ventilation rate, 0.73. Hughes and Hills derived equations based on mass transfer of oxygen from water into blood at the fish gill. Using the Fick equation to describe mass transfer of oxygen across the gill, they pointed out that log mean Po$_2$ is the important driving gradient. For diffusion in the water layer during laminar flow they assumed that k, the oxygen mass transfer coefficient in water, is proportional to $(W/L_{lam})^{1/3}$ where W is volume flow per pore and L_{lam} is pore length. For turbulent flow, k was assumed to be proportional to $(u^{0.83}/d^{0.17})$ where u is water velocity in the pore and d is pore width. The Fick equation was also used to estimate oxygen transfer into the blood. Values were scaled to body mass for the dimensional analysis. Using values from the literature, their calculations showed that the resistance to oxygen transfer in the pore water is five- to ten-fold greater than that through the tissue. They also concluded that the analysis adds strong support to the concept that water flow in the pores is usually laminar and that blood flows countercurrent to water.

Randall (1970) provided a comprehensive review of gas exchange by fish gills and discussed in some detail the fraction of water that does not flow over the gills (*i.e.,* the dead space). This is important in an analysis of water flow because the fraction of water that passes through the gill sieve must be known. Davis and Walters (1970) showed that much of the literature in this regard is in error because cannulae implanted in the operculum or cleithrum preferentially sample dead space and give Po_2 values much higher than mixed expired flow. Davis and Cameron (1971) modified a technique devised by Van Dam (1938) and showed that average %U (percentage of oxygen used from inspired water) for resting rainbow trout was 46% and ranged from 29% to 64%. They summarized the data for a variety of species and in general showed similar values. Higher values have been obtained for a single large trout (80%) by Van Dam (1938) and for tuna (71%) by Stevens (1972), but secondary lamellae of adjacent gill filaments of tuna are fused such that water is forced to pass through the gill sieve. Reasonable values are 50% for nontuna and 70% for tuna. Values of 70% and 50% for tuna and for nontuna are used in the present analysis as conservative estimates of the fraction of water passing through the sieve; however, this assumes that anatomic and physiological dead spaces are identical, whereas the latter is somewhat larger owing to underperfusion of some lamellae with blood, at least under resting conditions (see Blood Flow Through the Gills above).

Shelton (1970) reviewed the events that occur during respiration in fish. Early workers (cited in Shelton; Woskoboinikoff and Balabai, 1936; Van Dam, 1938) argued that most fish have two pumps, a pressure pump in the buccal cavity and paired suction pumps in the opercular cavity. Van Dam suggested that water flow was continuous throughout the respiratory cycle, and he tested this idea by connecting the buccal and opercular cavities with a tube and showed that water in the tube always moved in the direction toward the opercular cavity. He concluded that there was a pressure gradient between the cavities throughout the cycle. Pressure measurements by Hughes and Shelton (1958) showed that the hydrostatic pressure across the gills varied during each respiratory cycle, was positive for most but usually not all of the cycle, and that average differential pressure between the buccal and opercular cavities was about 1 cm water. Experiments on other species have confirmed these generalizations except in tuna, in which the differential pressure is about 2 cm water (Shelton, 1970; Stevens, 1972).

Holeton and Jones (1975) provide the only measurements of water velocity during the respiratory cycle in fish. They measured water velocity using a blood flow probe on three large (3 kg to 3.5 kg), lightly anesthetized carp (*Cyprinus carpio*). They reported that velocity normal to the probe was negligible, peak velocity more than doubled when ventilation was increased during hypoxia, and velocity in front of the sieve was pulsatile. They also made simultaneous measurements of pressures in the buccal and opercular cavities and differential pressure. They showed that the maximal differential pressure was about 0.5 cm water and only exceeded 1 cm for a short time during increased ventilation in hypoxic water. More important, they showed that the peak velocity in front of the sieve lags behind the peak differential pressure. The observations of Holeton and Jones are extremely significant because they show that a fundamental assumption on which models of gill irrigation are based is incorrect. As Hughes (1966) states, "It is assumed that the pressure gradient across them [the pores] remains constant and equal to the mean of the differential pressure measured simultaneously. . . ." The fact that there is a lag between peak velocity and peak differential pressure means that the boundary layer effects are significant (they account for the lag). It also means that all previous models based on this assumption are in error.

In most fish, therefore, the water flow is created by two pumps, the resistance to water flow is such that the average differential pressure is about 1 cm water, and about 50% of oxygen is removed as water passes over the gills. Estimates of the metabolic cost of irrigating the gills in nontunas have been reviewed by Jones (1971) and by Cameron and Cech (1970) and vary from 2% to 43% of total metabolism. Webb (1975) summarized this literature and concluded that 15% is typical. Tunas ram ventilate, and the metabolic cost of irrigating the gills is a small fraction (of the order of 1%) of total metabolic cost of swimming (*i.e.,* it is about one order of magnitude less than that in fish irrigating their gills with buccal and opercular pumps).

Information and ideas on gill water flow from current knowledge are summarized in Table 4-1, and companion Figure 4-13 that shows the feature of the gill sieve to scale. Most drawings in texts are misleading in the respect that elements are not drawn to scale. The secondary lamellae are more triangular rather than rectangular as can be seen in Figure 4-10.

Based on these data (Table 4-1), the following generalizations can be made:

Gill area is increased largely by increasing pore numbers rather than changing pore dimensions.
Over a size range of more than three orders of magnitude, pore velocity changes less than one order of magnitude.
During maximum oxygen uptake, pore velocity increases about one order of magnitude over the minimum value for fish of all sizes.
The pore velocities of tuna and bass are comparable even though the tuna can remove five times as much oxygen from the water per unit time.
Reasonable estimates of suction velocity (see below) are 0.01 to 0.10 cm/sec in a small fish (1 g) and are 0.10 to 1.0 cm/sec in a large fish (1 kg).
An average molecule of water is in the sieve for about 1 sec at low ventilation rates and about 0.1 sec at the highest ventilation rates (Table 4-2).

While previous work has made major advances in understanding how gills work, it has raised many new questions that make new analytical approaches of gill water flow desirable. For example, Hills and Hughes (1970)

Table 4.1
DIMENSIONS AND WATER VELOCITY IN FISH GILLS

MASS (g)	PORE DIMENSIONS d (cm)	b (cm)	L_{lam} (cm)	TOTAL NO. OF PORES (PER FISH)	TOTAL PORE AREA (cm²)	MAXIMUM DURING ACTIVITY V_{O_2} ml O₂/sec	$\dot{V}_g$ cm³H₂O/sec	VELOCITY (cm/sec)	MINIMUM = STANDARD V_{O_2} ml O₂/sec	$\dot{V}_g$ cm³H₂O/sec	VELOCITY (cm/sec)
a. Bass											
0.33	0.0025	0.0058	0.013	7060	0.10	38.5×10^{-6}	0.013	0.127	5.206×10^{-6}	0.0017	16.7×10^{-3}
2.71	0.0024	0.0068	0.026	37200	0.61	272×10^{-6}	0.090	0.148	35.10×10^{-6}	0.012	19.1×10^{-3}
26.0	0.0025	0.0080	0.052	95600	1.93	2.17×10^{-3}	0.725	0.325	274.0×10^{-6}	0.091	47.3×10^{-3}
41.1	0.0026	0.0088	0.063	112100	2.57	3.31×10^{-3}	1.10	0.430	415.7×10^{-6}	0.138	53.9×10^{-3}
116	0.0031	0.0088	0.080	155600	4.25	8.59×10^{-3}	2.86	0.673	1.065×10^{-3}	0.355	83.5×10^{-3}
189	0.0032	0.0125	0.083	182800	7.31	13.5×10^{-3}	4.49	0.615	1.666×10^{-3}	0.555	75.9×10^{-3}
288	0.0034	0.0132	0.092	204200	9.18	19.9×10^{-3}	6.63	0.721	2.445×10^{-3}	0.814	88.7×10^{-3}
452	0.0034	0.0161	0.106	242200	13.3	30.0×10^{-3}	10.0	0.752	3.675×10^{-3}	1.225	92.0×10^{-3}
618	0.0038	0.0176	0.124	265700	17.8	40.1×10^{-3}	13.3	0.749	4.886×10^{-3}	1.629	91.4×10^{-3}
837	0.0036	0.0176	0.146	302700	19.2	52.9×10^{-3}	17.6	0.918	6.439×10^{-3}	2.146	112×10^{-3}
b. Extrapolated from bass											
1667	0.0036	0.0173	0.166	474000	29.5	99.7×10^{-3}	33.2	1.12	12.0×10^{-3}	4.011	135×10^{-3}
c. Tuna											
1667	0.0021	0.0166	0.12	7186000	250	486×10^{-3}	143.0	0.57	83.6×10^{-3}	24.60	98.4×10^{-3}

d = pore width, b = height, L_{lam} = length. Total pore area is area of one spore ($d \times b$) multiplied by the number of pores. The morphometric data in Part a are for smallmouth bass, from Price (1931) cited in Steen (1971). Maximum oxygen uptake values are for largemouth bass (*Micropterus salmoides*) at 25°C (same size range, from Beamish, 1970) where oxygen uptake in ml O₂/sec = 1.091 × 10⁻⁴·$M^{0.9190}$ (M = mass in g). Minimum oxygen uptake values are for carp at 20°C (same size range) from Beamish (1964) where oxygen uptake in ml O₂/sec = 1.418×10⁻⁵·$M^{0.9090}$ (M = mass in g) V_g is water flow across the gills and is calculated by the Fick equation assuming percent utilization = 50% (see above) so that V_g = V_{O_2} (0.0030 ml O₂/ml water). Row **b** is extrapolated to a bass equal in mass to the tuna studied by Muir and Hughes (1969), which are given in Row **c**. Extrapolations were carried out on log-log transformed data for which the correlation coefficient was always greater than 0.88 for the original data. For the skipjack tuna, which represents the extreme in capacity to extract oxygen from the water, the morphometric data were taken from Muir and Hughes (1969) where d = the reciprocal of the number of secondary lamellae per cm minus the thickness of one secondary lamellae, 10 μ. The total cross-sectional pore area was taken from Brown and Muir (1970) and pore height was calculated from the area of one pore and pore width (d). The oxygen uptake data were taken from Gooding *et al.* (1981) who state, "the first five determinations of oxygen-consumption rate within about one hour of capture were 1.5 mg O₂·h⁻¹·g⁻¹ or more." V_g for tuna is calculated assuming a percent utilization of 70% (see above) so V_g – V_{O_2} × (0.0034 ml O₂/ml water). Water velocity is calculated as flow per unit area.

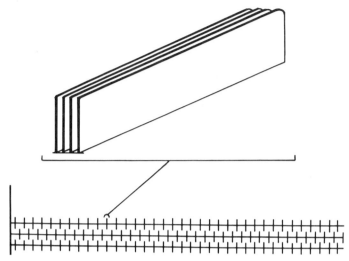

Figure 4-13
Schematic of gill sieve with secondary lamella drawn to scale. Data are from Muir for skipjack tuna gill, with a total weight of 1667 g and number of pores, 7,186,383. Filaments are short near the tips (2 mm) and long in the center (30 mm). The filament drawn represents the average length (18 mm). There are 30.5 to 43.0 secondary lamella per millimeter of filament length (average 32.3), and only every fifteenth one is drawn on the section of the whole filament. The schematic of a few pores on the large scale illustrates that the pore is actually very long and very thin such that relations equating the pore to a round capillary are inappropriate. The height of the pore, b, was calculated from the data and protocol of Muir: $b = wa \times l / 1.15$, where wa is the weighted average area of one side of a secondary lamella (0.428 mm^2) and l is weighted average pore length (1.2 mm). Average secondary lamella thickness is $10\ \mu$ and is drawn approximately to scale in the 10 times schematic. (From Stevens and Anantaraman, 1982)

concluded that 90% of the barrier to oxygen diffusion occurred in the *water* in the gill pore. If so, then clearly an understanding of the hydrodynamics of water flow is essential in describing the important features that limit oxygen movement in the water. In addition, Hughes (1972) argued that water flow in the sieve is laminar at low flows but turbulent at high flows. Obviously this has important consequences for estimating relations between water flow and oxygen transport and for estimating the cost of acquiring oxygen from the water. The lag between peak velocity and peak differential pressure, showing the importance of neglected boundary layer effects, was mentioned above.

Present Analysis

The following is a preliminary attempt to analyze the problem of water flow and oxygen transport; mathematical details will appear elsewhere (Stevens and Anantaraman, 1982). The present analysis estimates flow through pores from measured estimates of ventilation and pore geometry assuming viscous flow. The input variables to such a boundary layer model

Table 4.2

ESTIMATION OF REYNOLDS NUMBER FOR FLOW IN FRONT OF THE GILL FILAMENTS AND WITHIN THE PORES OF THE GILL SIEVE

MASS	AVERAGE FILAMENT LENGTH (cm)	IN FRONT OF SIEVE		WITHIN THE SIEVE			
		Maximum flow Re	Minimum flow Re	Maximum flow Re	Time in pore (sec)	Minimum flow Re	Time in pore (sec)
Bass							
0.33	0.38	4.9	0.64	0.016	0.10	1.88×10^{-3}	0.80
2.71	0.39	5.7	0.74	0.018	0.18	2.25×10^{-3}	1.4
26.0	0.40	13	1.9	0.041	0.16	6.02×10^{-3}	1.1
41.4	0.42	18	2.2	0.056	0.15	7.05×10^{-3}	1.2
116	0.47	32	4.0	0.105	0.12	13.0×10^{-3}	1.0
189	0.53	33	4.1	0.098	0.13	12.1×10^{-3}	1.1
288	0.61	44	5.4	0.122	0.13	15.2×10^{-3}	1.0
452	0.47	56	6.8	0.128	0.14	15.5×10^{-3}	1.2
618	0.87	65	8.0	0.143	0.17	16.9×10^{-3}	1.4
837	1.05	96	12	0.160	0.16	19.7×10^{-3}	1.3
Extrapolated from bass							
1667	1.70	192	23	0.19	0.15	23.2×10^{-3}	1.2
Tuna							
1667	2.78	159	27	0.086	0.21	14.7×10^{-3}	1.2

Reynolds number was calculated as $\mathrm{Re} = \dfrac{VD}{\nu}$ where V is velocity (Table 4-1), D is a characteristic distance and ν is the kinematic viscosity of water. For flow in front of the filaments, filament length was used as a characteristic distance. Within the sieve, half the separation of the secondary lamellae (d, in Table 4-1) was used (after standard descriptions of flow between plates; Van Dyke, 1970).

are the free stream velocity (*i.e.*, the velocity just in front of the gill sieve where there are no boundary layer effects) and suction velocity (*i.e.*, the velocity just behind the gill sieve). The velocity data in Table 4-1 are used as an estimate of the range of suction velocities in the model.

The magnitude of the problem can be appreciated by contrasting ideas for well-studied fish locomotion (see Chap. 6 and 7) with gill water flow. The swimming motions of fish are characterized by large Reynolds numbers. At these high Reynolds numbers, the problem of fish locomotion can be separated into two parts: the analysis of resistance offered by a streamlined body through calculations of the viscous shear stress in the thin boundary layer, and the generation of thrust force by analyzing the potential flow outside the boundary layer. In comparison, the fish gill system is not well defined, and experimental measurements of the unsteady flow through a nonuniform system are logistically difficult. The volumes of the buccal and opercular cavities change, and in most fish the gill filaments are free to move through the respiratory cycle.

It is well known that when a fluid flows past a fixed solid boundary, the fluid immediately in contact with the body is at rest, conforming with the condition of "no slip" that must hold for a viscous fluid. At the outer edge of the boundary layer, the fluid has practically full stream velocity relative to the body; therefore, the velocity changes continuously through the layer from 0 at the surface to full stream value at the outer edge of the boundary layer. Large velocity gradients within the boundary layer imply a steep gradient of shearing stress. Consequently, even though viscosity itself may be small, viscosity effects are not negligible and not all viscous terms in the equations of motion will be negligible.

In gill respiration, water is forced through the fine pores between the secondary lamellae; therefore, energy is required to overcome viscous forces. The pressure gradient required to drive a fluid through a pore is proportional to the rate of flow, and the work performed in driving gill flow is the product of the volume that passes through and the pressure gradient that causes the flow. The work required to drive a quantity of fluid through the gill pores is therefore proportional to the rate of flow. It also requires more work to drive a quantity of fluid through pores in a series of unsteady spurts than to drive it through at a steady rate over the same period of time.

The problem of analyzing gill water flow is a boundary layer problem, and it must be attacked in a series of steps such that each stage depends on the outcome of the previous analysis:

1. The form of the boundary layer in front of the gill sieve in the buccal cavity must be estimated in order to estimate the velocity profile at the front of the pore.
2. The form of the flow in the gill pores can then be estimated.
3. The effect of complicating factors must be evaluated. For example,

the presence of mucus will change shear stress and change velocity profiles. Variations in pore size between species and within species from the gill bar to the tip of the filament influence individual pore flows. Entrance and exit effects at the gill pore may influence velocity profiles, but this is unlikely given that the ratio of pore length to pore width is very large and the Reynolds number very low in this region (Table 4-2). Special effects will be extremely complex, and it is assumed that they will not change the generalizations of the present analysis.

4. The relation of water flow, as described above, to gas-exchange diffusion in the sieve can then be estimated. Such an analysis is much more complex than previously supposed, and it is inappropriate to review previous analyses.

The Boundary Layer Model in Front of the Gill Sieve

Assume that the fluid is directed through the buccal cavity, along the gill surface, and through the gill pores by means of a pressure gradient. The effect of suction is to produce a controlled flow of the incoming stream of fluid, resulting in a boundary layer flow along the surface of the gills. The following notations used are illustrated in Figure 4-14:

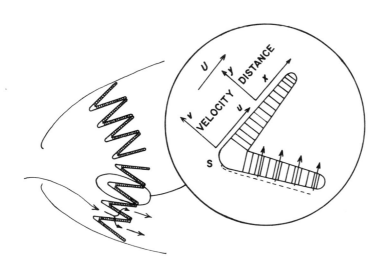

Figure 4-14
Schematic of the fish gill. There are four gill arches with two hemibranchs on either side. There are eight stagnation points S (one in front of each gill arch), and we examine water flow along one hemibranch. The dotted line is meant to indicate the growth of the boundary layer along the filament. The direction of water flow through the sieve is indicated by the arrows. (From Stevens and Anataraman, 1982)

$x =$ the distance in the direction of flow measured along the wall from the point where the boundary layer starts (*i.e.,* the ·gill bar). The maximum is the filament length, which varies from 0.2 cm in a 10-g bass to 15 cm in a 272-kg giant bluefin tuna (Hughes, 1966; Muir and Hughes, 1969). Note that mass is lost along x as water goes into the pores.

$y =$ the distance perpendicular to the boundary; it is measured from the surface.

$u =$ the component of velocity in the x direction.

$v =$ the component of velocity in the y direction.

$U =$ the velocity just outside the boundary layer.

Even at moderate flow velocities (1 cm/sec), the Reynolds numbers for flow in front of the gill filaments tend to be relatively small (of the order of 100 in 1-kg fish and 5 in 1-g fish—see Table 4-2). Under such conditions, the bulk flow of fluid behaves ideally, and the effects of viscosity are confined to the boundary layer because $u = 0$ at the wall (*i.e.,* the no-slip condition obtains). The above assumptions imply that the fluid momentum in the y direction is negligible compared to the momentum in the x direction. Recall that Holeton and Jones (1975) reported that velocity normal to the longitudinal axis of the fish was negligible immediately in front of the gill rakers; therefore the static pressure is assumed to vary only in the x direction. The pressure at any point in the boundary layer is therefore the same as that in the mainstream outside the boundary layer.

The flow in front of and through the gill sieve is characterized by low Reynolds numbers, and thus the boundary layer will be relatively thick. An approximate solution (from Vogel, 1981) to the Navier–Stokes equation for boundary layer thickness is

$$\delta = 5\sqrt{\frac{x \cdot \mu}{\rho\, U}} \tag{22}$$

where x is the distance along the gill filament and δ is the thickness at which velocity is 99% of U, the freestream velocity. According to Vogel (1981), the relation is useful down to a Reynolds number of 625 but can provide a crude estimate down to 100 or a little lower. Given the present state of knowledge, it is not considered inadequate to use equation 22 as an approximation, despite the obvious reservations. Reynolds numbers were calculated for flow in front of and within the sieve (Table 4-2). The average filament length was calculated from a linear regression of data given by Hughes (1972) for 38 measurements on 26 species ranging in size from 12 g to 1550 g. Reynolds numbers within the sieve are extremely low, thus the relation cannot tell us anything about flow within the sieve; it may however provide a crude estimate for flow in front of the sieve. (Reynolds numbers scale with mass as $M^{0.38}$ in front of sieve and as $M^{0.56}$ within the sieve). The boundary layer is zero at the stagnation point immediately in front of the gill bar but grows rapidly as water flows along the filament. Using the values for the tuna in Tables 4-1 and 4-2 for the condition of maximum flow yields a boundary layer thickness of 1.1 cm at the tip of the filament. The boundary layer grows rapidly such that it is more than one-half the final value (*i.e.*, 5 mm) only 20% of the way down the filament. Clearly this estimate is extremely crude, but it is presented to make the point that gill water flow is a boundary layer problem.

This calculation is crude not only because the Reynolds numbers are small but also because mass is lost as water flows along the filament; therefore, development of the boundary layer is more complex than suggested above. This calculation is of some biological significance, however, because it is likely that the amount of water that flows through the secondary lamellae closer to the tip of the filament depends on the boundary thickness there. At the low flows that characterize resting conditions the boundary layer will be thicker (and volume flow rate relatively lower) near the end of the filament than it is at the high flow rates that characterize high oxygen demand. Because the secondary lamellae near the tip of the filaments are only well perfused with blood (see Blood Flow Through the Gills) during periods of high oxygen demand, some matching the distribution of ventilation, and perfusion can be inferred.

The fact that mass is lost as water flows along the filament complicates the calculation of the boundary layer thickness considerably because it results in another term in the Navier–Stokes equation. Most of our efforts have been applied toward finding a reasonable approximation to the equations for this condition. What follows is a summary of efforts to date and a presentation of what is required to solve this problem (details will appear elsewhere; Stevens and Anantaraman, 1982).

The Integral Momentum Equation

The boundary layer equation expresses local conservation of momentum in the x direction at points within the boundary layer. A complete calculation of the boundary layer for a given body using the differential form of the equation encounters considerable mathematical difficulties because of the nonlinearity; in fact, very few exact solutions exist. In practice, however, one may not be interested in exact and complete solutions, so it is adequate and economical to use methods that are approximate (Schlichting, 1955; Rosenhead, 1963).

These approximate methods do not require that the differential boundary layer equations be satisfied for every particle within the fluid. Instead, it is assumed that the boundary layer equation is satisfied in a layer along the flow surface and near the region of transition to external flow by satisfying the boundary condition and certain compatibility conditions. Over the rest of the boundary layer, only a mean over the differential equation is applied, the mean being taken over the whole thickness of the boundary layer. Two parameters of the boundary layer, the momentum thickness and the displacement thickness, can then be calculated as approximations of bulk flow (see Head, 1961). It is useful to give a physical interpretation to these boundary layer thicknesses: the momentum thickness is a measure of the amount by which the total momentum of the fluid in the boundary layer has been reduced by viscosity effects, compared to the inviscid flow in the mainstream fluid; the displacement thickness indicates that the presence of the boundary layer has the effect of displacing the stream function or stream lines relative to flow in the absence of the boundary layer. Other measures of the boundary layer thickness are somewhat nebulous and cannot be described simply.

The solution to these equations is not straightforward. The momentum thickness grows with distance along the filament in the x direction, but the exact form of the relation is not known and the coefficients of the boundary layer equations have not been established. A large number of assumed forms of the relation have now been explored, but in no case was it possible to find coefficients that would satisfy the equations. Although it is not proven, it seems reasonable to conclude that either momentum thickness does not change with x given the prescribed flow conditions or that the coefficients that have been suggested (Thwaites, cited in Head, 1961) are not appropriate for low-flow conditions. The former explanation could reflect loss of fluid through the sieve, but this is probably not consistent with the ventilation distribution along the filaments because the distal pores are smaller. Therefore, the possibility remains that this advance in analysis may require refinement or perhaps new theories for such flow.

Flow Within the Gill Sieve

The easiest but least accurate method of describing gill sieve flow is to assume that fully developed Poiseuille-type flow (equation 21) through the sieve is driven by a single, well-defined, buccal-to-opercular pressure gradient. A rigorous approach to flow conditions between the secondary lamellae derives from the work of Blasius, who has provided solutions for flow over a flat plate or between two flat plates. Because of viscous friction, boundary layers will form on the walls of the pore, and their thickness will increase in the direction of the flow; however, at the very low Reynolds numbers that occur within the sieve (Table 4-2), boundary layer development between the lamellae will be restricted to a very short region at the sieve entrance, and the assumption of fully developed, Poiseuille-type flow is therefore reasonable.

For example, the Blasius solution (Schlicting, 1955) gives the displacement thickness, δ^*, as

$$\delta^* = 1.73 \sqrt{\frac{\mu x}{\rho u}} \tag{23}$$

Using values for the tuna gill pore ($x = 0.0012$ m, $U = 0.00572$ m/sec, $\frac{\mu}{\rho} = 1 \times 10^{-6}$), the calculated boundary layer thickness is about 27 times larger than the width of the pore. Clearly, boundary layers from adjacent lamellae will fuse to establish fully developed flow. On the other hand the pressure gradient driving flow through the sieve cannot be defined in terms of a single buccal-to-opercular pressure gradient as previous models have assumed (Hughes, 1965). Instead, an analysis that takes into account the growth of a boundary layer distal to the gill slits must be applied.

Conclusions

The solution to the problem of gill water flow requires more advanced hydrodynamic analysis than has previously been used. This in turn requires work in two areas. There must be some experimental work in which as many variables as possible are measured under conditions that simulate those in the gill, and many comparative physiologists have the equipment and background to approach this area. It also requires some intensive and extensive manipulation of the acquired data to model the low-flow situation. The advantages of collaboration with specialists in fluid mechanics or applied mathematics is obvious. The most important result from the work to date is the suggestion that distribution of flow through the sieve may be regulated to some extent by the boundary layer conditions in front of the sieve; therefore, an effective dead space at the tips of the filaments is in a sense autoregulated to go hand in hand with the changes in the pattern of blood circulation through the secondary lamellae.

Acknowledgments

We are grateful to Debra Montgomery and Nancy Wilson for typing the manuscript.

REFERENCES

Atabek, H. B. 1980. Blood flow and pulse propagation in arteries. In *Basic Hemodynamics and Its Role in Disease Processes*, edited by D. J. Patel and R. N. Vaishnav, 255–362. Baltimore: University Park Press.

Beamish, F. W. H. 1964. Respiration of fishes with special emphasis on standard oxygen consumption. *Can. J. Zool.* 42:177–188.

Beamish, F. W. H. 1970. Oxygen consumption of largemouth bass, *Micropterus salmoides,* in relation to swimming speed and temperature. *Can. J. Zool.* 48: 1221–1228.

Becker, E. L., Bird, R., Kelley, J. W., et al. 1958. Physiology of marine teleosts. Two hematologic observations. *Physiol. Zool.* 31:228–231.

Booth, J. H. 1979. The effects of oxygen supply, epinephrine, and acetylcholine on the distribution of blood flow in trout gills. *J. Exp. Biol.* 83:31–39.

Booth, J. H. 1978. The distribution of blood flow in the gills of fish: Application of a new technique to rainbow trout (*Salmo gairdneri*). *J. Exp. Biol.* 73:119–129.

Brown, C. E., and Muir, B. S. 1970. Analysis of ram ventilation of fish gills with application to skipjack tuna. *J. Fish. Res. Board Can.* 27:1637–1652.

Cameron, J. N., and Cech, J. J. 1970. Notes on the energy cost of gill ventilation in teleosts. *Comp. Biochem. Physiol.* 34:447–455.

Carey, F. G., and Teal, J. M. 1969a. Regulation of body temperature by the bluefin tuna. *Comp. Biochem. Physiol.* 28:205–213.

Carey, F. G., and Teal, J. M. 1969b. Mako and Porbeagle: Warm-bodied sharks. *Comp. Biochem. Physiol.* 28:199–204.

Chien, S. 1976. Significance of macrorheology and microrheology in atherogenesis. *Ann. N. Y. Acad. Sci.* 275:10–27.

Clark, A. J. 1927. *Comparative Physiology of the Heart.* New York: Macmillan.

Conte, F. P. 1969. Salt secretion. In *Fish Physiology,* edited by W. S. Hoar and D. J. Randall, Vol. I, 241–292. New York: Academic Press.

Davis, J. C., and Cameron, J. N. 1970. Water flow and gas exchange at the gills of rainbow trout. *J. Exp. Biol.* 54:1–18.

Davis, J. C., and Walters, K. 1970. Evaluation of opercular catheterization as a method of sampling water expired by fish. *J. Fish. Res. Board Can.* 27:1627–1635.

Farrell, A. P. 1980a. Vascular pathways in the gill of ling cod, *Ophiodon elongatus. Can. J. Zool.* 58:796–806.

Farrell, A. P. 1980b. Gill morphometrics vessel dimensions, and vascular resistance in ling cod, *Ophiodon elongatus. Can. J. Zool.* 58:807–818.

Farrell, A. P., Daxboeck, C., and Randall, D. J. 1979. The effect of input pressure and flow on the pattern and resistance to flow in the isolated perfused gill. *J. Comp. Physiol.* 133:233–240.

Farrell, A. P., Sobin, S. S., Randall, D. J., and Crosby, S. 1980. Intralamellar blood flow patterns in fish gills. *Am. J. Physiol.* 239:R428–R436.

Ferguson, G. G., and Roach, M. R. 1972. Physical factors in the initiation, growth, and rupture of human intracranial saccular aneurysms. *J. Neurosurg.* 37: 666–677.

Fisher, T. R., Coburn, R. F., and Forster, R. E. 1969. Carbon monoxide diffusing capacity in the bullhead catfish. *J. Appl Physiol.* 26:161–169.

Fung, Y. C., and Sobin, S. S. 1969. Theory of sheet flow in the lung alveoli. *J. Appl. Physiol.* 26:472–488.

Gooding, R. M., Neill, W. H., and Dizon, A. E. 1981. Respiration rates and low oxygen tolerance limits in skipjack tuna. *Fish. Bull.* 79:31–48.

Guyton, A. C., Lindsey, A. W., Abernathy, B., and Richardson, T. 1957. Venous return at various right atrial pressures and the normal venous return curve. *Am. J. Physiol.* 189(3):609–615.

Hales, S. 1733. Statical essays: Containing haemastatics. In *Classics of Cardiology,* edited by F. A. Willius, and T. E. Keys, 129–155. New York: Dover Publications.

Head, M. R. 1961. Approximate methods of calculating the two-dimensional laminar boundary layer with suction. In *Boundary Layer and Flow Control,* edited by G. V. Lachmann, vol. 2, 801–841. New York: Pergamon Press.

Helgason, S. S., and Nilsson, S. 1973. Drug effects on pre- and post-branchial blood pressure and heart rate in a free-swimming marine teleost, *Gadus morhua. Acta Physiol. Scand.* 88:533–540.

Hildebrand, M. 1974. *Analysis of Vertebrate Structure.* New York: Wiley.

Hills, B. A., and Hughes, G. M. 1970. A dimensional analysis of oxygen transfer in the fish gill. *Respir. Physiol.* 9:126–140.

Holbert, P. W., Boland, E. J., and Olson, K. R. 1979. The effect of epinephrine and acetylcholine on the distribution of red cells within the gills of the channel catfish. (*Ictaturus punctatus*). *J. Exp. Biol.* 79:135–146.

Holeton, G. F., and Jones, D. R. 1975. Water flow dynamics in the respiratory tract of the carp (*Cyprimus carpio* L.). *J. Exp. Biol.* 63:537–549.

Holeton, G. F., and Randall, D. J. 1967. Changes in blood pressure in the rainbow trout during hypoxia. *J. Exp. Biol.* 46:297–305.

Hughes, G. M. 1966. The dimensions of fish gills in relation to their function. *J. Exp. Biol.* 45:177–195.

Hughes, G. M. 1972. Morphometrics of fish gills. *Respir. Physiol.* 14:1–25.

Hughes, G. M., and Grimstone, A. V. 1965. The fine structure of the secondary lamellae in the gills of *Gadus pollachius. Q. J. Micr. Sci.* 106:343–353.

Hughes, G. M., and Morgan, M. 1973. The structure of fish gills in relation to their respiratory function. *Biol. Rev.* 48:419–475.

Hughes, G. M., and Shelton, G. 1958. The mechanism of gill ventilation in three freshwater teleostean fishes. *J. Exp. Biol.* 35:807–823.

Johansen, K., Franklin, D. L., and Van Citters, R. L. 1966. Aortic blood flow in free-swimming elasmobranchs. *Comp. Biochem. Physiol.* 19:151–160.

Jones, D. R. 1971. Theoretical analysis of factors which may limit the maximum oxygen uptake of fish. *J. Theoret. Biol.* 32:341–349.

Jones, D. R., Langille, B. L., Randall, D. J., and Shelton, G. 1974. Blood flow in dorsal and ventral aortas of the cod, *Gadus morhua. Am. J. Physiol.* 226:90–95.

Jones, D. R., and Randall, D. J. 1978. The respiratory and circulatory systems during exercise. In *Fish Physiology,* edited by W. S. Hoar, vol. VII, 425–501. New York: Academic Press.

Kiceniuk, J. W., and Jones, D. R. 1977. The oxygen transport system in trout (*Salmo gairdneri*) during sustained exercise. *J. Exp. Biol.* 69:247–260.

Lander, J. 1964. The shark circulation. B. Sc. Med. Dissertation. University of Sydney, Sydney, Australia.

Langille, B. L. 1975. A comparative study of central cardiovascular dynamics in vertebrates. Ph.D. Thesis, University of British Columbia, Vancouver, Canada.

Langille, B. L., and Adamson, S. L. 1981. Relationship between blood flow direction and endothelial cell orientation at arterial branch sites in rabbits and mice. *Circ. Res.* 48:481–488.

Langille, B. L., and Crisp, B. 1980. Temperature dependence of blood viscosity in frogs and turtles: Effect on heat exchange with the environment. *Am. J. Physiol.* 239:R248–R253.

Langille, B. L., and Jones, D. R. 1975. Central cardiovascular dynamics of ducks. *Am. J. Physiol.* 228:1856–1861.

Langille, B. L., and Jones, D. R. 1977. Dynamics of blood flow through the hearts and arterial systems of anuran Amphibia. *J. Exp. Biol.* 68:1–17.

Licht, J. H., and Harris, W. S. 1973. The structure, composition and elastic properties of the teleost bulbus arteriosis in the carp, *Cyprinus carpio*. *Comp. Biochem. Physiol.* 64A:699–708.

Lighthill, M. J. 1975. *Mathematical Biofluid Dynamics*. Philadelphia: Society for Industrial and Applied Mathematics.

Lipowsky, H. H., Kovalcheck, S., and Zweifach, B. W. 1978. The distribution of blood rheological parameters in the microvasculature of cat mesentery. *Circ. Res.* 43:738–749.

Lyon, E. P. 1926. A study of the circulation, blood pressure and respiration of sharks. *J. Gen. Physiol.* 8:279–290.

McDonald, D. A. 1974. *Blood Flow in Arteries*. Baltimore: Williams and Wilkins.

Milnor, W. R. 1979. Aortic wavelength as a determinant of the relation between heart rate and body size in mammals. *Am. J. Physiol.* 237:R3–R6.

Muir, B. S., and Brown, C. E. 1971. Effects of blood pathway on the blood-pressure drop in fish gills, with special reference to tunas. *J. Fish. Res. Board Can.* 28:947–955.

Muir, B. S., and Hughes, G. H. 1969. Gill dimensions for three species of tunny. *J. Exp. Biol.* 51:271–285.

Nerem, R. M., Rumberger, J. A., Jr., Gross, D. R., et al. Hot-film anemometer velocity measurements of arterial blood flow in horses. *Circ. Res.* 34:193–203.

Newstead, J. D. 1967. Fine structure of the respiratory lamellae of teleostean gills. *Z. Zellforsch. Mikrosk. Anat.* 79:396–428.

Nilsson, S. 1972. Autonomic vasomotor innervation in the gas gland of the swimbladder of a teleost (*Gadus morhua*). *Comp. Gen. Pharmacol.* 3:371–375.

Noordergraaf, A., Li, J. K.-J., and Campbell, K. B. 1979. Mammalian hemodynamics: a new similarity principle. *J. Theoret. Biol.* 79:485–489.

O'Brien, V., and Ehrlich, L. W. 1977. Simulation of unsteady flow at renal branches. *J. Biomechanics* 10:623–631.

Olson, K. R. 1979. The linear cable theory as a model of gill blood flow. *J. Theoret. Biol.* 81:377–388.

Patel, D. J., and Vaishnav, R. N. 1980. *Basic Hemodynamics and Its Role in Disease Processes*. Baltimore: University Park Press.

Piiper, J., Meyer, M., Worth, H., and Willmer, H. 1977. Respiration and circulation during swimming activity in the dogfish *Scyliorhinus stellaris*. *Respir. Physiol.* 30:221–239.

Price, J. W. 1931. Growth and gill development in small mouthed black bass. Studies, Ohio State University 4.

Priede, I. G. 1976. Functional morphology of the bulbus arteriosus of rainbow trout (*Salmo gairdneri* Richardson). *J. Fish Biol.* 9:209–216.

Randall, D. J. 1968. Functional morphology of the heart in fishes. *Am. Zoologist* 8:179–189.

Randall, D. J. 1970. Gas exchange in fish. In *Fish Physiology,* edited by W. S. Hoar and D. J. Randall, vol. 4, 253–292. New York: Academic Press.

Randall, D. J. 1976. Gill structure and function: Effects of gas and ion exchange. *Physiologist* 19:425.

Randall, D. J., Baumgarten, D., and Malyusz, M. 1972. The relationship between gas and ion transfer across the gills of fishes. *Comp. Biochem. Physiol.* 41A: 629–637.

Rosenhead, L. 1963. *Laminar Boundary Layers.* Oxford: Oxford University Press.

Ruud, J. T. 1954. Vertebrates without erythrocytes and blood pigment. *Nature* 173:848–850.

Satchell, G. H. 1970. A functional appraisal of the fish heart. *Fed. Proc.* 29:1120–1123.

Satchell, G. H. 1971. *Circulation in Fishes.* London: Cambridge University Press.

Satchell, G. H. 1978. Microcirculation in fishes. In *Microcirculation,* edited by G. Kaley and B. M. Altura, vol. II., 619–647. Baltimore: University Park Press.

Satchell, G. H., and Jones, M. P. 1967. The function of the conus arteriosus in the Port Jackson shark, *Heterodontus portusjacksoni. J. Exp. Biol.* 46:373–382.

Schlichting, H. 1955. *Boundary Layer Theory.* New York: Pergamon Press.

Shelton, G. 1970. The regulation of breathing. In *Fish Physiology,* edited by W. S. Hoar and D. J. Randall, vol. 4, 293–359. New York: Academic Press.

Short, S., Butler, P. J., and Taylor, E. W. 1977. The relative importance of nervous, humoral and intrinsic mechanisms in the regulation of heart rate and stroke volume in the dogfish *Scyliorhinus canicula. J. Exp. Biol.* 70:77–92.

Smith, D. G., and Rapson, L. 1977. Differences, in pulmonary microvascular anatomy between *Bufo marinus* and *Xenopus laevis. Cell Tissue Res.* 178:1–15.

Smith, L. S., and Bell, G. R. 1976. A practical guide to the anatomy and physiology of pacific salmon. Miscellaneous special publication #27. Department of the Environment, Fisheries and Marine Service, Ottawa.

Smith, L. S., Brett, J. R., and Davis, J. C. 1967. Cardiovascular dynamics in swimming adult sockeye salmon. *J. Fish. Res. Board Can.* 24:1775–1790.

Smith, W. C. 1918. On the process of disappearance of thee conus arteriosus in teleosts. *Anat. Rec.* 15:65–71.

Sobin, S. S., Tremer, H. M., and Fung, Y. C. 1970. Morphometric basis of the sheet-flow concept of the pulmonary alveolar microcirculation in the cat. *Circ. Res.* 26:397–414.

Steen, J. B. 1971. *Comparative Physiology of Respiratory Mechanisms.* New York: Academic Press.

Stevens, E. D. 1972. Some aspects of gas exchange in tuna. *J. Exp. Biol.* 56:809–823.

Stevens, E. D., and Anantaraman, A. 1982. Hydrodynamics of water flow in fish gills. Unpublished manuscript.

Stevens, E. D., Bennion, G. R., Randall, D. J., and Shelton, G. 1972. Factors affecting arterial pressures and blood flow from the heart in intact, unrestrained lingcod, *Ophiodon elongatus. Comp. Biochem. Physiol.* 43A:681–695.

Stevens, E. D., and Randall, D. J. 1967. Changes in blood pressure, heart rate and breathing rate during moderate swimming activity in rainbow trout. *J. Exp. Biol.* 46:307–315.

Sudak, F. N. 1965. Intrapericardial and intracardiac pressures and the events of the cardiac cycle in *Mustelus canis* (Mitchell). *Comp. Biochem. Physiol.* 14:689–705.

Taylor, E. W., Short, S., and Butler, P. J. 1977. The role of the cardiac vagus in the response of the dogfish *Scyliorhinus canicula* to hypoxia. *J. Exp. Biol.* 70:57–75.

Taylor, M. G. 1964. Wave travel in arteries and the design of the cardiovascular system. Edited by E. O. Attinger, *Pulsatile Blood Flow*, 343–372. New York: Mc-Graw-Hill.

van Dam, L. 1938. On the utilization of oxygen and regulation of breathing in some aquatic animals. Ph.D. thesis, University of Groningen, Groningen, Netherlands.

Van Dyke, M. 1970. Entry flow in a channel. *J. Fluid Mech.* 44:813–823.

Watson, A. D., and Cobb, J. L. S. 1979. A comparative study on the innervation and the vascularization of the bulbus arteriosus in teleost fish. *Cell Tissue Res.* 196:337–346.

Webb, P. W. 1975. Hydrodynamics and energetics of fish propulsion. *Bull. Fish. Res. Board Can.* 190:1–159.

West, J. B. 1979. *Respiratory Physiology—The Essentials,* 2nd ed. Baltimore: Williams & Wilkins.

West, N. H., Bramford, O. S., and Jones, D. R. 1977. A scanning electron microscope study of the microvasculature of the avian lung. *Cell Tissue Res.* 176:553–564.

West, N. H., Langille, B. L., and Jones, D. R. 1981. Cardiovascular system. *In Form and Function in Birds,* edited by A. S. King and J. McLelland, vol. 2, 235–339. New York: Academic Press.

Womersley, J. R. 1957. An elastic tube theory of pulse transmission and oscillatory flow in mammalian arteries. Wright Air Development Center, Technical Report, WADC-TR 56-614.

Wood, C. M. 1974. A critical examination of the physical and adrenergic factors affecting blood flow through the gills of the rainbow trout. *J. Exp. Biol.* 60:241–265.

SYMBOLS

A_b	cross sectional area of lamellar blood space at midsection	d	lamellar pore width
		E	elastic modulus
b	lamellar pore height	HR	heart rate
C_{da}	dorsal aorta compliance	h	lamellar sheet thickness
C_{va}	ventral aorta compliance	J_0, J_1	Bessel functions of the first kind of orders 0 and 1 respectively
c_o	pulse wave velocity		

K	constant	Q_l	flow in lamella
L	filament length	R	radius
L_{lam}	lamellar length	R_e	Reynolds Number based on R
m	lamellar sheet compliance		
P	pressure	R_g	gill vascular resistance
P_a	pressure in afferent filament artery	R_s	systematic vascular resistance
P_e	pressure in efferent filament artery	U	velocity
		u	axial velocity
P_l	pressure across lamella	v	normal velocity
P_{da}	dorsal aorta pressure	w	axial flow
P_{va}	ventral aorta pressure	α	Womersley parameter
ΔPg	differential pressure between ventral and dorsal aorta	δ	boundary layer thickness
		δ^*	boundary layer displacement thickness
Q	volume flow		
Q_a	flow in afferent filament artery	μ	viscosity
		ρ	density
Q_e	flow in efferent filament artery		

Chapter 5
ECOLOGIC IMPLICATIONS OF BUOYANCY CONTROL IN FISH
John H. Gee

CONTENTS

INTRODUCTION

Fish generate lift (buoyancy) to overcome weight in water by a number of mechanisms; of these, lift from the swimbladder and from hydrodynamic forces have received much attention. The hydrostatic role of the swimbladder along with its other functions of pressure and sound reception, respiration, and sound production have received considerable review (Jones and Marshall, 1953; Denton, 1961; Alexander, 1966a; Fänge, 1966; Steen, 1970; Blaxter and Tytler, 1978), and the recent studies of Magnuson (1970, 1973, 1978) have revealed many of the principles of hydrodynamic lift in fishes. Yet few studies have examined or compared the various lift-generating mechanisms in the light of their ecologic implications and consequences.

Apart from the extensive studies of Jones and Marshall (1953), Denton (1961, 1963), Denton and Marshall (1958), and Marshall (1960), few of the early workers directed their attention to the adaptive aspects of a particular mechanism of buoyancy regulation. Recent researchers have, however, emphasized the ecologic significance of their results and have related their findings to the mode of life of the fish under study. This review focuses on the various mechanisms used by fish to attain lift and evaluates the use of these

140

mechanisms in particular environments. The implications of buoyancy regulation in activities involving movements and migrations, maintaining position in fast-flowing waters, avoiding predation, reproducing, and using food and oxygen resources are also examined, and some of the evolutionary consequences of buoyancy control are discussed.

In its widest sense, buoyancy refers to the lift produced to offset the weight of the body in water. Buoyant (or static) lift is produced by incorporating lighter materials into the body such that the mass of the fish approaches the mass of the water displaced; hydrodynamic (dynamic) lift is produced by the movement of the body and fins through the water.

Four forces act on the body of a fish (Fig. 5-1): lift opposes weight in water, and thrust opposes drag. When in equilibrium, lift equals weight and the fish remains at a particular horizontal level neither rising nor falling. The appropriate amount of lift is extremely important for pelagic fishes. It not only saves energy by allowing the fish to hover at a particular depth, but it reduces the amount of energy required to maneuver and swim horizontally. Alexander (1966a) calculated that a fish swimming at a speed of one body length per second would be required to divert 60% of the energy required for movement into offsetting sinking. At speeds of three to four body lengths per second, this would be reduced to 20%.

WAYS OF GENERATING LIFT

Buoyant lift is attained by one or more of the following mechanisms: inclusion of gases within the body, development of large masses of lipids, use (by marine fishes) of low-density (salt-free) fluids often in combination with a reduction of high-density tissues such as muscle and bone (Table 5-1). In addition, most fishes appear to use some hydrodynamic lift, and a few species use this mechanism exclusively. A fish may use several of the above mechanisms, and the relative importance of any mechanism used to generate

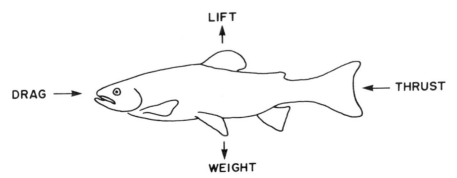

Figure 5-1
Forces that act on the body of a fish affecting equilibrium.

Table 5.1
RELATIVE AMOUNT OF LIFT PRODUCED PER UNIT VOLUME

| MECHANISM | LIFT (g/ml^{-1}) | |
	Fresh Water	Salt Water
Gas inclusion	0.999	1.025
Lipids	0.083-0.144	0.109-0.170
Low density fluids or tissues	NA	0.026

lift may shift with age, stage in the life cycle, or in response to a change in a particular environmental variable.

Gas Inclusions

Most gas inclusions are held in a swimbladder but in the catfish (*Hoplosternum thoracatum*) the swimbladder is greatly reduced, and gases held in the intestine are used to provide lift (Gee and Graham, 1978). Several air-breathing pelagic fishes have accessory respiratory organs associated with the mouth, pharynx, and buccal or opercular regions that produce some lift.

Gas inclusions change in volume following Boyle's law (or nearly so) as the fish experiences changes in pressure (depth). Deviations from Boyle's law are found in species that contain the gases in the body under higher or lower pressures than ambient. Gases held in the body under greater than ambient pressure (excess internal pressure) will not change as much with changes in depth as will those held at ambient pressure (Alexander, 1966a).

Tremendous partial pressure gradients may be found between the swimbladder contents of deep sea fishes and their surroundings, but ways of restricting passive gas losses in these situations are not clearly understood. Denton and associates (1970, 1972) suggested that guanine crystals in the swimbladder wall serve to lengthen the diffusion path and reduce the surface area for diffusion. Reduced permeability to oxygen is inversely related to the amount of guanine of the swimbladder (Kutchai and Steen, 1971; Lapennas and Schmidt-Nielsen, 1977; Ross, 1979; Kleckner, 1980a); furthermore, guanine content is positively related to depth of occurrence (Ross and Gordon, 1978; Kleckner, 1980b), correlating with increasing swimbladder oxygen with depth. Other possible mechanisms of reducing diffusion include collagen in the swimbladder (Fänge, 1966), but this role was discounted by Ross (1979); a foam consisting of lipids, lining the inside of the swimbladder of some deep-sea fishes (Patton and Thomas, 1971; Wittenberg *et al.*, 1980); and flattened overlapping cells composed of round platelets (Brown and Copeland, 1978).

Because of volume changes with pressure (depth), fish must be able to adjust swimbladder volume to provide the appropriate lift at a particular depth. Physostomes possess a pneumatic duct connecting the swimbladder to the pharynx and can spit gases out of the swimbladder in response to a decrease in pressure during ascent; this can be stimulated by a pressure reduction of 3% to 10% in cyprinids (Alexander, 1966a). Clearly, physostomes cannot gulp air when swimming far below the surface, but they can inflate the swimbladder to provide neutral buoyancy at a given depth by gulping the appropriate volume of air before descent. Some physostomes do not appear to secrete significant amounts of gas (Salmonidae), while others (Cyprinidae) secrete gases readily. *Pimephales promelas*, when undisturbed, uses both gulping and secretion to inflate the swimbladder with the former contributing on the average to 69% and the latter 31% of the increase. Resorption was used to reduce swimbladder volume as evidenced by a lack of spitting and a change in gas composition (Stewart and Gee, 1981).

Physoclists lack a pneumatic duct and must alter swimbladder volume by secreting or resorbing gases. Physoclists and many physostomes secrete gas by way of a countercurrent multiplication system called the *rete mirabile* (Steen, 1963a; Berg and Steen, 1968; Sund, 1977; Steen and Sund, 1977). The rete has the capacity to concentrate oxygen at very high partial pressures within the swimbladder; as a result, the composition of swimbladder gases is mainly O_2 in deep-water fishes, while in those closer to the surface the gas composition approximates atmospheric air. The efficiency of secretion is reduced with depth (hydrostatic pressure). One adaptation to increase efficiency is to lengthen the rete. Marshall (1972) and Wittenberg and colleagues (1980) describe a positive relationship between length of rete and depth. The longer the rete, the greater the ability to concentrate oxygen (Kuhn *et al.,* 1963) and the greater the rate of oxygen secretion (Kuhn and Marti, 1966).

Most but not all physoclists possess an oval (Marshall, 1971) where resorption of gases takes place (Steen, 1963b). Rates of gas secretion and absorption are reviewed by Blaxter and Tytler (1978), but as they have pointed out, the time taken either to inflate or deflate the swimbladder (difference between secretion and resorption) is most important. These rates depend on several factors relating to environments occupied and mode of life and are thus discussed below.

Swimbladder volume can also be altered by relaxing or contracting muscles in or about the swimbladder wall as first suggested by Delaroche (1809). That this can occur is seen by variation in internal pressure of 38 mm Hg to 114 mm Hg above ambient, which occurs commonly among freshwater fishes (Alexander, 1959; Gee *et al.,* 1974; Gee and Gee, 1976).

Altering internal pressure of swimbladder gas to change lift is a rapid and precise mechanism, but only a limited change can be made. It can, however, be used to adjust the shape of the swimbladder and bring about changes in orientation (attitude) as described by McCutcheon (1958) for the physoclist (*Lagodon rhomboides*). Gulping and spitting gas result in rapid and extensive changes in lift, but gulping exposes fish to aquatic and terrestrial predators, requires time and energy in traveling to the surface, and may be ineffective when ice cover is present. In addition, it is difficult to obtain, hold, and transport sufficient gas at the surface to maintain an optimal buoyancy at depths below the surface. Spitting gas is used as part of a fright response in some physostomes (Verheijen, 1962). The reduction in swimbladder lift may assist downward movement, while the rising bubble may serve to distract a predator. Secretion and resorption, while relatively slow, have none of the above restrictions and appear to be precise mechanisms of controling swimbladder lift.

Lipids

Lipids provide considerable lift because of their low specific gravity. Categories of lipids used for buoyancy control in fish include hydrocarbons (mainly squalene; specific gravity of 0.8562), wax esters (0.8578), diacyl glyceryl ethers (0.8907), and triglycerides (0.9154 to 0.9168). The last two groups also can be metabolized and used as energy stores in some fishes.

The location of lipids varies. Sharks possess high concentrations in the liver (Heller *et al.,* 1957; Corner *et al.,* 1969; Malins and Barone, 1970; Craik, 1978). In some myctophids, lipids are concentrated around the swimbladder wall (containing little or no gas; Butler and Pearcy, 1972). Lipids can also occur in the skull and spinal bones (Bone, 1972; Lee *et al.,* 1975), in intermuscular sacs (DeVries and Eastman, 1978), and in the dermis (Bone, 1972).

The amount of lipid may be regulated to control buoyancy because Bone and Roberts (1969) found a positive correlation between the size of the liver (and hence lift) and the density of other tissues; furthermore, Malins and Barone (1970) found that the ratio of diacyl glyceryl ethers to triglycerides was increased when *Squalus acanthius* was weighted. The mechanism by which changes in the amount or composition of lipids is controled remains obscure.

Low Density Fluids/Tissues

Many marine fishes attain neutral buoyancy primarily by lift generated by a high water content of their bodies combined with a reduction in skeletal structure and musculature. Denton and Marshall (1958) described some almost neutrally buoyant bathypelagic fishes with no swimbladders and with only moderate fat contents. They had poorly ossified skeletons, low protein and ash contents, and very watery bodies. The jaws and gill arches were the most firmly ossified. Similarly Blaxter and associates (1971) found that some mesopelagic fishes with no swimbladders had very high water contents ranging from 88% to 95%.

The nearly neutrally buoyant electric ray (*Torpedo nobiliana*) obtains its buoyant lift primarily from the high water content (90%) of its two electric organs (20% of total weight); additional lift comes from lipids in the liver and from hydrodynamic forces (Roberts, 1969).

Hydrodynamic Lift

The mechanics of hydrodynamic lift are reviewed by Magnuson (1978). Such lift is generated by the movement of the body, fins, or caudal keels through water. Any surface that has a camber or is held at a positive angle of attack will generate lift in a manner analogous to the wings on an airplane. Fish can control hydrodynamic lift by altering speed (lift increases with square of velocity) and/or fin geometry (area, angle of attack).

Scombrids have dense body tissues, and many species either lack or possess relatively small swimbladders. Their densities are much greater than that of seawater, and they swim rapidly and continuously, generating hydrodynamic lift to offset weight in water (Magnuson, 1978). Magnuson (1970) showed that in *Euthynnus affinis* such lift is produced by the body and fin camber, the angle of attack, the area of the pectoral fins, and the length of time they are extended. At slow speeds, the pectorals (fully extended) produce about 80% of the lift with the remainder produced by the peduncular keels. At high speeds the pectorals are appressed, reducing area, and lift anterior to the center of gravity (about 70%) is produced by the body, which has no camber but a positive angle of attack. In sharks, hydrodynamic lift is generated by the heterocercal tail and by the pectoral fins; however, the latter cannot be appressed, and lift must be regulated by altering swimming speed and/or angle of attack. Hydrodynamic lift is generated both anterior and posterior to the center of gravity in both scombrids and sharks to ensure longitudinal stability (Magnuson, 1970). The bodies of sturgeon (Aleev, 1963) and some sharks are cambered and produce lift at a zero geometric angle of attack. Again, lift posterior to the center of gravity for longitudinal stability is produced by the heterocercal tail (Alexander, 1965, 1966b; Simons, 1970).

Those species of myctophids that either lack or possess small swimbladders along with low amounts of lipid inclusions have long pectoral fins (Bone, 1973). These pelagic fish presumably use their fins to generate hydrodynamic lift to maintain position.

Advantages and Disadvantages of Particular Buoyancy Regulating Mechanisms

The mechanism of attaining lift profoundly influences the efficiency of movement, and Alexander (1972, 1977) has estimated the relative costs (in terms of drag) of using different lift-generating mechanisms. First, the amount of drag produced is a function of the mechanism in use. Alexander (1977) has assessed the basic drag produced on a hypothetical fish, without any buoyancy aids, swimming at a range of speeds (Table 5-2). If hydrodynamic lift is generated by the pectorals to overcome weight, a reasonable estimate of the additional drag on these hydrofoils would be 0.1 N; however, if lipids such as squalene or wax esters were used, there would be a potential increase in volume and surface area resulting in additional drag amounting to 20% of basic drag. If the more dense triglycerides were used, the additional drag would be 33% of basic drag.

Childress and Nygaard (1973) showed that an increased lipid content in several species of myctophids was accompanied by a reduction in water content of the body and concluded that there would be no net increase in volume or drag. A swimbladder also increases volume and surface area of the body but to a much lesser extent because of the almost negligible density of its gases and amounts to additional drag of only 4% of basic drag (Table 5-2). Total drag experienced by a fish is therefore a function of its swimming speed and the mechanism used to produce lift. At slow swimming speeds gas inclusions result in less drag than hydrodynamic lift (Fig. 5-2), but at higher speeds gas inclusions and hydrodynamic lift are almost equally effective. At very high swimming speeds hydrodynamic lift becomes most efficient.

The above calculations represent a cost to the fish in terms of drag alone when swimming at a constant depth. They ignore costs of maintaining swimbladder volume (secretion of gas) required to offset diffusion, which increases with depth. To assess such a cost, Alexander (1972) estimated the cost of replacing gas lost from the swimbladder (using the permeability of the swimbladder wall of the eel, *Conger*; Denton *et al.*, 1970) to be

Table 5.2

ESTIMATES OF DRAG INCURRED BY A HYPOTHETICAL 28-CM 220-G FISH USING EITHER HYDRODYNAMIC LIFT, LIPIDS, OR A SWIMBLADDER TO OVERCOME A DENSITY 5% GREATER THAN WATER AND ASSUMING THAT IN THE CASE OF LIPIDS THERE IS NO ACCOMPANYING DECREASE IN WATER CONTENT OF THE BODY TO ACCOMMODATE THE ADDITION OF LIPIDS

Swimming speed (m·sec^{-1})	0.10	0.21	0.34	0.52
Basic drag (N)	0.007	0.031	0.068	0.130
Additional drag				
Hydrodynamic lift	0.01	0.01	0.01	0.01
Lipids–squaline/wax esters	0.0014	0.0062	0.0136	0.0260
–triglycerides	0.0023	0.0102	0.0224	0.0429
Swimbladder	0.0003	0.0012	0.0027	0.0052

(Data from Alexander, 1977)

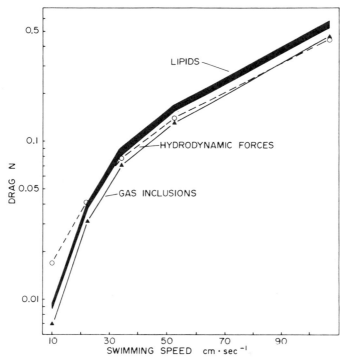

Figure 5-2

Relationship between drag and swimming speed for three lift-generating mechanisms on a hypothetical fish, assuming that in the case of lipids there is no accompanying decrease in body water content to accommodate the addition of lipids. Lipids are shown as a broad band with squalene and wax esters at the lower range and triglycerides at the top range of the band. (Modified from data given by Alexander, 1972, 1977)

$2 \text{ cm}^3 \text{ O}_2 \cdot \text{kg}^{-1} \cdot \text{hr}^{-1}$ at 100 m and $35 \text{ cm}^3 \text{ O}_2 \cdot \text{kg}^{-1} \cdot \text{hr}^{-1}$ at 1000 m. These values of oxygen consumption must be added to those required to offset drag, assuming that in the case of lipids there is no accompanying decrease in water content of the body to accommodate the addition of lipids. These too were estimated by Alexander (1972) for a hypothetical fish using either hydrodynamic lift, triglycerides, wax esters, or a swimbladder and were 25, 17, 10, and $2 \text{ cm}^3 \text{ O}_2 \cdot \text{kg}^{-1} \cdot \text{h}^{-1}$.

Clearly then, the energy advantages of using a swimbladder accrue to those fishes that swim relatively slowly (minimizing drag) in shallow water (minimizing gas diffusion from the swimbladder); however, the main disadvantage of using gas inclusions for lift is that volume (lift) changes with vertical movements. Several species such as garfish and flying fish remain at the surface and avoid the problem (Bone 1973). Those that alter depth must compensate for change in hydrostatic pressure and lift. Some species may be close to neutral buoyancy at the upper part of their range and may compensate for the increased negative buoyancy at the lower depth by increasing their reliance on hydrodynamic lift and secreting gas (Kanwisher and Ebeling, 1957). Fishes that are at or near neutral buoyancy at the lower depth range must remove gas by either resorption or spitting (physostomes) or hold the gas under pressure on ascent. Herring (*Clupea harengus*) can release gas on ascent by way of a duct from the swimbladder to the anus (Brawn, 1962). The disadvantage of volume changes with depth are partially compensated by the relatively rapid ways in which swimbladder volume can be adjusted.

With lipids the total lift produced is fixed and cannot be adjusted rapidly; however, extensive vertical movements are possible because the lift generated is unaffected by changes in hydrostatic pressure. Similarly, lift produced by a reduction of high-density tissues combined with inclusion of salt-free fluids cannot be adjusted rapidly but is not affected by changes in depth. Such lift functions only in marine waters, and because muscle and skeletal systems are reduced, movement is restricted to slow and unsustained swimming (Blaxter, *et al.,* 1971).

Hydrodynamic lift can be adjusted rapidly by altering swimming speed and/or fin geometry and is also unaffected by changes in hydrostatic pressure. The main disadvantage is that it requires continuous expenditure of energy, not only for constant movement but to generate lift forces and overcome the additional induced drag (Magnuson, 1978).

DISTINCTIVE FEATURES OF AQUATIC ENVIRONMENTS AFFECT LIFT MECHANISMS

The mechanisms used to attain lift are influenced by particular variables associated with aquatic environments. The basis for defining aquatic environments (Fig. 5-3) follows one originally used by Jones and Marshall (1953) and subsequently modified by Marshall (1971). Variables that appear to be most important in influencing, either directly or indirectly, the lift mechanisms used are hydrostatic pressure, supply of food, and water currents or turbulence (Table 5-3).

Hydrostatic pressure increases linearly with depth, and its effect on gas inclusions is to reduce the volume by one-half when pressure is doubled. Pressure at sea level is 1 atm, and it doubles to 2 atm at a depth of 10 m, then to 4 atm at 30 m, and 8 atm at 70 m. As a result, changes in volume of gas inclusions with vertical excursions are potentially extreme in the epipelagic waters (Fig. 5-3); thus, species that alter depth rapidly use mainly hydrodynamic lift or lipids (Table 5-3).

At high hydrostatic pressures encountered in the bathypelagic and benthopelagic environments, fish with gas inclusions experience increased rates of diffusion of swimbladder gases and decreased efficiency of gas secretion. At extreme depths (6000 m), the specific gravity of swimbladder gases is so high that the lift produced is quite reduced.

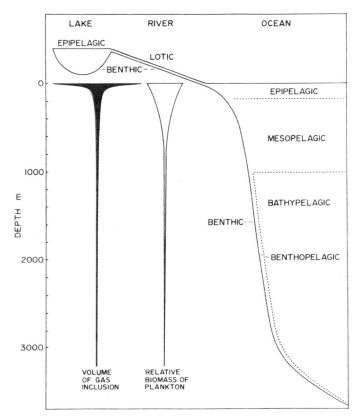

Figure 5-3
Major aquatic environments showing the extent to which a given volume of a gas inclusion would change with depth. Changes in the relative biomass of plankton with depths are also shown. (Modified from Marshall, 1971)

Production of food is greatest in the epipelagic environment including its boundary with the mesopelagic (Fig. 5-3). In the lower mesopelagic, food production is reduced to between 50% and 10% and is reduced further to between 10% and 1% in the bathypelagic environment (Marshall, 1971).

The problem of food scarcity in the middle and lower mesopelagic is solved by fishes making vertical diel migrations to the upper mesopelagic or epipelagic waters where feeding occurs at night. Myctophids making the most extensive vertical migrations use lipids or hydrodynamic lift, or if they possess a swimbladder, it is supplemented by these two mechanisms (Bone, 1973). There is no evidence of such movements in bathypelagic fishes. Here the swimbladder is regressed in all species, and the lipid content is low (Marshall, 1971). Marshall (1960, 1971, 1972) has argued that this is part of an extreme economy of organization that has evolved in response to the scarcity of food. Weight is reduced primarily by a reduction of high-density tissues as bathypelagic fishes characteristically show a reduction of muscles along the trunk

Table 5.3
AQUATIC ENVIRONMENTS AND THEIR CHARACTERISTIC FEATURES THAT INFLUENCE THE STRATEGIES USED TO GENERATE LIFT

ENVIRONMENT	DESCRIPTION	SPECIAL PROBLEMS	LIFT STRATEGIES
Lotic	Rivers and streams excluding benthic area; depth less than 15 m; food generally abundant; light present	Great variation in water velocity in time and space; important to hold station; other environmental factors variable	Gas inclusions ubiquitous; physostomes very common (variety of teleost fishes) Hydrodynamic lift supplements swimbladder lift and its relative contribution increases in fast water velocities
Epipelagic	Depth 0–150 m; marine waters and freshwater lakes; photosynthetic zone; food abundant	Extensive changes in volume of gas inclusions with depth owing to change in hydrostatic pressure	Gas inclusions used by physostomes (Cyprinidae, Salmonidae, Clupeidae) in freshwater and coastal marine; physoclists (Percidae) in freshwater but outnumber physostomes in marine Hydrodynamic lift used by fast-swimming sharks and Scombridae Lipids and hydrodynamic lift used by slow-swimming sharks
Mesopelagic	Depth 150–1000 m; marine waters and freshwater lakes; light varies from dim to darkness; food not abundant	Vertical migration to epipelagic where feeding occurs; extreme variation in hydrostatic pressure is encountered	Gas inclusions (all physoclists; e.g., Myctophidae) used by one-third of species Lipids, hydrodynamic lift, or gas inclusions combined with lipids and hydrodynamic lift used by many species making vertical migrations (Myctophidae, Stomiatidae, and stromateoid fishes) Low-density fluids/ tissues used by some Gonostomatidae

continued

Table 5.3

AQUATIC ENVIRONMENTS AND THEIR CHARACTERISTIC
FEATURES THAT INFLUENCE THE STRATEGIES USED
TO GENERATE LIFT (*continued*)

ENVIRONMENT	DESCRIPTION	SPECIAL PROBLEMS	LIFT STRATEGIES
Bathypelagic	Depth greater than 1000 m; food scarce; light limited to bioluminescence	Limited food supply limits energy-expensive functions reducing buoyancy options	Gas inclusions are generally absent as gas retention and secretion expensive at high pressure Lipids rarely used as expensive to develop and maintain Hydrodynamic lift not compatible with reduced skeletal and muscle systems Low-density fluids/tissues commonly used (some Gonostomatidae)
Benthopelagic	A thin zone (several meters) between substrate and bathypelagic; dark; food scarce	Fish must swim long distances slowly searching for sparse food; hydrostatic pressure high	Gas inclusions: used by some species (Macrouridae, Eretmorphoridae, Brotulidae), gas secretion inefficient. Gas bladder used also for sound production and reception Lipids used by Squalidae, Chimaeridae Low-density fluids/tissues used by Ateleopidae and Alepocephalidae
Benthic	Bottom of marine waters (all depths), and of lakes and rivers; food and light as described for neighboring environments	Fish sedentary; commonly encounter currents or turbulence and important to hold position; concealment important in shallow waters	Gas inclusions, when present, are reduced in volume Hydrodynamic lift is generated when currents are encountered; fish possessing gas inclusions reduce the volume to compensate for excessive hydrodynamic lift Generally all forms of lift are minimized (Percidae, Cottidae, Gobiidae, shallow water; Zoarchidae, Liparidae, Bathypteroidae, deep water)

and tail and a poorly ossified skeleton with only jaws and gills arches firmly ossified. The gills are reduced, and some species have no scales. These fish are slow swimmers, and the description of Denton and Marshall (1958) is most apt: these fish resemble floating traps.

Childress and Nygaard (1973) showed with a survey of 37 midwater species that body water content progressively increases with depth of occurrence and that this was accompanied by decreases in protein, lipid, and skeletal ash content. They argued that the replacement of organic matter with low-density fluids allowed fish to not only obtain lift but also to attain increased size. The advantage of size according to Childress and Nygaard is that it enables fish to capture a wider range of food items.

Fishes encounter water currents and turbulence in benthic and lotic environments. In marine waters, benthic fish in shallow coastal areas experience turbulence from wave action and from water currents, particularly near estuaries. Tidal action creates strong currents in shallow and deep waters along coastal shelves. Below the bathypelagic, benthic fishes commonly encounter velocities of 4 to 40 cm $\cdot$ sec^{-1} (Hollister and Heezen, 1966). In streams and rivers both lotic and benthic environments are characterized by fluctuations in water velocity; the ability to hold position in such conditions is of great importance. In benthic environments fish are negatively buoyant and lift is reduced; in lotic environments swimbladders are found in most species although some lift is generated by hydrodynamic forces.

RELATIONSHIP BETWEEN LIFT STRATEGY AND MODE OF LIFE

Limitations of particular mechanisms of attaining lift and characteristics of a given environment interact to determine the overall strategy used to provide lift. Such a strategy might use several lift mechanisms and must be complementary to the various activities that make up the mode of life of a species. This relationship is examined for a number of activities.

Holding Position Against Current

If fishes, in the face of fluctuations in current and turbulence, are to maintain position with a minimum expenditure of energy they must carefully regulate the forces of lift and weight.

Benthic

The negative buoyancy of benthic fishes generates frictional forces between the body and the substrate and this aids the fish in holding position when exposed to currents (Alexander, 1966a). Although streamlined to reduce drag, benthic fishes exposed to currents face two problems when increased velocities are encountered. The increased flow over the body causes an increase in viscous drag that can exceed frictional drag of the body against the substrate causing the fish to slip back, and at higher speeds, the fish lifts up off the bottom owing to increased hydrodynamic lift that exceeds its weight in water. These relationships are described by Arnold and Weihs (1978) for plaice. The behavioral responses of plaice to resist both slip-back and lift-off are described by Arnold (1969).

Deep-water benthic species seldom possess a swimbladder; however, its occurrence among shallow-water species (next to epipelagic or lotic environments) is common, and many species regulate swimbladder volume precisely to increase lift when velocity or turbulence diminish and decrease lift as velocity or turbulence increase. Such a reduction increases weight and the resulting frictional drag against the substrate, altering the velocity at which lift-off and slip-back occur to higher speeds. The longnose dace (*Rhinichthys cataractae*) and the darters (*Percina caprodes* and *Percina shumardi*) are benthic, and all occur in both rapids of rivers as well as along exposed shores of large lakes. Whenever strong current (river) or turbulence (wave action on lake shore) is encountered, swimbladder lift is reduced by at least 40% over that generated in still water (Gee, 1968; Gee and Machniak, 1972; H. Balesic, unpublished data).

That swimbladder lift is greatly increased in slow-moving or still water by some benthic species suggests that some time may be spent swimming up off the substrate. The darter (*Percina maculata*), a benthic stream fish, obtains most of its food by foraging just off the bottom (Smart and Gee, 1979). In still water its swimbladder provides near neutral buoyancy, while in strong current it contributes little or no lift (no gas present).

Lotic

Fish considered here are pelagic, possess a swimbladder, and although most common in still waters, and moderate currents (<45 cm $\cdot$ sec^{-1}), they periodically encounter fast velocities. The contribution of lift from gas inclusions and hydrodynamic forces is altered with changes in velocity as described for benthic fishes. Excessive lift created by fish swimming to hold position in increasing velocities of water is compensated by a reduction in swimbladder lift of between 20% and 65% (Gee *et al.*, 1974).

There is an inverse relationship between water velocity and the contribution of swimbladder lift to total lift (Fig. 5-4). The amount of hydrodynamic lift increases with the square of the velocity unless the fish alters the angle of attack or geometry of the hydrofoils. Such changes must occur because the decrease in swimbladder lift is either linear or becomes progressively less with higher velocities. The reason for a particular combination of swimbladder lift and hydrodynamic lift at a given water velocity is not clear, but appears to be related to the efficiency (in terms of minimizing drag) of each lift mechanism

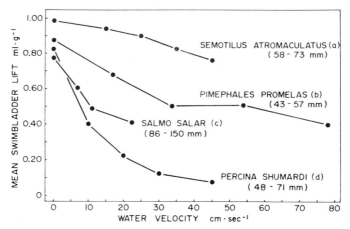

Figure 5-4

Mean ($n = 8$–10) swimbladder lift generated at different velocities of water. (From (a) Berezay and Gee, 1978; (b) Gee, 1977; (c) Neave *et al.,* 1966; (d) H. Balesic, unpublished data.)

at a particular velocity. In slow currents or still water, many lotic fishes hover or swim slowly, so gas inclusions would be most appropriate (Fig. 5-2). At faster velocities fish must swim faster to hold position against current, and either hydrodynamic lift is most efficient or the generation of such lift is unavoidable owing to the morphology of the fish. Whatever the reason, experimental observations clearly show that fish reduce swimbladder lift and increase hydrodynamic lift when current increases and vice versa. In addition, observations on swimming behavior during adjustment of swimbladder lift to a change in velocity show that fishes swim with a negative angle of attack when exposed to strong current after acclimation to still water, suggesting excessive lift and a positive angle of attack when exposed to still water after acclimation to strong current, suggesting insufficient lift (Berezay and Gee, 1978; Stewart and Gee 1981). Once the adjustment of swimbladder lift is complete, fish swim horizontally.

Factors Affecting Extent and Rate of Change of Swimbladder Lift by Benthic and Lotic Fishes Exposed to Fluctuations in Water Velocity

A range of environmental factors and conditions influence the amount of swimbladder lift generated by benthic and lotic fishes in either still water or water current (Table 5-4). Those that affect extent of the change are water temperature, velocity, and their interaction; size of fish; the seasonally related factors of photoperiod, condition, and degree of gonad development; and the strength of the water velocity in which the fish was reared. The extent of adjustment and ability to minimize swimbladder lift is related to mode of life and to the success and ease of holding position in fast water velocities (Gee, 1972).

Water temperature profoundly affects the ability to alter swimbladder lift. Of those species studied (*Pimephales promelas*: Gee, 1977; *Semotilus atromaculatus*: Berezay and Gee, 1978; *Percina shumardi*: H. Balesic, unpublished data), the extent of adjustment is restricted at extreme low (< 10°C) and high (>25°C) temperatures. This has important implications for holding position during the period of spawning as well as being a contributing factor to downstream dispersal. (Saunders, 1965; Gee, 1977; Berezay and Gee, 1978; Luoma and Gee, 1980).

In comparing the ability to alter swimbladder volume of North American stream fishes with those in Central America, Gee and Gee (1976) found that

Table 5.4
FACTORS AFFECTING SWIMBLADDER LIFT GENERATED BY BENTHIC AND LOTIC FISHES IN STILL WATER AND CURRENT

FACTOR	WHERE EFFECT SHOWN	EFFECT ON SWIMBLADDER LIFT	SPECIES	SOURCE
Temperature	Still water and current	Variable; depends on species	*Pimephales promelas* *Percina shumardi*	Gee (1977) H. Balesic (unpublished data)
		Interacts with velocity	*Semotilus atromaculatus*	Berezay and Gee (1978)
Photoperiod	Still water and current	Lift is least with 12 hr light; in shorter or longer periods lift increases	*P. promelas*	Luoma and Gee (1980)
Velocity in which fish reared	Still water and current	Rearing in fast velocities gives lower lift than when reared in still water	*Rhinichthys cataractae* *R. atratulus*	Gee (1974)
Size of fish	Still water and current	Inverse	*R. cataractae* *R. atratulus*	Gee (1972)
	Current only	Inverse	*Noturus gyrinus*	Machniak and Gee (1975)
	Still water only	Inverse	*S. atromaculatus* *Ictalurus melas*	Berezay and Gee (1978) Machniak and Gee (1975)
Swimming speed	Still water only	Inverse	*S. atromaculatus*	Berezay and Gee (1978)
Water velocity	Current only	Inverse	*P. promelas* *Salmo salar* *P. shumardi*	Gee (1977) Neave *et al* (1966) H. Balesic (pupublished data)
Coefficient of condition	Current only	Inverse	*P. promelas*	Luoma and Gee (1980)
Percent gonad development	Current only	Inverse	*P. promelas*	Luoma and Gee (1980)

many of the Central American group did not adjust buoyancy and those that did were unable to adjust to the same extent as North American species. These differences can be related to differences in the flow regime of North and Central American streams: the former show a pronounced and prolonged period of freshet conditions in the spring while the latter show repeated freshet conditions over shorter times (fewer than 6 hr), which result from daily short bursts of rain during the wet season (Gee and Gee, 1976). Under such conditions it may not be economical to reduce swimbladder volume for such a short time, and fish may swim against the water current adjusting their swimming behavior to overcome excessive lift or else seek areas where velocity is reduced.

Thus stream fish, particularly temperate species, show considerable plasticity in control of swimbladder lift. Evidence of additional plasticity comes from experiments on *Rhinichthys cataractae* and *R. atratalus*. The development of the swimbladder of both is influenced by the water velocity in which they are reared (Gee, 1974). Thus some benthic and lotic species possess behavioral and developmental plasticity in swimbladder volume that provides them with the potential to modify the amount of lift from the swimbladder to meet the particular conditions of water velocity in which they develop.

The rate of adjustment of swimbladder volume by benthic and lotic fishes to compensate for changes in water velocity varies. Surprisingly, physostomes and physoclists are quite similar in their average rate of decrease in swimbladder volume. If anything, physostomes are a little slower. At the average rate observed, physostomes could eliminate all gas from their swimbladders in 115 hr, while physoclists would require 80 hr (Table 5-5). This suggests that physostomes, because they are so slow, may rely more on spitting than resorbtion. Similarly, there is little difference in times to inflate the swimbladder by physostomes and physoclists (Table 5-6). At rates observed for *Percina* (two species) it would take about 100 hr to completely fill an emptied swimbladder. Among physostomes with surface access, an average of 59 hr was required. Physostomes without surface access inflated their swimbladders (by secretion) as fast or faster than physoclists (Table 5-6). The physostomes studied (except the Salmonidae, which are very rapid at such adjustments) were Ostariophysi, where the swimbladder is involved in sound detection. Rapid changes in volume interfere with this sensory function because of the particular viscoelastic properties of the swimbladder wall (Alexander 1961, 1966a). This may explain the slow rate of volume changes in the species studied.

Temperature affects the rate of inflation in *Percina shumardi* (H. Balesic, unpublished data), with inflation at 6°C slower than at 12°C or 20°C. Similarly, *Pimephales promelas* inflates swimbladder volume much faster at 21°C than at 6°C. These findings suggest that rate of gas secretion is temperature dependent. McNabb and Mecham (1971) found inflation rates in

Table 5.5

COMPARISON BETWEEN PHYSOSTOMES AND PHYSOCLISTS IN
THE RATE OF DECREASE IN SWIMBLADDER VOLUME (LIFT)
WHEN EXPOSED TO WATER VELOCITIES OF 25 TO 40 CM · SEC^{-1}
AFTER ACCLIMATION TO STILL WATER. IN SOME SPECIES
DIFFERENT SIZE GROUPS (FORK LENGTH; MM) WERE ANALYZED

SPECIES		SWIMBLADDER LIFT ml · g^{-1}			TIME TO ATTAIN MINIMUM LIFT (HR)	RATE OF CHANGE (ml/g^{-1}h^{-1})
		Still	Current	Difference		
Physostomes						
Roeboides		1.01	0.87	0.14	24	0.0058
guatemalensis						
Brycon chagrensis		0.93	0.70	0.23	48	0.0048
Bryconamericanus		0.83	0.59	0.24	24	0.0100
emperador						
Hoplias		0.82	0.42	0.40	72	0.0056
microlepis						
Rhinichthys		0.99	0.27	0.72	96	0.0075
cataractae[a]						
R. atratulus[b]		0.99	0.67	0.32	132	0.0024
Pimephales	20–30	1.00	0.77	0.23	12	0.0192
promelas[c]	47–63	1.00	0.57	0.43	24	0.0179
Pimelodella		0.79	0.62	0.17	24	0.0071
chagresi						
Noturus gyrinus[d]	24–41	1.05	0.80	0.25	96	0.0026
	44–59	0.95	0.80	0.15	192	0.0008
	61–101	0.90	0.77	0.13	192	0.0008
Semotilus		0.98	0.75	0.23	6	0.0383
atromaculatus[e]					(Mean)	0.0094
Physoclists						
Rivulus brunneus		0.96	0.83	0.13	24	0.0054
Brachyrhaphis		0.94	0.70	0.24	48	0.0050
episcopi						
Neoheterandria		0.84	0.65	0.19	24	0.0079
tridentiger						
Poecilia sphenops		0.99	0.67	0.22	6	0.0367
Aequidens coeruleo-		0.95	0.64	0.31	24	0.0129
punctatus						
Geophagus		0.93	0.80	0.13	24	0.0054
crassilabris						
Neetroplus		0.92	0.73	0.19	24	0.0079
panamensis						
Percina caprodes[f]		0.91	0.29	0.62	48	0.0129
Percina shumardi[f]		0.82	0.15	0.67	96	0.0070
					(Mean)	0.0112

[a]Gee, 1968; [b]Gee, 1970; [c]Gee, 1977; [d]Machniak and Gee, 1975; [e]Berezay and Gee, 1978;
[f]Balesic, unpublished data
(Data from Gee and Gee, 1976, except where noted.)

Table 5.6
COMPARISON BETWEEN PHYSOSTOMES AND PHYSOCLISTS IN THE RATE OF INCREASE IN SWIMBLADDER VOLUME (LIFT) WHEN EXPOSED TO STILL WATER AFTER ACCLIMATION TO FAST-FLOWING WATER (25 to 40 CM · SEC^{-1}). IN SOME SPECIES DIFFERENT SIZE GROUPS (FORK LENGTH; MM) WERE ANALYZED

SPECIES		SWIMBLADDER LIFT, ml · g^{-1}			TIME TO ATTAIN MINIMUM LIFT (HR)	RATE OF CHANGE, (mg · g^{-1}H^{-1})
		Still Water	Current	Difference		
Physostomes						
Rhinichthys atratulus[a]		0.97	0.63	0.34	36	0.0094
R. cataractae[b]	access	0.90	0.35	0.55	24	0.0229
	no access	0.92	0.34	0.58	48	0.0121
Noturus gyrinus[c]	24–41	0.90	0.78	0.12	192	0.0006
	44–59	0.92	0.78	0.14	192	0.0007
	61–101	0.98	0.83	0.15	96	0.0016
Pimephales promelas[d]						
20–30 {	access	1.00	0.80	0.20	3	0.0667
	no access	1.00	0.80	0.20	6	0.0333
47–63 {	access	0.98	0.58	0.40	24	0.0167
	no access	0.98	0.58	0.40	48	0.0083
Physoclists						
Percina caprodes[e]		0.83	0.18	0.65	48	0.0135
P. shumardi[e]		0.80	0.02	0.78	96	0.0081

[a]Gee, 1968; [b]Gee, 1970; [c]Machniak and Gee, 1975; [d]Gee, 1977; [e]Balesic, unpublished data

Lepomis macrochirus to be independent of temperature, but the secretion of oxygen increased at higher temperatures. Rate of deflation is independent of temperature in *P. promelas, Semotilus atromaculatus,* and *P. shumardi* (Gee, 1977; Berezay and Gee, 1978; Balesic, unpublished data). Stream fishes, then, can react to increases in water velocity over a range of temperatures with equal ability; however, inflation rates when still water is encountered are temperature dependent. It would be interesting to determine whether physostomes that use both gulping gas and secretion to inflate swimbladder volume rely more on gulping gas at colder temperatures to compensate for a slower rate of inflation.

Migration

Migrations usually involve extensive movements in either vertical or horizontal planes, often exposing fish to two or more environments. Such movements have implications for the mechanism used to generate lift. The efficient use of energy during migration is often critical to survival or successful reproduction.

A fish attaining neutral buoyancy by either lipids or low-density tissues or fluids can move in either plane with the same expenditure of energy. Those using hydrodynamic lift must expend more energy to move upward as opposed to horizontally but can save an equivalent amount by coasting downward. There are no additional costs of locomotion to vertical migrants using these mechanisms of lift. This is not so for fish using gas inclusions because on descent, the volume of gas is reduced owing to increased hydrostatic pressure and increased rates of diffusion gas loss. In addition, secretion of gas becomes more difficult with increased depth. A fish using gas inclusions is faced with two possibilities of compensating for loss of lift: it can either secrete gas to increase lift or increase swimming to generate more hydrodynamic lift. Alexander (1972) has estimated the energy costs for both solutions, and his findings indicate that for short vertical migrations within the upper epipelagic environment, gas secretion is the most economical; for more extensive migrations hydrodynamic compensation is most efficient (Fig. 5-5).

As a result of these calculations, it would be expected that species making extensive diel vertical migrations between epipelagic and mesopelagic waters could use several strategies (Table 5-7) including swimbladder lift in surface waters, substituting it with hydrodynamic lift with depth; lift from lipids; hydrodynamic lift; a combination of lift from the swimbladder gas and from lipids at the top of the migration, supplementing lift with that generated from hydrodynamic forces with depth. Species making limited vertical movements would be expected to use swimbladder lift exclusively.

The most appropriate source of information to test these ideas is with observations on myctophids. These species either perform extensive vertical migrations or are nonmigratory, and they gain lift from lipids, gas inclusions, and hydrodynamic forces. Myctophids generate hydrodynamic lift from their pectoral fins (Bone, 1973), and the amount of lift can be estimated by knowing

Figure 5-5
Relationship between estimated daily work requirements to provide lift using a swimbladder (volume kept constant; *solid lines*) or a swimbladder supplemented with hydrodynamic lift with increasing depth (mass of gas constant; *broken lines*). In *A*, fish migrate from surface to deeper waters and *B* from 100 m to deeper waters. Estimates of work for swimbladder lift adjusted to constant volume for two regimes (*a*) and (*b*), of dissolved O_2. (Redrawn from Alexander, 1972, with permission from the Society of Experimental Biologists)

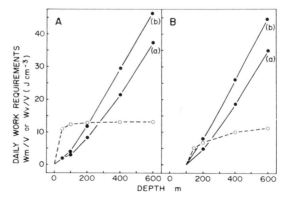

Table 5.7
RELATIONSHIP BETWEEN LIPID CONTENT (% WET WEIGHT), SWIMBLADDER VOLUME, SIZE OF PECTORAL FINS, DEPTH RANGE OF VERTICAL MIGRATION, AND STRATEGY USED TO GAIN BUOYANT LIFT *

SPECIES	STRATEGY	LIPID	RELATIVE SIZE Swimbladder	RELATIVE SIZE Pectoral fins	DEPTH (m) Day	DEPTH (m) Night
Myctophum punctatum	1	2.0–2.6[g]	Significant	Long	700	40[d]
Protomyctophum thompsoni	1	4.9[h]	Significant	Long	200–400	200–400[a,b,c]
Diaphus theta	2	22.1[i]	Reduced	Short	230–600	0–140[a,b,c]
Stenobrachia leucopsarus	2	15.6–18.7[i]	None	Short	230–600	0–185[a,b,c]
Stenobrachia nannochir	2	18.9[i]	None	Short	600–700 below 440[b]	600–700
Lampanyctus ritteri	2	14.2–16.0[h,i]	None	Short	100–200	400–500[c]
Tarletonbeania crenularis	3	4.2[g]	Reduced	Long	300–600	0–5[c]
Notoscopelus kryoeri	3	3.7[g]	None	Short	extensive migration[d]	
Ceratoscopelus maderensis	4	8.2[g]	Significant	Long	650[d]	100[e]
Diaphus rafinesqui	4	8.9[g]	Significant	Short	400	100[e]
Lobianchia gemellari	5	3.7[g]	Significant	Short	450–650	350–490[f]

[a]Taylor, 1968; [b]Frost and McCrone, 1978; [c]Pearcy et al., 1977; [d]Goodyear et al., 1972; [e]Badcock, 1970; [f]Nafpaktitis, 1968; [g]Bone, 1973; [h]Nevenzel et al., 1969; [i]Butler and Pearcy, 1972

*Strategies as follows: 1-swimbladder lift at surface; hydrodynamic lift at depth, 2-lipids, 3-hydrodynamic lift, 4-swimbladder lift and lipids at surface; hydrodynamic lift and lipids at depth, and 5-swimbladder lift exclusively.

the size of the fin and the swimming speed of the fish. This information along with measures of lipid content and observations on swimbladder volumes can be related to information on the extent of vertical movements (Table 5-7). In general, the mechanisms used to attain lift by myctophids relate well to the extent of their vertical movements. Species using the first four strategies listed above make extensive movements. *Lobianchia gemellari,* using swimbladder lift exclusively, makes very little vertical movement. There are, however, two exceptions: *Protomyctophum thompsoni* and *Stenobrachia nannochir,* which in terms of their lift mechanisms have the potential for extensive vertical movements (these have not been observed). *Notoscopelus kryoeri* uses hydrodynamic lift at all depths because although its pectoral fins are relatively small, it is a streamlined, fast-swimming species (Bone, 1973).

The information in Table 5-7 must be regarded with some reservation. Swimbladder volumes of all myctophids have not been measured, and in most cases it is difficult to do so. Although vertical migrations by myctophids occur with regularity and with little seasonal variation (Pearcy and Laurs, 1966; Pearcy *et al.,* 1977), several other factors influence the extent and range of depth of vertical movements, including size, age of fish (Nafpaktitis, 1968; Clarke, 1973; Frost and McCrone, 1978), and sex (Nafpaktitis, 1968). In addition, a significant proportion of some species do not migrate at all. Even with these reservations in mind, the information on myctophids provides strong support for the ideas of Alexander (1972), that is, it is metabolically more efficient for fish undertaking vertical migrations to use the swimbladder in surface waters and hydrodynamic lift with depth, or lift from lipids. Indeed it appears unlikely that any fish can either secrete gas fast enough on descent or resorb gas fast enough on ascent to undertake an extensive diel vertical migration and at the same time maintain a constant buoyancy at all depths using lift from the swimbladder (Blaxter and Tytler, 1978).

Vertical migrations are often made at particular stages in the life cycle of a species and can often occur only after morphologic and physiological changes to the lift-generating mechanism. The American eel (*Anguilla rostrata*) moves over 2000 m vertically on its spawning migration to the Sargasso Sea (Kleckner, 1980b), but before maturation and the start of the migration, there is a metamorphosis involving an increase in the guanine content, reducing the rate of gas diffusion, and an increase in length and diameter of the retial capillaries, increasing the rate of gas secretion (Kleckner, 1980a and b; Kleckner and Krueger, 1981); thus extending the depth at which the swimbladder volume can be maintained. Considerable variation in morphology occurs among stromateoid fishes (Horn, 1970, 1975) and myctophids (Butler and Pearcy, 1972; Bone, 1973) with age that alters the primary source of lift from one mechanism to another. These changes in source of lift relate to changes in the environment occupied.

Negatively buoyant fishes using hydrodynamic lift on long distance horizontal migrations can save considerable energy in two ways. First, by alternating a downward glide (no propulsion) with active· swimming upward to regain the original depth, energy savings could range between 20% and 49% (beat-and-glide swimming; Weihs, 1973; see Chap. 11). Second, by using selective tidal stream transport (Greer Walker *et al.*, 1978), where a benthic fish (*e.g.*, plaice) swims up off the bottom and moves with a particular tidal current (either ebb or flood), many species move considerable distances (Arnold, 1981) with energy savings up to 40% (Weihs, 1978) compared to continuous swimming in a particular direction.

The response of a decreasing swimbladder volume when water velocity increases in a lotic environment is analogous to the reduction in swimbladder volume on ascent during a vertical migration; fish in both situations correct for excessive lift. Similarly, fish correct for insufficient lift when they either encounter still water after experiencing fast-flowing water in a lotic environment or low descent during a vertical migration. Responses to changes in water velocity involve substantial alterations in swimbladder lift, but these are equivalent to traversing relatively short vertical distances. When alterations in swimbladder volume by lotic benthic fish in response to changes in water velocity are equated to vertical movements (in surface waters), most of these fishes reduce volume equivalent to a vertical movement of 80 m or less (Table 5-8).

The stimulus initiating the response to alter swimbladder volume in the two situations must be quite different. Fishes in both epipelagic and lotic environments are very sensitive to pressure changes (Blaxter and Tytler, 1978). In epipelagic environments fish alter swimbladder volume in response to changes in hydrostatic pressure (depth), but the stimulus to alter swimbladder volume in response to changes in water velocity is not clear.

Predator Avoidance, Feeding, and Reproduction

The activities involved in avoiding detection and capture by predators, obtaining food, and reproducing require control of both the amount of lift

Table 5.8
EQUATING THE CHANGE IN SWIMBLADDER VOLUME BY BENTHIC
FISHES IN RESPONSE TO AN INCREASE IN WATER VELOCITY
TO DISTANCE MOVED DOWNWARD FROM THE WATER SURFACE
IN AN EPIPELAGIC ENVIRONMENT

	<34	34–67	67–94
Percent reduction in swimbladder volume when exposed to water current			
Number of species observed (Gee and Gee, 1976)	21	12	6
Increase in hydrostatic pressure required to obtain a similar reduction in volume (atm)	<1.5	1.5–3.0	3.0–9.0
Depth moved downward from surface to attain a similar reduction in volume (m)	0.5	5–20	20–80

and its distribution along the length of the body. Depth in the water column, attitude, postures, and vertical and horizontal maneuvers must all be regulated.

Fishes hide or are camouflaged to reduce chances of detection. Some juvenile epipelagic and mesopelagic species living temporarily in surface waters remain hidden among tentacles of jellyfishes using all four mechanisms to gain the appropriate lift (Horn, 1970, 1975, 1977; Bone and Brook, 1973). A number of species like pipefish (*Siphostoma*) and needlefish (*Strongylura*) are camouflaged and are adept at controlling the amount and center of buoyancy, producing particular attitudes such that in appearance and posture they resemble the surrounding vegetation (Sazima and Vieda, 1979).

Control and rapid alteration of lift play an important role in escape once prey detect the presence of a predator. Sticklebacks (*Gasterosteus aculeatus*, *Pungitius pungitius*, and *Culaea inconstans*) shows a "freezing" response after detecting a predator. The fish becomes very still with virtually no fin movements and a reduced frequency of opercular beats. Before this response, some species show a rapid series of darts or erratic swimming behavior and following the response either rise to the surface or sink slowly to the bottom (Benzie, 1965; McPhail, 1969; Weselowski, 1974; Wootten, 1976). A number of species reduce swimbladder volume rapidly on detecting a predator and drop to the substrate (Cyprinidae: Verheijen, 1962; Umbridae: Gee, 1981).

Control of attitude is most important in the search for food. Harrison (1967) noted that many fishes adopt a "heads up" attitude to see prey silouetted from below. The hawk fish (*Cirrhites pinnulatus*) is negatively buoyant, but its head lifts up off the bottom because of lipids in the skull possibly elevating the head sufficiently to see prey as it perches on coral (Phleger, 1974).

The speed and pattern of locomotion used in searching for prey is in part determined by the mechanism used to generate lift. Species relying on hydrodynamic lift generally search over large areas at relatively fast speeds (*e.g.*, scombrids and some sharks) moving along horizontal and vertical planes. Those using lipids or low-density tissues or fluids are typically slower (basking shark *Cetorhinus maximus*: Hallacher, 1977; *Acanthonus armatus*: Horn *et al.*, 1978) and again are capable of movement on horizontal and vertical planes. Fishes possessing a swimbladder either move slowly, hover, or both and generally search only over a horizontal plane. Some (*e.g.*, Centrarchidae: Keast and Webb, 1966) adopt a sit-and-wait strategy at neutral buoyancy or patrol slowly while watching for very slight movements of prey. Others (*e.g.*, Salmonidae: Kalleberg, 1958; Schultz and Northcote, 1972) alternate hovering and scanning the substrate for prey with short distance cruises. The ability to hover requires precise buoyancy control and is critical to the discovery of food in many species. Fishes using low-density fluids or tissues usually have reduced musculature, and hence the ability to swim is reduced. Fishes such as deep-sea angler fish (Lophiiformes) either attract or trap prey.

It is important for some species to maintain a particular distance from either the water surface or the substrate when searching for food. The actual distance is a function of the sensory mechanisms used to locate food. A variety of species search for food by swimming just off the bottom using elongate tactile pelvic fin rays or barbels to detect food (Moridae: Iwamoto, 1975; Marshall and Bourne, 1964; Gadidae: Brawn, 1969; Pearson *et al.*, 1980; Ictaluridae: Keast and Webb, 1966). *Ictalurus nebulosus* swims slowly over the substrate with ventral chemotactile barbels just touching the substrate (Keast and Webb, 1966). It searches for prey with a negative angle of attack with the large anal fin apparently providing some lift in a manner similar to the heterocercal tail of sharks; the pectoral fins are extended and may act as hydrofoils. Thus both swimbladder and hydrodynamic lift act together to hold the appropriate horizontal position and maintain the correct angle of attack for feeding. Similar body attitudes during food searching are reported by macrourids and halosaurs by Marshall and Bourne (1964).

Movements associated with the capture of prey once sighted require that the fish orient and approach the potential prey with precise control of lift. This is especially so for species that stalk prey and fixate it before lunging and striking (*e.g., Esox lucius*: Hoogland *et al.,* 1959; Neill and Cullen, 1974).

The archerfish (*Toxotes*) must not only maintain correct horizontal position just below the water surface once prey is sighted above the water, but some species must also maintain a precise attitude. *T. jacula* (Lüling, 1963) and *Colisa* spp. (Vierke, 1975) spit from an almost vertical position directly below the potential prey, but *T. chatareus* spit using a variety of attitudes depending on the height of the prey above the water. The precise angle is determined after a short period of binocular fixation of the prey (Dill, 1976).

Fishes feeding on individual zooplankton (*e.g., Notemigonus chryso-leucas*: Keast and Webb, 1966) must orient toward each prey upon sighting before striking. They must be capable of maneuvering quickly to alter position and attitude to capture as many prey as possible over the shortest time.

The ability to regulate lift is critical in all phases of reproduction. Many species prepare the substrate on or into which eggs are laid, often involving the removal and manipulation of objects, and such activities often require intricate maneuvering and precise control of buoyancy. Similarly in courtship, communication occurs between males and females where a series of signals are exchanged that consist of movements and postures that are obviously dependent on control of lift and the center of buoyancy. Mating, in which the sexes come together and either release gametes simultaneously or else sperm is transferred to the female, also requires postures and positions dependent on buoyancy control.

The development of gametes and their subsequent sudden release into the environment could have a definite influence on the forces of lift of females. As they become gravid, significant lift could result from eggs (low density), which often represent 15% to 25% of the weight of the fish. Some sharks appear to compensate for such changes by altering the density of other tissues (Bone and Roberts, 1969). As eggs develop and fill the body cavity they can impinge on space taken by the swimbladder, reducing its volume. In addition, distention of the ventral surface could alter the hydrodynamic properties of the body. Compensation for such changes must be reversed rapidly once eggs are released into the environment.

Obtaining Oxygen in Hypoxic Water

Survival strategies in hypoxic water affect the lift generated by fishes using gas inclusions. Such strategies rely at least in part on using oxygen contained within gas inclusion without immediate replacement with other gases, resulting in temporary loss of lift. This problem is faced by fishes using either aquatic or aerial respiration.

Aquatic Respiration

The gas contained in the swimbladder represents a potential supply of oxygen that can be used during periods of hypoxia in the surrounding water; however, the amount available in the swimbladder of fishes living near the surface is very slight and can only provide for the requirements of the fish for a few minutes (Jones and Marshall, 1953). Those living in deeper waters have a greater proportion of oxygen and hence supply, and it is maintained at a much higher pressure. Blaxter and Tytler (1978) have calculated for a fish at neutral buoyancy with 90% oxygen in the swimbladder that at 10 m depth the amount of oxygen would be sufficient for 0.3 hr; at 90 m for 3 hr; at 990 m for 30 hr; and at 6999 m for 210 hr.

During exposure to hypoxic water, the amount of oxygen in the swimbladder declines as described in a number of studies (see Jones and Marshall, 1953 for a review) and more recently by Green (1971) for two species of *Eucionstomus*. Although oxygen is removed from the swimbladder during hypoxia, the extent to which it is used in respiration by the fish is unknown. If the oxygen in the swimbladder is removed faster than gases can be secreted, swimbladder volume and lift will decrease during the initial exposure to hypoxic water.

Fish can survive prolonged exposure to severe hypoxia by performing aquatic surface respiration (Kramer and Mehegan, 1981). In this response, fish rise to the water surface and irrigate their gills with the relatively oxygen-rich surface water. Here the upper 1 mm contains significant amounts of dissolved oxygen as calculated by Lewis (1970). The response is common in temperate and tropical fishes (Lewis, 1970; Gee *et al.,* 1978; Kramer and McClure, 1982). During aquatic surface respiration, activity is generally reduced, minimizing metabolic oxygen demand, and precise buoyancy control is required to maintain the fish at the surface and at the correct attitude, allowing the mouth to be positioned at the surface. Efficient aquatic surface respiration by pelagic species appears to demand a neutral or even positive buoyancy (Chiasson, 1980; Gee, unpublished data).

Observations on the physostome (*Pimephales promelas*) indicate that oxygen is removed from the swimbladder, and its volume declines in the initial 12 hours of hypoxia (dissolved $O_2 < 0.5$ ppm); however, buoyancy is corrected to the original level (0.95 ml $\cdot$ g^{-1}) and then increased to positive levels (1.01 to 1.09 ml $\cdot$ g^{-1}) most likely by gulping air into the swimbladder (Chiasson, 1980). In four species of Eleotridae (physoclists) G. H. Gee (unpublished data) found that sudden exposure to hypoxia resulted in a decline of about 10% in the swimbladder volume, which occurred within 10 to 30 minutes. This loss was corrected back to the initial neutral buoyancy and then increased slightly to positive levels (1.02 ml $\cdot$ g^{-1}) within 4 hours by secretion of gases and a decrease in internal pressure of swimbladder gas. In addition to this increase in buoyancy, the center of buoyancy was moved forward slightly such that the head was tilted upward (about 30 degrees) locating the lips at the water surface (Fig. 5-6). In further observations (J. H. Gee, unpublished data), it was found that the extent of reduction in swimbladder volume was influenced by the level of dissolved oxygen in the surrounding water and the rate at which progressive hypoxia occurred.

The eleotrid (*Dormitator latifrons*) shows a marked increase in swim-bladder lift to positive buoyancy during exposure to hypoxia, such that the

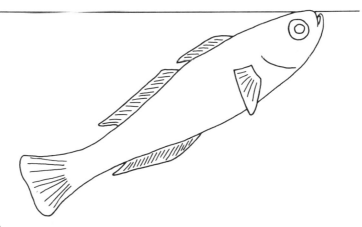

Figure 5-6
Hypseleotris gali, a pelagic species, performing aquatic surface respiration. (Drawn from a photograph)

dorsal surface of the head is emmersed, and aerial respiration takes place using a highly vascularized pad that develops on the head (Todd, 1973). This fish can actively secrete oxygen and carbon dioxide into the swimbladder over 9 hours to increase buoyancy in hypoxic water. Carbon dioxide rises to 8.5% and oxygen to 42% of the swimbladder volume once positive buoyancy is reached.

Benthic Gobiidae use aquatic surface respiration, and many species (eight of nine observed; J. H. Gee, unpublished data) appear to use gas inclusions to provide additional lift in hypoxic water in order to use the surface water efficiently. These fishes were observed to move into shallow waters in response to progressive hypoxia, arch the head upwards, gulp a bubble into the mouth, and hold it for a variable period of time. The bubble appears to have a hydrostatic function, providing lift to the head and in some cases anchoring the lips at the water surface by providing positive buoyancy to the anterior region (four of eight species). In addition, the bubble appears to provide oxygen either directly or indirectly to the gills. In three of nine species the bubble came in direct contact with the gills and here, once inspired, the frequency of branchial breathing was either reduced or ceased entirely (J. H. Gee, unpublished data). In the remaining species the bubble did not come in contact with the gills but oxygen still could diffuse from the bubble into the water flowing over it in the mouth before irrigating the gills. In these species, the frequency of branchial breathing either remained unchanged or was reduced slightly. This behavior allowed benthic fish, with a subterminal–ventral mouth, to exploit the surface without "beaching" in the shallows, thereby permitting rapid escape from predators.

The need to control lift during initial exposure to hypoxia appears to have played a role in the evolution of aerial respiration. The hypothesis is that both aquatic surface respiration and the associated corrections and adjustments of lift necessary to its performance are prerequisite steps in the evolution of air breathing in teleost fishes. Pelagic physostomes could make the buoyancy alterations required to perform aquatic surface respiration by gulping air into the swimbladder; if these fish then made some metabolic use of the oxygen added to the swimbladder, further gulping would be necessary to correct lift, leading to additional uptake of aerial oxygen and ultimately, leading to aerial respiration. Pelagic physoclists could increase lift and adjust their attitude during initial stages of aquatic surface respiration by either secreting gas into the swimbladder or by gulping air and holding it in the mouth. The latter is purely speculative, but it is interesting to note that apart from the skin, all air-breathing physoclists have accessory respiratory tissues located in proximity to the mouth.

The benthic Gobiidae (physoclists) do gulp air into the mouth and gain considerable lift to the anterior part of the body. That such behavior could eventually lead to aerial respiration using tissues associated with either the mouth or gills is supported by observations on the varying degree of success to which different species of gobies capture and hold bubbles either within the mouth or opercular (gill) regions (J. H. Gee, unpublished data).

Aerial Respiration

Air-breathing fishes also face problems associated with control of lift when the air-breathing organ also has a hydrostatic function. Because oxygen is removed without replacement by another gas (Johansen, 1970), the lift created by the gas in the air-breathing organ may potentially diminish between air breaths. To reduce the conflict between the two opposing roles, both the extent and rate of decline in lift should be minimized. Gee (1981) found that *Umbra limi* used the following mechanisms to resolve the conflict:

1. Changes in swimbladder lift occurred in the interbreath interval, but these were kept to a range of positive values as the fish adapted to a mode of life at the surface.
2. A large volume of gas was inspired, compressed to provide the appropriate lift, and then internal pressure was reduced to compensate for uptake of oxygen from the swimbladder.
3. Aquatic respiration was used as much as possible, reducing the rate of decline in buoyancy between air breaths.
4. Hydrodynamic lift was used to compensate for loss of swimbladder lift in the latter part of the interbreath period.

The use of these mechanisms was determined by the presence or absence of simulated predator disturbance and the amount of dissolved oxygen. An additional mechanism would be adoption of a benthic mode to counter the costs of maintaining a particular vertical position but not the extra costs caused by locomotion. Such a strategy is used by the catfishes (*Brochis splendens* and *Hoplosternum thoracatum*; Gee and Graham, 1978).

DEVELOPMENT OF ACCESSORY ROLES FOR BUOYANCY MECHANISMS

Both costs and benefits are associated with each of the mechanisms used to generate lift. It is, however, incorrect to evaluate a particular mechanism solely by its direct contribution to lift. In many situations, direct accessory benefits are associated with a particular lift-generating mechanism. Such benefits are not apparent or else are very indirect (*e.g.,* distinctive life history strategy of bathypelagic fishes; Childress *et al.,* 1980) with either lipids or low-density tissues and fluids, but the evolution of the swimbladder and of locomotary patterns providing hydrodynamic lift have lead to the development of several complimentary roles for these mechanisms.

The use of hydrodynamic lift resulting from continuous swimming becomes more efficient in terms of energy expended as other complimentary roles are developed from such movement. Such roles, as illustrated by the tunas, include searching for either food or a mate, escape from a predator, or irrigation of gills using ram gill ventilation. Freadman (1979) showed that there were considerable metabolic savings made by shifting the ventilatory work from branchial to swimming musculature. In addition, this form of gill irrigation produces a more streamlined flow of water along the sides of the body, apparently reducing frictional drag (Freadman, 1981). Continuous swimming is almost a necessity for feeding by tuna because their food is often scant and contagiously distributed (Stevens and Neill, 1978).

The swimbladder can be made much more economical when accessory roles are developed. The role of pressure reception is important in detecting changes in depth using either proprioceptors in the swimbladder wall (Qutob, 1962) or the Weberian apparatus of the Cypriniformes. The reception of sound is also an auxillary function of gas inclusions because the amplitude of vibrations in water resulting from sound waves is increased in the vicinity of gas (Alexander, 1966a). Gas inclusions that are located at least in part near the otolith organs (Clupeidae, Anabantidae, etc) or, as in the case of the Cypriniformes, connected to the otoliths by the Weberian apparatus, are used for hearing. In addition, gas inclusions can be used as resonators to produce sound used in reproductive behavior or during aggressive encounters (Marshall, 1962). The occurrence of gas inclusions as a lift mechanism among some benthopelagic fishes (Macrouridae) probably results in part from its accessory functions of sound production and reception.

Respiration is an accessory function of some gas inclusions in fishes found in epipelagic and lotic environments. Wittenberg and associates (1980) suggested that swimbladder oxygen could be used to sustain benthopelagic fish over periods of rapid swimming of up to 200 minutes; however, there is potential conflict between hydrostatic and respiratory roles of gas inclusions unless strategies are developed to make them compatible.

Mechanisms by which lift can be created are diverse, and the success to which each can be used is much influenced by the environment, and variables of food productivity, hydrostatic pressure, and water currents are important. The mechanism of lift used by a fish influences most of its activities, some mechanisms more so than others because of their accessory functions. These activities include locomotion, migration, feeding, reproduction, and avoiding predation. Thus the strategies of obtaining lift have a profound influence on the mode of life of a fish, and both are dictated to by the environment.

Acknowledgments

This review was prepared largely while I was on a research leave supported by a Visiting Research Fellowship from Macquarie University and from funds from the Natural Sciences and

Engineering Research Council of Canada. I thank Dr. D. W. Cooper, Head, School of Biological Sciences, Macquarie University for providing space and facilities and the Macquarie University Library for assistance in locating literature. Dr. P. A. Gee provided much assistance with library research.

REFERENCES

Aleyev, Y. G., 1963. Functional basis of the exterior structure in fish. *Izdat. Akad, Nauk SSSR,* Moscow (in Russian with English summary).

Alexander, R. McN. 1959. The physical properties of the swimbladder in intact Cypriniformes. *J. Exp. Biol.* 36:315–332.

Alexander, R. McN. 1961. Visco-elastic properties of the tunica externa of the swimbladder in Cyprinidae. *J. Exp. Biol.* 38:747–757.

Alexander, R. McN. 1965. The lift produced by the heterocercal tails of selachii. *J. Exp. Biol.* 43:131–138.

Alexander, R. McN. 1966a. Physical aspects of swimbladder function. *Biol. Rev.* 41:141–176.

Alexander, R. McN. 1966b. Lift produced by the heterocercal tail of *Acipenser. Nature* 210:1049–1050.

Alexander, R. McN. 1972. The energetics of vertical migration of fishes. *Symp. Soc. Exp. Biol.* 26:273–294.

Alexander, R. McN. 1977. Swimming. In Alexander, R. McN. and G. Goldspink, *Mechanics and Energetics of Animal Locomotion* edited by R. McN. Alexander and G. Goldspink, 222–248. New York: Academic Press.

Arnold, G. P. 1969. The reactions of the plaice (*Pleuronectes plastessa* L.) to water currents. *J. Exp. Biol.* 51:681–697.

Arnold, G. P. 1981. Movements of fish in relation to water currents. In *Animal Migration, Society for Experimental Biology Seminar Series B,* edited by Aidley, 55–79. Cambridge: Cambridge University Press.

Arnold, G. P., and Weihs, D. 1978. The hydrodynamics of rheotaxis in the plaice (*Pleuronectes platessa* L.). *J. Exp. Biol.* 75:147–169.

Badcock, J. 1970. The vertical distribution of mesopelagic fishes collected on the Sond cruise. *J. Marine Biol. Assoc. U.K.* 50:1001–1004.

Benzie, V. L. 1965. Some aspects of the anti-predator responses of two species of stickleback. D. Phil. Thesis, Dept. of Zoology, University of Oxford.

Berezay, G., and Gee, J.H. 1978. Buoyancy response to changes in water velocity and its function in creek chub (*Semotilus atromaculatus*). *J. Fish. Res. Board Can.* 35:295–299.

Berg, T., and Steen, J.B. 1968. The mechanism of oxygen concentration in the swim-bladder of the eel. *J. Physiol.* 195:631–638.

Blaxter, J.H.S., and Tytler, P. 1978. Physiology and function of the swimbladder. *Adv. Comp. Physiol. Biochem.* 7:311–367.

Blaxter, J.H.S., Wardle, C.S., and Roberts, B.L. 1971. Aspects of the circulatory physiology and muscle systems of deep-sea fish. *J. Marine Biol. Assoc. U.K.* 51:991–1006.

Bone, Q. 1972. Buoyancy and hydrodynamic functions of the integument in the castor oil fish, *Ruvettus pretiosus* (Pisces: Gempylidae). *Copeia* 1972:78-87.

Bone, Q. 1973. A note on the buoyancy of some lantern-fishes (Myctophoidei) *J. Marine Biol. Assoc. U.K.* 53:619-633.

Bone, Q., and Brook, C.E.R., 1973. On *Schedophilus medusophagus* (Pisces: Stromateoidei). *J. Marine Biol. Assoc. U.K.* 53:753-761.

Bone, Q., and Roberts, B.L. 1969. The density of elasmobranchs. *J. Marine Biol. Assoc. U.K.* 49:913-937.

Brawn, V.M. 1962. Physical properties and hydrostatic function of the swimbladder of herring (*Clupea harengus* L.). *J. Fish. Res. Board Can.* 19:635-656.

Brawn, V.M. 1969. Feeding behaviour of cod (*Gadus morhua*). *J. Fish. Res. Board Can.* 26:583-596.

Brown, D.S., and Copeland, D.E. 1978. Layered membranes: a diffusion barrier to gases in teleostean swimbladders. *Tissue Cell* 10:785-796.

Butler, J.L., and Pearcy, W.G. 1972. Swimbladder morphology and specific gravity of myctophids off Oregon. *J. Fish. Res. Board Can.* 29:1145-1150.

Chiasson, A.G. 1980. Adaptive responses to hypoxia in the fathead minnow *Pimephales promelas:* Buoyancy control and uptake of aquatic and aerial O_2. M. Sc. Thesis, Zoology Dept., University of Manitoba.

Childress, J.J., and Nygaard, M.H. 1973. The chemical composition of midwater fishes as a function of depth of occurrence off southern California. *Deep-Sea Res.* 20:1093-1109.

Childress, J.J., Taylor, S.M., Cailliet, G.M., and Price, M. H., 1980. Patterns of growth, energy utilization and reproduction in some meso- and bathypelagic fishes off southern California. *Marine Biol.* 61:27-40.

Clarke, T.A., 1973. Some aspects of the ecology of lantern fishes (Myctophidae) in the Pacific Ocean near Hawaii. *Fish. Bull.* 71:401-434.

Corner, E.D.S., Denton, E.J., Forster, F.R.S., and Forster, G.R. 1969. On the buoyancy of some deep-sea sharks. *Proc. R. Soc.* 171B:415-429.

Craik, J.C.A. 1978. The lipids of six species of shark. *J. Marine Biol. Assoc. U.K.* 58:913-921.

Delaroche, F. 1809. Observations sur la vassie aérienne des poisons. *Ann. Museum Hist. Nat. Marseille* 14:184-289.

Denton, E.J. 1961. The buoyancy of fish and cephalopods. *Progr. Biophysics Biophysical Chem.* 11:177-234.

Denton, E.J. 1963. Buoyancy mechanisms of sea creatures. *Endeavour* 22:3-8.

Denton, E.J., Liddicoat, J.D., and Taylor, D.W. 1970. Impermeable silvery layers in fish. *J. Physiol.* 207:64-65.

Denton, E.J., Liddicoat, J.D., and Taylor, D.W. 1972. The permeability to gases of the swimbladder of the conger eel (*Conger conger*). *J. Marine Biol. Assoc. U.K.* 52:727-746.

Denton, E.J., and Marshall, N.B. 1958. The buoyancy of bathypelagic fishes without a gas-filled swimbladder. *J. Marine Biol. Assoc. U.K.* 37:753-767.

DeVries, A.L., and Eastman, J.T. 1978. Lipid sacs as a buoyancy adaptation in an Antarctic fish. *Nature* 271:352-353.

Dill, L.M. 1976. Refraction and the spitting behavior of the archerfish (*Toxotes chatareaus*). *Behav. Ecol. Sociobiol.* 2:169-184.

Fänge, R. 1966. Physiology of the swimbladder. *Physiol. Rev.* 46:299–322.

Freadman, M.A. 1979. Swimming energetics of striped bass (*Morone saxatilis*) and bluefish (*Pomatomus saltatrix*): gill ventilation and swimming metabolism. *J. Exp. Biol.* 83:217–230.

Freadman, M.A. 1981. Swimming energetics of striped bass (*Morone saxatilis*) and bluefish (*Pomotomus saltatrix*): hydrodynamic correlates of locomotion and gill ventilation. *J. Exp. Biol.* 90:253–265.

Frost, B.W., and McCrone, L.E. 1978. Vertical distribution, diel vertical migration, and abundance of some mesopelagic fishes in the eastern subarctic Pacific Ocean in summer. *Fish. Bull.* 76:751–770.

Gee, J.H. 1968. Adjustment of buoyancy by longnose dace (*Rhinichthys cataractae*) in relation to velocity of water. *J. Fish. Res. Board Can.* 25:1485–1496.

Gee, J.H. 1970. Adjustment of buoyancy in blacknose dace, *Rhinichthys atratulus*. *J. Fish. Res. Board. Can.* 27:1855–1859.

Gee, J.H. 1972. Adaptive variation in swimbladder length and volume in dace, genus *Rhinichthys*. *J. Fish. Res. Board Can.* 29:119–127.

Gee, J.H. 1974. Behavioral and developmental plasticity of buoyancy in the longnose, *Rhinichthys cataractae*, and blacknose, *R. atratulus* (Cyprinidae) dace. *J. Fish. Res. Board Can.* 31:35–41.

Gee, J.H. 1977. Effects of size of fish, water temperature and water velocity on buoyancy alteration by fathead minnows, *Pimephales promelas*. *Comp. Biochem. Physiol.* 56A:503–508.

Gee, J.H. 1981. Coordination of respiratory and hydrostatic functions of the swimbladder in the central mudminnow, *Umbra limi*. *J. Exp. Biol.* 92:37–52.

Gee, J.H., and Gee, P.A. 1976. Alteration of buoyancy by some Central American stream fishes, and a comparison with North American species. *Can. J. Zool.* 54:386–391.

Gee, J.H., and Graham, J.B. 1978. Respiratory and hydrostatic functions of the intestine of the catfishes *Hoplosternum thoracatum* and *Brochis splendens* (*Callichthyidae*). *J. Exp. Biol.* 74:1–16.

Gee, J.H., and Machniak, K. 1972. Ecological notes on a lake-dwelling population of longnose dace (*Rhinichthys cataractae*). *J. Fish. Res. Board Can.* 29:330–332.

Gee, J.H., Machniak, K., and Chalanchuk, S.M. 1974. Adjustment of buoyancy and excess internal pressure of swimbladder gases in some North American freshwater fishes. *J. Fish. Res. Board Can.* 31:1139–1141.

Gee, J.H., Tallman, R.F., and Smart, H.J. 1978. Reactions of some great plains fishes to progressive hypoxia. *Can. J. Zool.* 56:1962–1966.

Goodyear, R.H., Zahuranec, B.J., Pugh, W.L., and Gibbs, R.H. 1972. Ecology and vertical distribution of Mediterranean midwater fishes. Mediterranean Biological Studies, Final Report 1:91–229. Smithsonian Institution, Washington, D.C.

Green, J.M. 1971. Studies on the swimbladders of *Eucinostomus gula* and *E. argenteus* (Pisces: Gerridae). *Bull. Marine Sci.* 21:567–590.

Greer Walker, M., Harden Jones, F.R., and Arnold, G.P. 1978. The movements of plaice (*Pleuronectes platessa* L.) tracked in the open sea. *J. Cons. Int. Explor. Mer.* 38:58–86.

Hallacher, L.E. 1977. On the feeding behavior of the basking shark, *Cetorhinus maximus*. *Environ. Biol. Fish.* 2:297–298.

Heller, J.H., Heller, M.S., Springer, S., and Clark E. 1957. Squalene content of various shark livers. *Nature London.* 179:919–920.

Hollister, C.D., and Heezen, B.C. 1966. Ocean bottom currents. In R.W. Fairbridge, *Encyclopedia of Oceanography*, edited by R. W. Fairbridge, 576–583. New York: Reinhold.

Hoogland, R., Morris, D., and Tinbergen, N. 1959. The spines of sticklebacks (*Gasterosteus* and *Pygosteus*) as a means of defence against predators (*Perca* and *Esox*). *Behaviour* 10:205–236.

Horn, M.H. 1970. The swimbladder as a juvenile organ in stromateoid fishes. *Breviora* 359:1–9.

Horn, M.H. 1975. Swim-bladder state and structure in relation to behavior and mode of life in stromateoid fishes. *Fish. Bull.* 73:95–109.

Horn, M.H. 1977. Observations on feeding, growth, locomotor behavior, and buoyancy of a pelagic stromateoid fish *Icichthys lockingtoni. Fish. Bull.* 75:453–456.

Horn, M.H., Grimes, P.W., Phleger, C.F., and McClanahan, L.L. 1978. Buoyancy function of the enlarged fluid-filled cranium in the deep-sea Ophidiid fish *Acanthonus armatus. Marine Biol.* 46:335–339.

Iwamoto, T. 1975. The abyssal fish *Antimora rostrata* (Günther). *Comp. Biochem. Physiol.* 52B:7–11.

Johansen, K. 1970. Air breathing in fishes. In *Fish Physiology*, edited by W.S. Hoar and D.J. Randall, vol. 4, 361–411. New York, London: Academic Press.

Jones, F.R.H., and Marshall, N.B. 1953. The structure and functions of the Teleostean swimbladder. *Biol. Rev.* 28:16–83.

Kalleberg, H. 1958. Observations in a stream tank of territoriality and competition in juvenile salmon and trout (*Salmo salar* L. and *Salmo trutta* L.) *Rep. Inst. Freshwater Res. Drottningholm* 39:55–98.

Kanwisher, J., and Ebeling, A. 1957. Composition of the swim-bladder gas in bathypelagic fishes. *Deep-Sea Res.* 4:211–217.

Keast, A., and Webb, D. 1966. Mouth and body form relative to feeding ecology in the fish fauna of a small lake, Lake Opinicon, Ontario. *J. Fish. Res. Board Can.* 23:1845–1874.

Kleckner, R.C. 1980a. Swimbladder wall guanine enhancement related to migratory depth in silver phase *Anguilla rostrata. Comp. Biochem. Physiol.* 65A:351–354.

Kleckner, R.C. 1980b. Swim bladder volume maintenance related to initial oceanic migratory depth in silver-phase *Anguilla rostrata. Science* 208:1481–1482.

Kleckner, R.C., and Krueger, W.H. 1981. Changes in swimbladder retial morphology in *Anguilla rostrata* during premigration metamorphosis. *J. Fish. Biol.* 18:569–577.

Kramer, D.L., and Mehegan, J.P. 1981. Aquatic surface respiration, an adaptive respiratory response to hypoxia in the guppy, *Poecillia reticulata. Environ. Biol. Fish.* 6:299–313.

Kramer, D.L., and McClure, M. 1982. Aquatic surface respiration, a widespread adaptation to hypoxia in tropical freshwater fishes. *Environ. Biol. Fish.* 7:47–55.

Kuhn, W., Ramel, A., Kuhn, H.J., and Marti, E. 1963. The filling mechanism of the swimbladder. Generation of high pressures through hairpin countercurrent multiplication. *Experientia* 19:497–511.

Kuhn, H.J., and Marti, E. 1966. The active transport of oxygen and carbon dioxide into the swimbladder of fish. *J. Gen. Physiol.* 49:1209–1220.

Kutchai, H., and Steen, J.B. 1971. The permeability of the swimbladder. *Comp. Biochem. Physiol.* 39A:119–123.

Lapennas, G.N., and Schmidt-Nielsen, K. 1977. Swimbladder permeability to oxygen. *J. Exp. Biol.* 67:175–196.

Lee, R.F., Phleger, C.F., and Horn, M.H. 1975. Composition of oil in fish bones: possible function in neutral buoyancy. *Comp. Biochem. Physiol.* 50B:13–16.

Lewis, M.W. 1970. Morphological adaptations of cyprinodontoids for inhabiting oxygen deficient waters. *Copeia* 1970:319–326.

Lüling, K.H. 1963. The archerfish. *Sci. Am.* 209:100–129.

Luoma, M.E., and Gee, J.H. 1980. Seasonal factors affecting buoyancy attained in still water and current by fathead minnows, *Pimephales promelas. Can. J. Fish Aquat. Sci.* 37:670–678.

Machniak, K., and Gee, J.H. 1975. Adjustment of buoyancy by tadpole madtom, *Noturus gyrinus*, and black bullhead, *Ictalurus melas*, in response to a change in water velocity. *J. Fish. Res. Board Can.* 32:303–307.

Magnuson, J.J. 1970. Hydrostatic equilibrium of *Euthynnus affinis*, a pelagic teleost without a gas bladder. *Copeia* 1970:56–85.

Magnuson, J.J. 1973. Comparative study of adaptations for continuous swimming and hydrostatic equilibrium of scombrid and xiphoid fishes. *Fish. Bull.* 71:337–356.

Magnuson, J.J. 1978. Locomotion by scombrid fishes: hydromechanics, morphology, and behavior. *Fish Physiol.* 7:239–313.

Malins, D.C., and Barone, A. 1970. Glyceryl ether metabolism: Regulation of buoyancy in dogfish *Squalus acanthias. Science* 167:79–80.

Marshall, N.B. 1960. Swimbladder structure of deep-sea fishes in relation to their systematics and biology. *Discovery Rep.* 31:1–122.

Marshall, N.B. 1962. The biology of sound-producing fishes. *Symp. Zool. Soc. Lond.* 7:45–60.

Marshall, N.B. 1971. *Explorations in the Life of Fishes.* Cambridge, MA: Harvard University Press.

Marshall, N.B. 1972. Swimbladder organization and depth range of deep-sea teleosts. *Symp. Soc. Exp. Biol.* 26:261–272.

Marshall, N.B., and Bourne, D.W. 1964. A photographic survey of benthic fishes in the Red Sea and Gulf of Aden, with observations on their population density, diversity, and habits. *Bull. Museum Comp. Zool. Harvard University* 132:223–249.

McCutcheon, F.H. 1958. Swimbladder volume, buoyancy and behavior in the pinfish, *Lagodon rhomboides* (Linn.). *J. Cell Comp. Physiol.* 52:453–480.

McNabb, R.A., and Mecham, J.A. 1971. The effects of different acclimation temperatures on gas secretion in the swimbladder of the bluegill sunfish, *Lepomis macrochirus. Comp. Biochem. Physiol.* 40A:609–616.

McPhail, J.D. 1969. Predation and the evolution of a stickleback (*Gasterosteus*). *J. Fish. Res. Board Can.* 26:3183–3208.

Nafpaktitis, B.G. 1968. Taxonomy and distribution of the lanternfishes, genera *Lobianchia* and *Diaphus*, in the North Atlantic. *Dana Rep.* 73:131.

Neave, N.M., Dilworth, C.L., Eales, J.G., and Saunders, R.L. 1966. Adjustment of buoyancy in Atlantic salmon parr in relation to changing water velocity. *J. Fish. Res. Board Can.* 23:1617–1620.

Neill, S.R. St. J., and Cullen, J.M. 1974. Experiments on whether schooling by their prey affects the hunting behaviour of cephalopods and fish predators. *J. Zool. Lond.* 172:549–569.

Nelson, E.M. 1961. The comparative morphology of the definitive swim bladder in the Catostomidae. *Am. Midland Naturalist* 65:101–110.

Nevenzel, J.C., Rodegker, W., Robinson, J.S., and Kayama, M. 1969. The lipids of some lantern fishes (Family Myctophidae). *Comp. Biochem. Physiol.* 31:25–36.

Patton, S., and Thomas, A.J. 1971. Composition of lipid foams from swim bladders of two deep ocean fish species. *J. Lipid Res.* 12:331–335.

Pearcy, W.G., and Laurs, R.M. 1966. Vertical migration and distribution of mesopelagic fishes off Oregon. *Deep-Sea Res.* 13:153–165.

Pearcy, W.G., Krygier, E.E., Mesecar, R., and Ramsay, F. 1977. Vertical distribution and migration of oceanic micronekton off Oregon. *Deep-Sea Res.* 24:223–245.

Pearson, W.H., Miller, S.E., and Olla, B.L. 1980. Chemoreception in the food-searching and feeding behavior of the red hake, *Urophycis chuss* (Walbaum). *J. Exp. Marine Biol. Ecol.* 48:139–150.

Phleger, C.F., 1974. Bone lipids of Kona coast reef fish: skull buoyancy in the hawkfish, *Cirrhites pinnulatus. Comp. Biochem. Physiol.* 52B:101–104.

Qutob, Z. 1962. The swimbladder of fishes as a pressure receptor. *Archs. Neer. Zool.* 15:1–67.

Roberts, B.L. 1969. The buoyancy and locomotory movements of electric rays. *J. Marine Biol. Assoc. U.K.* 49:621–640.

Ross, L.G. 1979. The permeability to oxygen and the guanine content of the swimbladder of a physoclist fish, *Pollachius virens. J. Marine Biol. Assoc. U.K.* 59:437–441.

Ross, L.G., and Gordon, J.D.M. 1978. Guanine and permeability in swimbladders of slope-dwelling fish. In *Physiology and Behaviour of Marine Organisms,* edited by D.S. McLusky and A.J. Berry, 113–121. Proceedings of the 12th European symposium on marine biology. Oxford and New York: Permagon Press.

Saunders, R.L. 1965. Adjustment of buoyancy in young Atlantic salmon and brook trout by changes in swimbladder volumes. *J. Fish. Res. Board Can.* 22:335–352.

Sazima, I., and Vieda, V.S. 1979. Is the night-time resting behavior of young needlefish an example of nocturnal disguise? *Biotropica* 11:308–309.

Schultz, D.C., and Northcote, T.G. 1972. An experimental study of feeding behavior and interaction of coastal cutthroat trout (*Salmo clarki clarki*) and dolly varden (*Salvelinus malma*). *J. Fish Res. Board Can.* 29:555–565.

Simons, J.R. 1970. The direction of the thrust produced by the heterocercal tails of two dissimilar elasmobranchs: the Port Jackson shark, *Heterodontus portusjacksoni* (Meyer), and the piked dogfish, *Squalus megalops* (Macleay). *J. Exp. Biol.* 52:95–107.

Smart, H.J., and Gee, J.H. 1979. Coexistence and resource partitioning in two species of darters (Percidae), *Etheostoma nigrum* and *Percina maculata. Can. J. Zool.* 57:2061–2071.

Steen, J.B. 1963a. The physiology of the swimbladder in the eel *Anguilla vulgaris.* III. The mechanism of gas secretion. *Acta Physiol. Scand.* 59:221–241.

Steen, J.B. 1963b. The physiology of the swimbladder in the eel *Anguilla vulgaris* II. The resorption of gases. *Acta Physiol. Scand.* 58:138–149.

Steen, J.B. 1970. The swim bladder as a hydrostatic organ. In *Fish Physiology,* edited by W.S. Hoar and D.J. Randall, vol. 4, 413–443. New York and London: Academic Press.

Steen, J.B., and Sund, T. 1977. Gas deposition by counter-current multiplication in eel swim-bladder: experimental verification of a mathematical model. *J. Physiol.* 267:697–702.

Stevens, D.H., and Neill, W.H. 1978. Body temperature relations of tunas, especially skipjack. In *Fish Physiology,* edited by W.S. Hoar and D.J. Randall, vol. 7, 316–359. New York and London: Pergamon Press.

Stewart, D.B., and Gee, J.H. 1981. Mechanisms of buoyancy adjustment and effects of water velocity and temperature on ability to maintain buoyancy in fathead minnows, *Pimephales promelas,* Rafinesque. *Comp. Biochem. Physiol.* 68A:337–347.

Sund, T. 1977. A mathematical model for counter-current multiplication in the swim-bladder. *J. Physiol.* 267:679–696.

Taylor, F.H.C. 1968. The relationship of midwater trawl catches to sound scattering layers off the coast of northern British Columbia. *J. Fish. Res. Board Can.* 25:457–472.

Todd, E.S. 1973. Positive buoyancy and air-breathing: a new piscine gas bladder function. *Copeia* 1973:461–464.

Verheijen, F.J. 1962. Gas splitting by alarmed fish disturbs their hydrostatic equilibrium. *Science* 137:864–865.

Vierke, J. 1975. Das wasserspucken der arten der gattung *Colisa* (Pisces: Anabantidae). *Bonn. Zool. Beitn.* 24:62–104.

Weihs, D. 1973. Mechanically efficient swimming techniques for fish with negative buoyancy. *J. Marine Res.* 31:194–209.

Weihs, D. 1978. Tidal stream transport as an efficient method for migration. *J. Cons. Int. Explor. Mer.* 38:92–99.

Weselowski, R.F. 1974. Comparison of populations of brook stickleback *Culaea inconstans* (Kirtland) with and without predation by a piscivorous fish. M.Sc. Thesis, Dept. of Zoology, University of Manitoba.

Wittenberg, J.B., Copeland, D.E., Haedrich, R.L., and Child J.S. 1980. The swimbladder of deep-sea fish: the swimbladder wall is a lipid-rich barrier to oxygen diffusion. *J. Marine Biol. Assoc. U.K.* 60:236–276.

Wootton, R.J. 1976. *The Biology of the Sticklebacks.* London and New York: Academic Press.

Chapter 6
HYDROMECHANICS OF BODY AND CAUDAL FIN PROPULSION
George T. Yates

CONTENTS

INTRODUCTION

The study of the hydrodynamics of fish locomotion is not only of great interest to the fluid dynamicist, but has a pertinent interface with studies of aquatic animal metabolism and energetics, feeding and migration, growth and spawning, as well as other behavioral and physiological adaptations that may depend on environmental parameters. In hope of taking full benefit of multidisciplinary interactions, this chapter discusses the hydrodynamic aspects of aquatic animal swimming by exploring what the biologist and the hydrodynamicist can accomplish with close collaboration, rather than what they can do separately. Emphasis is placed on the studies of thrust generation based on hydrodynamic principles of fish locomotion and subsequent application of these theories to studies on metabolism and biochemical energy conversion. In this way, more useful data become available, thus reducing the number of unknowns for the investigation of the natural phenomena in

177

question. For example, the metabolic rate of a fish in self-propulsion can be measured in various cases to a relatively high precision, compared to the formidable task of making direct flow measurements on the pressure and skin-friction distributions over the entire surface of a swimming fish. With further reference to the scaling effects (when the data cover a range of animal sizes), such joint studies often yield interesting relationships between the physiological and dynamic parameters that would otherwise be difficult to achieve.

The chapter is organized from the perspective of hydrodynamics. The subject matter is presented in an order that traces the development of the theories; the biological classifications play a diminished role in the organization. The earlier theoretical hydrodynamic models dealing with fish swimming applied existing aerodynamic works related either to slender body theory (Lighthill, 1960; Taylor, 1952) or to two-dimensional wing theory (Wu, 1961). Consequently, priority is given to the problems of carangiform and lunate-tail (thunniform) locomotion of different groups of fishes. In this rather broad area, experimental results are sufficiently abundant to render refined investigations possible, and the hydromechanical efficiency and physiological functions are considered on the basis of data from both comparative zoology and dynamic similarity. Following the examination of the theories, further modifications are discussed that expand their application. Several new developments are considered and example calculations are carried out to illustrate the application of the theories.

New modifications of the elongated body theory for carangiform and subcarangiform swimming take into account the interaction of the caudal fin with the vortex sheets shed from upstream median fins. A substantial contribution to thrust and efficiency can be realized through this interaction. Immediately following this discussion, two extensions of the elongated body theory are considered. The first takes a brief look at the effects of large amplitude lateral motions; the second treats elongated median fins on which propulsive waves are propagated. Investigation of amiiform, gymnotiform, and balistiform locomotion is permitted by this new degree of freedom of the body motion. The results are incomplete, and agreement with observations is tentative; it is hoped that this section will serve to stimulate research in these areas.

Lunate tail swimming is summarized next, and various methods in unsteady aerodynamics are applied. For this mode of propulsion, a reexamination of the pitching axis and the heave-pitch phase is undertaken. Minimizing the root mean square moment or power used to produce moment suggests that the axis of the pitching motion should be moved further forward on the fin than previously indicated. Finally, measurements of metabolic rate at various activity levels, coupled with direct observations of pertinent kinematic parameters such as fish mass, length, swimming velocity, and frequency and wavelength of tail beat, provide the basis necessary to identify that portion of the energy budget that goes toward locomotion. Direct and indirect evidence about the swimming drag coefficient, concerning both its functional dependence on the Reynolds number and its order of magnitude, are discussed. Comparison between the drag coefficient and the power coefficient available for swimming, converted from data on metabolic rate with estimated muscle efficiency and hydromechanical efficiency, indicates their similar dependence on the Reynolds number and their comparable magnitude.

In contrast to many areas of engineering, where measurements can be made and repeated with a high degree of accuracy, the individual variability and the complexity of the natural processes do not at present permit the same level of precision in this most exciting field of study. The need for better understanding permeates both the physical and life sciences, and solution techniques are insufficiently refined for many of the complex problems encountered in aquatic swimming. An attempt is made in this chapter to survey the existing hydrodynamic approaches related to body and median fin propulsion and to outline some new works. Throughout, assumptions are made that simplify the problem and render tractable solutions in the hope of pointing out the important parameters and giving elucidating results. The applicability and the limitations of the theories are kept in mind, and whenever possible, comparisons to relevant experiments are referenced.

MOMENTUM AND ENERGY

Before discussing the detailed computation of the hydrodynamic forces acting on a fish, it is instructive to look at the overall momentum and energy balance during swimming. This illustrates some of the interconnections between the various disciplines involved in the study of aquatic animal swimming.

Balance of Forces and Moments

The conservation of linear and angular momentum requires the vector sum of all the forces and the moment of forces acting on a body to equal the time rate of change of the linear and angular momentums of the body, respectively. This balance of fluid forces and body inertia must hold at every instant of time for an undulating fish. In addition to the action of pressure forces, the fluid forces acting on the fish are comprised of two major types: those caused by the acceleration of a mass of fluid (inertia) and those caused by the resistance of the fluid to shearing motion (viscosity). The relative importance of inertia over viscosity in any fluid flow is indicated by the Reynolds number (Re $= UL/v$), where U and L are some characteristic velocity and length associated with the particular flow and v is the kinematic viscosity of the fluid ($v \simeq 0.01$ cm^2/sec for water).

The vast majority of fish inhabiting our oceans and streams swim at a

Reynolds number, based on mean swimming speed and body length, between 10 thousand and 5 million. In this range of Reynolds numbers and for streamlined shaped bodies, the viscous forces are confined to a very narrow region close to the body. This viscous boundary layer is so thin that the pressure gradient normal to the body surface is very small and can be neglected. Under this assumption, forces calculated by inviscid theory are expected to represent the inertial forces exerted by the fluid on the animal. The viscous forces acting in the boundary layer can in principle be calculated separately. Because the current understanding of unsteady three-dimensional boundary layer development is inadequate to accurately specify the boundary layer character (laminar or turbulent) everywhere along the body and the nature of the wake, the calculation of drag force remains a very challenging task. The ability to separate the computation of inertial and resistive forces makes the problem tractable, and the forces acting on the swimmer by the fluid are thus decomposed into thrust $T(t)$, calculated from inviscid flow theory, and drag $D(t)$, calculated in principle from the boundary layer. It should be noted that inviscid flow theory may result in negative thrust (*i.e.*, drag) for clumsy motions or for inertial braking and also should include the drag associated with lift (induced drag). The partitioning of the fluid forces is thus somewhat ambiguous and must be carefully stated. The splitting of forces into T and D may be further influenced by the particular application in question because, for example, it may be desirable to lump the induced drag with D or to consider the propulsive force generated by drag based locomotion as thrust.

In the absence of any external forces, conservation of linear momentum in the direction of forward swimming gives

$$T(t) - D(t) = ma(t) \tag{1}$$

where m is the mass and $a(t)$ the acceleration of the fish. For a periodic swimming motion, the average forward speed is constant, the time average of the acceleration is zero, and thus the mean thrust must equal the mean drag

$$\bar{T} = \bar{D} \tag{2}$$

Viewed behind the fish, this means that the momentum deficit in the wake, caused by the boundary layer dragging fluid along with the fish, is exactly equal to the momentum increment generated by the thrust-producing undulations.

Defining the thrust, C_T, and drag, C_D, coefficients as

$$C_T = \frac{\bar{T}}{\frac{1}{2}\rho U^2 S} \tag{3}$$

and

$$C_D = \frac{\overline{D}}{\frac{1}{2}\rho U^2 S} \qquad (4)$$

where U is the average swimming speed, ρ the density of the fluid, and S the wetted surface area, we can write equation 2

$$C_T = C_D \qquad (5)$$

The chief merit of using C_T and C_D is that they are nondimensional coefficients.

Similarly, a balance of the transverse momentum gives

$$T_L(t) - D_L(t) = ma_L(t) \qquad (6)$$

for the instantaneous lateral forces and acceleration. The oscillatory nature of the lateral motion may limit the maximum obtainable D_L, and the lateral accelerations of the body are balanced predominantly by the transverse component of the inertial force. The fluid motion (and hence the kinetic energy of the fluid) in the lateral direction may thus be more extensive than the fluid motion in the longitudinal direction, as observed by McCutchen (1976). For steady forward swimming, the mean value of the acceleration again vanishes, and

$$\overline{T}_L = \overline{D}_L \qquad (7)$$

and the symmetry of the motion and the nature of the viscous forces indicate that $\overline{D}_L = \overline{T}_L = 0$.

For aquatic animals the gravitational force or potential energy is generally treated separately: neutrally buoyant swimmers are usually taken in static equilibrium; in the case of the scombrids and other negatively buoyant fishes, the forces in the vertical direction must be balanced dynamically, and they can be considered independently (Magnuson, 1973).

Rate of Work

In addition to the balance of forces, the rate at which energy is used must be properly accounted for. The mean rate of energy expenditure in overcoming the fluid resistance will be approximately $\overline{D}U$, and this energy must be supplied by the swimming muscles. If $\overline{P}$ is taken as the mean metabolic rate of the fish, then $\overline{P}$ with some efficiency η equals the power going into the drag

$$\eta C_P = C_D \qquad (8)$$

where the power coefficient is defined as

$$C_P = \frac{\overline{P}}{\frac{1}{2}\rho U^3 S} \tag{9}$$

The inefficiencies of the energy conversions include the loss of the heat of reaction within the muscle (chemical-to-mechanical conversion), the increased internal friction loss and power required within the circulatory and respiratory systems, as well as the loss of energy associated with vortex shedding. These effects are usually taken in two major groups: the muscle efficiency, η_m, and the hydromechanical efficiency, η_h. Typically, η_m ranges between 0.2 and 0.3 and depends on species, temperature, size, or other factors (Goldspink, 1977). The hydromechanical efficiency can easily exceed 0.8 and may obtain values greater than 0.9 (Chopra and Kambe, 1977; Magnuson, 1978).

For steady swimming at speeds where aerobic processes dominate, the power input for locomotion $\overline{P}$ can be determined by measuring the animal's oxygen consumption and by applying standard energy conversion factors. The extensive literature on the metabolism and swimming speeds of fish makes it plain that the physical details of an experiment must be clearly specified, and Brett (1965a, 1967) has shed considerable light on this with his careful experiments. In a comparative mechanophysiologic study, Wu and Yates (1978) show the importance of the kinematic and dynamic variables of the swimming for interpreting the data. Before examining and interpreting these data on the overall forces and energetics, it is necessary to isolate the important kinematic variables that describe the motion and to estimate the fluid forces using hydrodynamic theory.

BODY FORM AND KINEMATICS

The detailed description of the fish morphology and of the swimming movements is needed before estimates of the fluid forces can be accurately made. Breder (1926) classified swimmers by the extent of the body that is involved in locomotion, and the variety of shapes and types of movements used by fish shows marked variation. Likewise, fin configurations are highly varied throughout the aquatic world. No attempt to cover the entire range of motions is made, and this chapter is restricted to the most common or typical class of motions, concentrating on the body and median fin types of propulsion used by anguilliform, carangiform, and thunniform swimmers.

The body morphology is assumed to be described by the functions $b_1(x)$, $b_2(x)$, and $g(x,y)$, which are defined for the body in its stretched straight position (Fig. 6-1). The outline of the side view is prescribed by b_1 and b_2. The body is assumed symmetric about the xy plane, and the body thickness is given

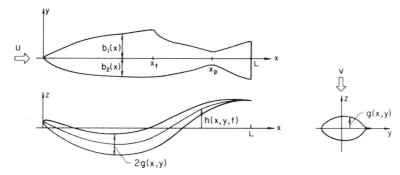

Figure 6-1
Illustration of the coordinate system used and the functions that prescribe the body shape $b(x)$, thickness $g(x,y)$, and centerline motion $h(x,y,t)$. The (x,y,z) frame is translating with the fish swimming speed U in the negative x-direction. For the linearized boundary conditions, the lateral fluid velocity V is shown in the cross-flow plane.

by $g(x,y)$. These three functions completely specify the physical dimensions of the fish, and no assumptions have been made about the swimming motions.

During swimming, muscle contractions cause lateral movements of the body away from its stretched straight configuration. These locomotory movements are described by another function $h(x,y,t)$, and the location of the body surface is then

$$z = h(x,y,t) \pm g(x,y); \qquad (0 < x < L) \text{ and } (-b_2 < y < b_1) \qquad (10)$$

where L is the overall body length and the (x,y,z) reference frame moves with the velocity of the fish.

Taking the fish to be swimming at a constant mean forward speed U in the negative x direction, several new quantities are identified. The maximum amplitude of the lateral body motion is denoted by h_0, and the frequency of the periodic lateral movements by f. If the motion is wavelike (*i.e.*, if the body movements propagate from one region of the body to another), the speed of the wave propagation (c) is introduced. The wave speed is measured in a reference frame moving with the mean swimming speed. The role of the Reynolds number has already been discussed, and these new length and time scales allow other Reynolds numbers to be formed based, for example, on the fish height and lateral velocity. It is important to form the appropriate Re when any specific region of the flow is under special investigation; thus, in the examination of pectoral fin locomotion, the dimensions and velocities of the fin rather than the body should be used in the Reynolds number.

Figure 6-2 was compiled using data collected by Wu and Yates (1978) and by Beamish (1978) for a wide range of sizes and speeds of carangiform and subcarangiform swimmers. The log U versus log L plot illustrates several

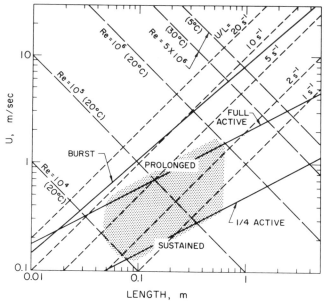

Figure 6-2

Variation of swimming speed U with body length. The range of reported activity levels of fish is shown by the shaded region. The burst performance represents a bound on the swimming capabilities and is shown by the solid line (Wu and Yates, 1978). Lines of constant Reynolds number (Re) and lines of constant specific speed (U/L) are indicated for reference.

important features of the carangiform mode of swimming. Lines of constant Re (based on L and U) and lines of constant specific speed (in L/sec) are indicated for reference. Through changes in the density and viscosity, which depend on temperature, salinity, and pressure, the Reynolds number can be influenced by environmental conditions, as illustrated by the Re = 5×10^6 lines, which are given at two different temperatures in Figure 6-2.

The swimming capabilities of any given fish can be roughly categorized into three levels of performance (Brett, 1965a and b, 1967; Hoar and Randall, 1978): sustained (speeds that can be maintained almost indefinitely), prolonged (speeds maintained for 1 or 2 hours with a steady effort, but leading to fatigue), and sprint or burst (speeds achieved at maximum effort lasting for only about 30 seconds). The physiological basis of each of these activity levels is different; each level may have different dependence on body size, temperature, and environmental conditions. Apparently, the physiological parameters involved in characterizing different levels of activity are quite complex because they have been noted (Brett, 1965a and b for the salmon, and Beamish, 1978) to include such factors as temperature, pre-exercise, maturity, sex, varying use of red and white musculature, buildup of an oxygen debt, and fatigue. Further, the metabolic process may vary with the kinematics of the bodily motion, which in turn may be modulated by the fluid reaction, and with the efficiency of energy conversion (Lighthill, 1973).

The effects of animal size (the so-called scale effects) are also evident in Figure 6-2. Brett (1965a and b) found the upper limit of the prolonged performance to be approximately proportional to $L^{0.5}$, "indicating a rapid decay in the relative ability to maintain a sustained speed as size increases." Other reports (Brett, 1967; Magnuson, 1970; Hunter, 1971; Hunter and Zweifel, 1971), however, indicate that a better overall average value would be $L^{0.6}$. Reanalysis of Brett's (1965a) data for the 60-minute critical speed (the speed that ends in fatigue after 1 hour of continuous swimming) gives the solid line (slope 0.524) passing through the prolonged region shown in Figure 6.2 It is interesting to point out that Brett's one fourth active speeds give the solid line passing through the sustained region in Figure 6.2, with a slope of 0.527. Note that there are no systematic studies on the swimming performance of fish in excess of 60 cm. There is no doubt that investigations expanding the size range studied will lead to a better understanding of swimming capacities.

Considerable attention has been given to the specific burst speeds, body lengths per second, that for various species of streamlined fish tend to decrease as the fish length increases. An interesting approach was taken by Wardle (1975), who used isolated muscle blocks from the various sizes of fish to estimate the upper limits of swimming speed, but as yet no adequate data are available to verify these results. Wu and Yates (1978) suggest the line illustrated in Figure 6-2 with a slope of 0.88.

Another important flow parameter that helps characterize the flow is the reduced frequency

$$\sigma = \frac{\omega L}{U} = \frac{2\pi f L}{U} \tag{11}$$

where $\omega = 2\pi f$ is the radian frequency. The reduced frequency is a measure of the importance of unsteady effects in the flow, and is 2π times the ratio of the time it takes the fish to swim one body length to the time for one complete tail beat (alternately, it is 2π divided by the stride length). This ratio has far reaching fluid dynamic importance. If σ is small, the undulatory effects of the tail motion are small compared to the longitudinal motion and the fluid behavior can be modeled by freeze-frame (quasisteady) analysis. Quasisteady theory assumes that the body is temporarily fixed in one position (as by a photograph) and uses steady-flow theory to calculate the fluid forces on it. The body position is then advanced and again frozen during the calculation of the fluid flow. Subsequent addition of the forces found for all body positions gives the total force experienced over one cycle. For a range of intermediate and large values of σ, both the longitudinal and transverse motions are important, and unsteady effects profoundly influence the fluid forces.

In assessing the values of σ for which unsteady effects are important, comparison with traditional wing theories and experiments are useful. Typically, σ is based on the wing chord for two-dimensional or high-aspect ratio wings, and in these cases the unsteady effects are already fully evident near $\sigma = 0.2$. The reduced frequency defined by equation 11 is based on the body length, and for the purpose of comparing with these results from aerodynamics, a more appropriate length scale may be the fin chord, body height, or wave amplitude. Consequently, the reduced frequency, more relevant for comparison, would be lowered in most cases by a factor of about ten below the value obtained using equation 11. Because measurements of the fish length and tail-beat frequency are readily available and because fin geometries are not consistently reported in the literature, the definition in equation 11 is retained unless otherwise stated. The one exception will be the case of lunate tail swimmers (see section on lunate tail propulsion), where the fin chord can be more easily identified and is used in place of L.

The reduced frequency for a wide range of carangiform swimmers is shown in Figure 6-3. The filled data points are for near maximum sustained speed, and the open points connected with solid lines represent individual fish over their full range of swimming speeds. As the speed (and hence Re) of a fish increases, σ decreases, with the decrease becoming less pronounced at higher

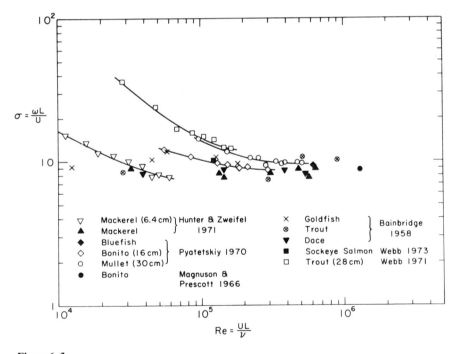

Figure 6-3
Dependence of the reduced frequency (σ) on the Reynolds number (Re) for a variety of fish. Filled points are for swimming near the maximum prolonged speeds. Open points and solid lines represent the performance of an individual fish.

speeds. Except for the very low speeds (less than one body length per second), all σ are within a factor of two regardless of speed or fish length. The higher speeds particularly show scale independence, with σ lying between 8 and 10 for all Re. The effects of body size are clearly shown by the solid lines. Each line represents a different size fish and has very similar behavior with Re. An essential consequence for σ in this range is that the unsteady effects are important, and the much simplified quasisteady approach must be abandoned.

Fewer data are available for the ratio of the forward speed to the propulsive wave speed U/c. Data from Webb (1975), Pyatetskiy (1970), and Batty (1981) indicate that U/c increases as specific swim speed increases. From the limited size and activity range that has been investigated to date, U/c appears to increase as fish size increases, for the same specific swimming speed.

The description of the body geometry and motion (equation 10) is quite general and encompasses a wide variety of motions used by fish. The motion includes swimmers in the anguilliform, subcarangiform, carangiform, thunniform, ostraciiform, tetraodontiform, balistiform, amiiform, and gymnotiform modes of swimming. (Locomotion by fins out of the plane of symmetry are, however, precluded and are the subject of Chapter 7.) In order to find the propulsive forces generated by body and median fin motions, certain simplifying assumptions must be introduced, and the dynamics must be included. The next several sections address these subjects.

ELONGATED BODY THEORY

Within the framework of inviscid potential flow theory, the hydrodynamic forces can be estimated on a slender fish. Most fish are characterized by a body geometry that is very long in comparison to the body thickness and height (Fig. 6-1). This slenderness is used to simplify the computation of the hydrodynamic forces and gives rise to the so-called elongated (or slender) body theory, in which b/L, g/L, h/L, $|dh/dx|$, and $|db/dx|$ are all assumed to be much less than 1. This assumption is justified for a rather large number of species. The results obtained by making the slenderness assumption are good for very slender bodies and retain their validity even for moderately slender bodies, where the error in using the theory on fish with a slenderness ratio as large as 0.4 may be tolerable. At any rate, the dependence on the parameters can be determined, and comparison with experimental data will help determine the range of validity of the results.

Because the body is long in the x-direction and the body cross-section changes slowly along the body length, it is assumed that the solution can be calculated at each cross-section and that the solution depends only on the flow quantities and fish geometry at that position and is not influenced by the body extremities. In this way, the problem reduces to solving a two-dimensional flow over a cylinder in the cross-flow plane (*yz* plane in Fig. 6-1). Special considerations must be given to the head and tail regions where the body can no longer be assumed to be slender. In the regions where a vortex sheet is present, modifications must also be made because the sheet was generated at an upstream trailing edge, is convected posteriorly with the flow, and thus carries upstream information back along the body.

In order to obtain some simple results and because the effects of body thickness are not expected to be large (Newman and Wu, 1973; Lighthill, 1970) the body is assumed to have zero thickness, and $g(x,y)$ is taken to be identically zero.

The lateral motion at each cross-section is assumed to be independent of y, such that h is a function of x and t only. This constraint will be removed for the case of amiiform swimming in the section on elongated median fin propulsion. The relative fluid velocity at any cross-section $V(x,t)$ is given by the linearized total (Lagrangian) time derivative of h

$$V(x,t) = Dh(x,t) = \left(\frac{\partial}{\partial t} + U \frac{\partial}{\partial x}\right)h(x,t) \tag{12}$$

According to the slender body approximation, the solution at each longitudinal cross-section is equivalent to that of an infinitely long plate moving transversely with velocity $V(x,t)$ (see the *yz* plane in Fig. 6-1).

Lateral Pressure Force

The lateral momentum of the water per unit length of the fish is then $m(x) V(x,t)$, where $m(x)$ is the "added mass" of the fish per unit length for transverse motion of the body. A rather surprising and simple result, which follows from a detailed analysis of inviscid hydrodynamics (Yih, 1977), is that $m(x)$ is proportional to the mass of fluid displaced by a circle circumscribing the body cross-section. The added mass, which has the dimensions of mass per unit length, is thus often written

$$m(x) = \rho\beta\pi b^2(x) \tag{13}$$

where ρ is the fluid density, $b(x) = (b_1 + b_2)/2$, and β is a coefficient that depends on the body thickness and the extent of the fins as described by $g(x,y)$. For many fishlike cross-sections, β is found to vary only slightly from one (Lighthill, 1970). If more precise analysis is desired, β can be retained, but to simplify the discussion and in accordance with the zero thickness approximation, β is taken as unity.

The instantaneous lateral force per unit length on the fish L_a is equal and opposite to the total time rate of change of the lateral momentum of the fluid

$$L_a(x,t) = -D[m(x)V(x,t)] \qquad (0 < x < x_f) \qquad (14)$$

where x_f is the anteriormost position where vortex shedding occurs. This result was first found by Lighthill (1960) and is valid at body cross-sections where there are no vortex sheets present (*i.e.*, anterior or leading edge regions illustrated in Fig. 6-4).

Posterior to the leading edge region, dorsal and ventral fins are often present. Many fish, like swordfish and some species of tuna, are able to completely retract these fins into small grooves in the body and have well-rounded dorsal and ventral body edges. For these fish the lateral force is again given by equation 14 if the fins are retracted. Other species such as salmon and trout cannot completely retract these fins, some species of tuna and sharks have permanently extended dorsal or ventral fins, and still other species have a lenticular body cross-section. In these cases, as a consequence of the fluid viscosity, further restrictions on the flow are needed. Because a real fluid cannot negotiate sharp corners, a vortex sheet is expected to be shed from the body or fin trailing edges, and the pressure is expected to be bounded. This is the Kutta condition, which is imposed at sharp trailing edges and subsequently modifies the potential flow velocity and pressure field. The presence of this trailing edge vortex sheet makes the longitudinal variation of the added mass unimportant in calculating the lateral force (Wu, 1971c); thus,

$$L_f(x,t) = -mD(V) \qquad (x_f < x < x_p) \qquad (15)$$

where x_p is the value of x for which b is a minimum (the position of the caudal peduncle), and the body has been assumed symmetric about the xz plane, $b_1(x) = b_2(x) = b(x)$. There is no inherent difficulty in treating the nonsymmetric case; however, the formulas are somewhat cumbersome and the important features are contained in the symmetric case. Here and in the remaining analysis, the body outline $b(x)$ is assumed to be a single-valued

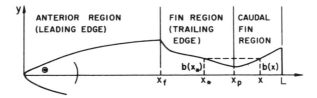

Figure 6-4
Identification of various regions of the body for calculation of the hydrodynamic forces. Vortex shedding is assumed in the fin region between x_f and x_p and at the caudal fin trailing edge $x = L$.

function of x; thus, fins with rearward-slanted leading or trailing edges are permitted, but forward-slanted or swallow-tail fins are excluded.

Moving posterior from the caudal peduncle to the caudal fin region, the body usually has rounded edges similar to the anterior region, and no further vorticity is shed into the fluid until the edge of the caudal fin at $x = L$. The only free vorticity present is transported with velocity U from the upstream fins. The deformation of the sheet caused by body thickness and self-induced velocities that generally cause the rolling up of the sheet are neglected, and the sheet is taken at $z = 0$. The lateral force must be modified again and is given by

$$L_c(x,t) = - D(Vm) + V_* D(m)$$
$$= - mDV - (V - V_*) D(m)   (x_p < x < L) \qquad (16)$$

where

$$V_*(x,t) = V(x_*,t_*) \qquad (17)$$

has dimensions of velocity and represents the effects of the vortex sheet on the body. V_* depends on x_*, which is the value of x in the trailing edge region $(x_f < x_* < x_p)$ where $b(x_*) = b(x)$ and the retarded time t_*, which is the time taken for the vorticity shed at x_* to be convected with the velocity U to the x location in caudal fin region (Fig. 6-4)

$$t_* = t - \frac{x - x_*}{U} \qquad (18)$$

Because the shed vorticity is assumed to travel downstream along a straight line parallel to the body axis, its influence on L_c is only through the single variable x_*.

Other fin geometries such as fin asymmetry, the absence of shedding in the peduncle regions, or multiple fins separated by nonshedding regions occur in nature and can be solved with appropriate modifications of the theory. The results are cumbersome, and for simplicity we shall consider only these three regions on a symmetric fish and examine the effect of the vortex sheet interaction on thrust and power.

Leading-Edge Suction

In addition to the lateral force that acts normal to the body surface, another force acts along the leading edges of the body. In the approximation of zero thickness the fluid velocities become infinite along body edges which do not shed vorticity. The pressure is also infinite, but the force, which is the surface integral of the pressure, is finite. This pressure integral along the body edges produces a leading edge suction force (Batchelor, p 412, 1967). The component of the sectional suction that contributes to the thrust is (Wu, 1961)

$$T_s(x,t) = \frac{1}{2} V^2 \frac{dm}{dx} \qquad (0 < x < x_f) \qquad (19)$$

In the regions where vortex shedding takes place, the velocity and pressure at the body edges are finite, and

$$T_s(x,t) = 0 \qquad (x_f < x < x_p) \qquad (20)$$

In the caudal region the suction force is modified owing to the vortex sheet that was shed upstream

$$T_s(x,t) = \frac{1}{2}(V - V_*)^2 \frac{dm}{dx} \qquad (x_p < x < L) \qquad (21)$$

where V_* is given above.

Thrust

The vector sum of these sectional forces along the entire body gives the total force acting on the fish. The component of this force in the x-direction is the thrust

$$T(t) = \int_0^L \left[L_n(x,t) \frac{\partial h}{\partial x}(x,t) + T_s(x,t) \right] dx \qquad (22)$$

and

$$L_n \frac{\partial h}{\partial x} + T_s = -\frac{\partial h}{\partial x} D(mV) + \frac{1}{2} V^2 \frac{dm}{dx} \qquad (0 < x < x_f) \qquad (23a)$$

$$= -m \frac{\partial h}{\partial x} D(V) \qquad (x_f < x < x_p) \qquad (23b)$$

$$= -m \frac{\partial h}{\partial x} D(V) - (V - V_*) \frac{\partial h}{\partial x} D(m) + \frac{1}{2}(V - V_*)^2 \frac{dm}{dx}$$

$$(x_p < x < L) \qquad (23c)$$

The sectional forces for the entire body can be represented by equations 16, 21, and 23c if the appropriate values of V_* are taken as

$$V_*(x,t) = 0 \qquad (0 < x < x_f) \qquad (24a)$$

$$= V(x,t) \qquad (x_f < x < x_p) \qquad (24b)$$

$$= V(x_*,t) \qquad (x_p < x < L) \qquad (24c)$$

Taking a time average over one tail-beat cycle or averaging over a very long time, the mean thrust is

$$\overline{T} = \int_0^L \overline{[L_n(x,t) \frac{\partial h}{\partial x}(x,t) + T_s(x,t)]}dx$$

$$= -m\overline{\left(\frac{1}{2}V^2 - V\frac{\partial h}{\partial t}\right)}\bigg|_{x=L} + \int_{x_f}^{x_p} \overline{\left(\frac{1}{2}V^2 - V\frac{\partial h}{\partial t}\right)}\frac{dm}{dx}dx$$

$$+ \int_{x_p}^L \overline{\left(\frac{1}{2}V_*^2 - V_*\frac{\partial h}{\partial t}\right)}\frac{dm}{dx}dx = \overline{T_e} + \overline{T_f} + \overline{T_i} \quad (25)$$

where a bar over any variables means the time average of that quantity. $\overline{T_e}$ is the thrust associated with the vortex sheet shed from the tail and is the total thrust in the absence of any vortex shedding from any body fins. $\overline{T_f}$ gives the contribution from the dorsal and ventral fins, and $\overline{T_i}$ arises from the interaction of the vortex sheets shed by body fins with the caudal fin.

Power

The time average rate of work done by the fish in making the lateral undulations

$$\overline{P_h} = -\int_0^L \overline{L_n(x,t) \frac{\partial h}{\partial t}(x,t)}\, dx =$$

$$\overline{UmV\frac{\partial h}{\partial t}}\bigg|_{x=L} - U\int_{x_f}^{x_p} \overline{V\frac{\partial h}{\partial t}\frac{dm}{dx}}\, dx$$

$$- U\int_{x_p}^L \overline{V_*\frac{h}{\partial t}\frac{dm}{dx}}\, dx = \overline{P_e} + \overline{P_f} + \overline{P_i} \quad (26)$$

represents the mechanical power input needed to produce the hydrodynamic thrust (equation 25). The three terms $\overline{P_e}$, $\overline{P_f}$, $\overline{P_i}$ represent the power required from the caudal fin trailing edge, the body fins, and the interaction of the vortex sheet from the body fins with the caudal fin, respectively.

Only part of this energy is used in overcoming the viscous drag or in producing thrust, and the rest is lost to the fluid in the wake at the average rate $\overline{E}$. If $\overline{P}$ in the energy balance (equation 8) is taken as the mechanical power $\overline{P_h}$

$$\overline{P_h} = \overline{TU} + \overline{E} \tag{27}$$

and the hydromechanical efficiency of the energy conversion can be identified

$$\eta_h = \frac{\overline{TU}}{\overline{P_h}} \tag{28}$$

Special Case

It is instructive to apply these formulas to a specific example. Several further restrictions are assumed, and when specific values are needed, numbers representative of fish are taken. The specific assumptions will alter the detailed numerical values, but the order of magnitude and the dependence of $\overline{T}$, $\overline{P_h}$, and η_h on the parameters should be qualitatively the same. The body motion is taken to be a constant amplitude rearward propagating wave, of wave length λ

$$h(x,t) = h_1 \cos (kx - \omega t) \tag{29}$$

where h_1 is constant and $k = 2\pi/\lambda$. Then

$$V(x,t) = -\omega h_1 (1 - U/c) \sin (kx - \omega t) \tag{30}$$

where $c = f\lambda = \omega/k$. The time averages indicated in $\overline{T}$, $\overline{P_h}$ can now be evaluated, and except for those terms involving V_*, are all independent of x.

$$C_{Te} = \frac{\overline{T_e}}{\frac{1}{2}\rho U^2 L^2} = \frac{\sigma^2}{2}\left(\frac{h_1}{L}\right)^2 (1 - U^2/c^2) \frac{A_L}{L^2} \tag{31}$$

where $A_L = \pi b^2(L)$ and C_{Te} is the nondimensional thrust coefficient.

$$C_{Tf} = \frac{\overline{T_f}}{\frac{1}{2}\rho U^2 L^2} = C_{Te}\left(\frac{b_f^2 - b_p^2}{b_L^2}\right) \tag{32}$$

$$C_{Pe} = \frac{\overline{P_e}}{\frac{1}{2}\rho U^3 L^2} = \sigma^2\left(\frac{h_1}{L}\right)^2 (1 - U/c) \frac{A_L}{L^2} \tag{33}$$

$$C_{Pf} = \frac{\overline{P_f}}{\frac{1}{2}\rho U^3 L^2} = C_{Pe}\left(\frac{b_f^2 - b_p^2}{b_L^2}\right) \tag{34}$$

The thrust and power caused by the vortex sheet interaction must be integrated along the body. These integrals can be easily done numerically once the body geometry $b(x)$ is specified. By taking $A(x) = \pi b^2(x)$ to vary linearly with x in the trailing edge and caudal fin region $x_f < x < L$, the integrals are evaluated and give the simple expressions.

$$C_{Ti} = \frac{C_{Te}}{\eta_e} \left(1 - \frac{b_p^2}{b_L^2}\right) \left[\frac{1}{2}\left(1 - \frac{U}{c}\right) - \frac{\sin \theta_*}{\theta_*}\right] \tag{35}$$

$$C_{Pi} = C_{Pe} \left(1 - \frac{b_p^2}{b_L^2}\right) \left(-\frac{\sin \theta_*}{\theta_*}\right) \tag{36}$$

where $\theta_* = \dfrac{L^*}{L} \sigma(1 - U/c)$ and $L^* = L - x_f$ and it has been assumed that the caudal fin reaches the same height as the dorsal fin and does not extend beyond this point ($b_f = b_L$).

Combining these results gives

$$C_T = C_{Te} \left[1 + \frac{1}{\eta_e}\left(1 - \frac{b_p^2}{b_L^2}\right)\left(1 - \frac{\sin \theta_*}{\theta_*}\right)\right] \tag{37}$$

$$C_{Ph} = C_{Pe} \left[1 + \left(1 - \frac{b_p^2}{b_L^2}\right)\left(1 - \frac{\sin \theta_*}{\theta_*}\right)\right] \tag{38}$$

and

$$\eta_h = \frac{C_T}{C_{Ph}} \tag{39}$$

where

$$\eta_e = \frac{C_{Te}}{C_{Pe}} = \frac{1}{2}\left(1 + \frac{U}{c}\right) \tag{40}$$

is the hydromechanic efficiency if there is no vortex sheet interaction. The thrust and power coefficients and the efficiency are all functions of the body or fin height at x_p and L, the reduced frequency σ, the amplitude of the body motion h_1/L, the ratio of forward speed to wave speed and the distance L_* between the body fins and the caudal fin.

The quantity $(1 - b_p^2/b_L^2)$ is greater than 0.75 for fish with tail fins more than twice the height of their caudal peduncle and typically is between 0.8 and 0.95. The dorsal and ventral fin morphology limit variations of L_*, and L_*/L is expected to be between 0.25 and 0.75 for most fish. The reduced frequency never falls below 7 at the fastest speeds and ranges to about twice this at slow swimming (Fig. 6-2). U/c approaches 1 at high speeds and is usually greater than 0.5 for speeds above one body length per second (Wu and Yates, 1978). For a given fish b_p, b_L, and $L*$ are fixed quantities, and variations in performance are determined by σ and U/c.

If the contribution from the body fins is included but the vortex sheet interaction is neglected, both the thrust and power are augmented by the factor $(2-b_p^2/b_L^2)$, and the efficiency remains unchanged ($\eta = \eta_e$). If the vortex sheet interaction is taken into account, the thrust and power are further increased and are given by equations 37 and 38 respectively. When typical values are substituted into these formulas, the thrust increases by nearly a factor of 2 and the power by a slightly smaller amount. The thrust always increases proportionally more than the power and thus gives an increased efficiency of about 10%, and η is found to be less sensitive to variations in the parameters.

Observation of rainbow trout by Webb (1971) can be used to estimate the power and thrust predicted by this hydrodynamic theory. The first column in Table 6-1 lists the relevant dimensional quantities that need to be recorded during the steady swimming. In the second column nondimensional quantities are found; these nondimensional parameters are particularly useful when comparing the performance of different fish or different experiments. The thrust, power, and efficiency are obtained by substituting into equations 37, 38, and 39 and are given in the third column. These results are expected to overpredict the thrust and power because the trout is not symmetric; vortex shedding may not occur continuously from the dorsal fin to the caudal peduncle, and the wave amplitude was assumed constant along the entire body length. Because these approximations tend to give overestimates, the thrust and power and should be regarded as upper bounds. Returning to the dimensional quantities

Table 6-1
SWIMMING PARAMETERS FOR TROUT, SALMO GAIRDNERI
(WEBB, 1975)

$U = 0.457$ m $\cdot$ sec^{-1}	$\sigma = \omega L/U = 14.0$	$C_{Te} = 0.0137$ (31)[b]
$L = 0.282$ m	$U/c = 0.59$	$C_{Pe} = 0.0172$ (33)[b]
$h_1 = 0.0215$ m	$\theta_* = \dfrac{L_*}{L}\sigma\left(1 - \dfrac{U}{c}\right) = 2.87$	$\eta_e = 0.80$ (40)[b]
$b_L = 0.0305$ m		$C_T = 0.0279$ (37)[b]
$f = 3.6$ Hz	$h_1/L = 0.076$	$C_{Ph} = 0.0314$ (38)[b]
$c = 0.77$ m $\cdot$ sec^{-1}	$A_L = \pi b_L^2/L^2 = 0.037$	$\eta_h = 0.89$ (39)[b]
$b_p/b_L = (0.30)$[a]	$\dfrac{b_L^2 - b_p^2}{b_L^2} = 0.91$	
$L_*/L = (0.50)$[a]	$Re = UL/v = 1.29 \times 10^5$	
$S = 0.03113$ m^2		

[a]not available (assumed value)
[b]equation used to evaluate coefficient

$$\overline{T} = 0.232 \text{ newtons}$$

$$\overline{P_h} = 0.119 \text{ watts}$$

It should be kept in mind that equations 31 to 39 and the results of Table 6-1 were obtained by assuming a very special shape of fish and does not necessarily represent swimming in nature. The swimming motion was chosen for convenience of the computation, to render simple formula, to identify the important parameters, and to investigate their influence on the results. For any given fish the thrust, power, and efficiencies should be computed from equations 25, 26, and 28, where the body motion $h(x,t)$ and shape $b(x)$ should be measured and used as input.

LARGE AMPLITUDE UNDULATORY PROPULSION

The results presented in the preceding section are restricted by the assumption of small lateral oscillations of the body; extension to large amplitude is considered in this section. Large amplitude theory may be applied to carangiform swimming where the tail-beat amplitude is large and may be used as a first attempt at isolating the reactive forces experienced during anguilliform swimming. The salient features of anguilliform locomotion are that the entire body is involved in the propulsion, and the amplitude of the lateral motion may be a significant proportion of the body length.

For large amplitude theory, the boundary conditions are very cumbersome when applied at $z = 0$ and are most conveniently prescribed in a local frame fixed on the body at each cross-section. Because of its unsteady translation and rotation, this frame is not inertial and care must be taken in the formulation. Lighthill (1971) dealt with the reference frame difficulties by extending his (1970) physical interpretation of the perturbation theory results. He used the Lagrangian description for the body motion and considered momentum conservation evaluated with a time-varying control volume of which the backward-facing surface moves and rotates with the fish tail. By replacing the factor V in the first term of equation 25 with the velocity of the fluid normal to the backbone V_n, Lighthill found the mean thrust

$$T = -m\left(\frac{1}{2}\overline{V_n V} - \overline{V_n \frac{\partial h}{\partial t}}\right)\bigg|_{x = L} \tag{41}$$

The mean rate of energy waste

$$\overline{E} = \frac{1}{2} m\overline{V_n^2 V_s}\bigg|_{x = L} \tag{42}$$

is modified by replacing V by V_n and U by V_s, where V_s is the fluid velocity tangent to the backbone. The overall energy balance (equation 27) gives the mean power consumption $\overline{P_h} = \overline{TU} + \overline{E}$. In the limit, as the lateral motions become small $V_n \simeq V$ and $V_s \simeq U$ and the results of the preceding section are recovered. Using experimental data, Lighthill applied his theory in a manner analogous to that done for elongated body theory and obtained similar results. The experimental variations in the data preclude a quantitative comparison of the theories, and his calculations are not repeated here.

Further extensions of large amplitude theory have been made to include the effects of body elasticity and centerline curvature. Katz and Weihs (1979) use a noninertial body frame of reference to find the sectional fluid forces. They include the effects of passive chordwise flexibility, determined by the time-dependent force balance on the body, which is assumed to be linearly elastic. By distributing flow singularities along the body centerline, Wu and Yates (1976) and Yates (1977) examine the motion of a slender body of circular cross-section performing a prescribed motion. The effects of body center-line curvature are thus brought out.

Application of the finite amplitude theory has been made to turning and fast-starting maneuvers. Lighthill's (1971) study was adapted by Weihs (1972) for turning, where the mean motion of the center of mass describes a curvilinear path. Contributions from upstream fins were obtained by indicial aerodynamic methods and added to the caudal fin contribution. A similar analysis was used by Weihs (1973) and applied to the investigation of an optimum shape for rapid starts. In both cases, comparison with observations seem in general agreement (Webb, 1978a and b).

ELONGATED MEDIAN-FIN PROPULSION

A variety of species accomplish propulsion by passing a wave along an elongated dorsal or ventral fin. The body is held straight, and a fin wave propagates posteriorly or anteriorly along the dorsal or ventral fin or both and thus propels the animal in the opposite direction. These modes of swimming are called *amiiform, gymnotiform,* or *balistiform* and are often seen among eels during slow maneuvering near the bottom or in crevices (further discussion of these modes is found in Chap. 7, by Blake). Modification of the elongated body theory is required for this type of movement; the function h describing the body motion must now include dependence on the distance of the dorsal and ventral fins from the body centerline. Because h is now a function of y, the lateral fluid velocity on the body surface, V, is also modified.

To see some of the essential contributions of this new degree of freedom, the special case of a constant amplitude wave times an integer power of y is considered.

$$h(x,y,t) = \left(\frac{y}{b_o}\right)^n H(x,t) \qquad n = 0, 1, 2, 3, \ldots \qquad (43)$$

where

$$H(x,t) = h_1 \cos k(x - ct)$$ (44)

and h_1 is a constant. This particular body motion (equation 43) may differ somewhat from observed body and fin movements and is used to simplify the mathematic analysis. The exact description of the motion can be used but requires the numerical evaluation of integrals that can be evaluated analytically for the motion given by equation 43. In contrast to the last two sections, in which the amplitude of the body motions generally increased along the body, the mode of swimming considered here is frequently characterized by a constant amplitude wave. The theory can be carried out for h_1 of the same order of magnitude as b_0, but the results presented here assume that h_1/b_0 is small. When $n = 0$, h is independent of y and the results of the section on elongated body theory are recovered.

The body is again assumed to have zero thickness and to be symmetric with the height given by the function $b(x)$. b is required to vanish at the nose and tail and is a monotonically increasing function from these two extremities to the position of the maximum height b_0 at x_0. The lateral fluid velocity can be written

$$V(x,y,t) = \left(\frac{y}{b_0}\right)^n W(x,t)$$ (45)

where

$$W(x,t) = h_1\omega\left(1 - \frac{U}{c}\right)\sin k(x - ct)$$ (46)

The slenderness assumption reduces the problem to finding the local velocities and presures for a two-dimensional cross flow of velocity V at each cross-section, and the solution procedure presented for elongated bodies follows when $V(x,t)$ is replaced by $V(x,y,t)$. This new dependence on y changes the force computation because the lateral forces must be obtained from an integral of the pressure at each cross-section.

The contribution to the mean thrust from the leading edge suction is

$$\overline{T_s}(x,t) = \frac{1}{2}\,\overline{W^2}\,\frac{d}{dx}\,(m_s) \qquad (0 < x < x_0)$$ (47)

where

$$m_s(x) = m_e(x)\left[1 + \frac{n(n+1)}{16}\left(\frac{b}{b_0}\right)^{2n-2}\left(\frac{h_1}{b_0}\right)^2\right]$$ (48)

$$m_e(x) = \rho\pi b^2 \, C_n\left(\frac{b}{b_0}\right)^{2n} \tag{49}$$

and

$$C_n = 1, \frac{1}{8}, \frac{1}{12}, \frac{9}{256}, \frac{9}{320}, \ldots \qquad n = 0, 1, 2, 3, 4, \ldots \tag{50}$$

$m_s(x)$ can be thought of as an effective added mass for the mean sectional thrust from leading edge suction. The pressure acting on the body surface also contributes to the mean sectional thrust

$$\overline{T_p}(x,t) = -\frac{d}{dx}\left[\left(\frac{1}{2}\,\overline{W^2} - \overline{W\frac{\partial H}{\partial t}}\right)m_p(x)\right] - \frac{1}{2}\,\overline{W^2}\,\frac{d}{dx}(m_s) \tag{51}$$

where

$$m_p(x) = m_e(x)\left[1 + \frac{n(n+1)}{16}\frac{\left(1 - \dfrac{U}{c}\right)}{\left(1 + \dfrac{U}{c}\right)}\left(\frac{b}{b_0}\right)^{2n-2}\left(\frac{h_1}{b_0}\right)^2\right] \tag{52}$$

The total mean thrust

$$\overline{T} = -m_p(x_0)\left[\frac{1}{2}\,\overline{W^2} - \overline{W\frac{\partial H}{\partial t}}\right]_{x_0} \tag{53}$$

or

$$C_T = \frac{m_p(x_0)}{m(x_0)}\,C_{Te}\bigg|_{x_0} \tag{54}$$

depends only on the flow quantities evaluated at x_0. C_{Te} is given by equation 31, and $m(x) = \rho\pi b^2(x)$. The total mean power is

$$\overline{P_h} = m_e(x_0)UW\frac{\overline{\partial H}}{\partial t}\bigg|_{x_0} \tag{55}$$

or

$$C_{Ph} = \frac{m_e(x_0)}{m(x_0)}\,C_{Pe}\bigg|_{x_o} \tag{56}$$

where C_{Pe} is given by equation 33. The efficiency is thus

$$\eta_h = \frac{U\overline{T}}{\overline{P}_h} = \eta_e \frac{m_p(x_0)}{m_e(x_0)} \tag{57}$$

where

$$\eta_e = \frac{1}{2}\left(1 + \frac{U}{c}\right) \tag{58}$$

is the same as equation 40.

In this example the effective added mass for thrust, power, and suction are all different. Over the range of values of U/c, $m_p(x)$ is always greater than $m_e(x)$ and less than $m_s(x)$ with m_p being equal to m_s when $U/c = 0$ and reducing to m_e for $U/c = 1$. The shape of the sectional fin motion (n in equation 43) plays a dominant role as evidenced by the drop of m_e by a factor of eight when n is changed from 0 to 1. Subsequent increases in n result in further reducing m_e as indicated by C_n (equation 50). The dramatic drop in m_e is offset somewhat by a modest increase in m_p and m_s with increasing n and by their quadratic dependence on h_1/b_0. As expected, this mode of propulsion produces less thrust and requires less power than do the classical results of the section on elongated body theory. This first order theory further indicates that the thrust is not reduced as much as the power and thus gives about a 5% increase in the propulsive efficiency.

Application of these formulas can be made to the swimming of an eel (*Gymnarchus niloticus*) using the observations of Blake (1980). Table 6-2 summarizes the results and Blake's data. The calculated C_T values using equation 54 are well below the rigid body C_D values measured by Blake, except when $n = 0$. This discrepancy can in part be expected because the theory is restricted to small amplitude fin motion; however, it is unlikely that this accounts for the entire difference. The vortex shedding and its interaction

Table 6.2
SWIMMING OF ELECTRIC FISH GYMNARCHUS NILOTICUS
(BLAKE, 1980)

$U = 0.171$ m $\cdot$ sec^{-1}	$h_1/L = 0.0223$	$C_{Te} = 0.0011$ (31)[b]
$c = 0.204$ m/sec	$h_1/b_0 = 0.268$	$C_{Pe} = 0.0012$ (33)[b]
$L = 0.30$ m	$\dfrac{A_o}{L^2} = \pi b_0^2/L^2 = 0.0218$	$\eta_e = 0.92$ (40)[b]
$h_1 = 0.0067$ m		
$b_0 = (0.025)$ m[a]	$U/c = 0.838$	
$f = 2.4$ Hz	$\sigma = \omega L/U = 26.5$	
$S = 0.0146$ m^2	Re $= UL/v = 5.13 \times 10^4$	

[a]not available (assumed value)
[b]equation used to evaluate coefficient

in the posterior portion of the animal may have an important influence that is yet to be investigated for this mode of propulsion.

Using actuator disk theory, Blake predicts the hydromechanical efficiency of this amiiform swimmer. He estimates the velocity increment in the wake of the fin, needed as input to the momentum theory he uses, by requiring the thrust to equal the measured dead drag. Blake obtains efficiencies below 71% in comparison to over 90% found using the current theory. There is a need for more detailed observations and further refinements of the theories to bring observations and predictions into finer focus.

LUNATE TAIL PROPULSION

There is a wide class of aquatic swimmers for which the assumptions of slender body theory no longer are expected to apply. Although the body itself remains long and thin and slender body theory is expected to be valid for the flow over the body, the caudal and pectoral fins are often at variance with the slenderness assumption. The commercially important tuna and the sport fish, marlin, and swordfish have caudal fins much higher than they are long. The caudal fins on these swimmers have a characteristic crescent-moon shape and are referred to as lunate tails. Many marine mammals including dolphins and whales have lunate tail flukes that are horizontal rather than vertical. For these swimmers the elongated body theory must be abandoned, and the propulsive appendage is usually considered independent of the rest of the body. In the simplest case, the local thrust production is estimated using two-dimensional wing theory. This assumption holds whenever the variations of the flow quantities along the span of the fin are small. To help quantify the two-dimensional nature of such fins, the aspect ratio $A_R = s^2 / S_t$ is introduced, where s is the span and S_t is the projected planform area of the fin. Two-dimensional theories ($A_R = \infty$) have been found to give good results, in some cases for wings with an aspect ratio as low as 4.

Hydrodynamic Forces

The time-dependent forces and moments acting on an infinitely long airfoil can be calculated using unsteady aerodynamics (Theodorsen, 1935; and von Kármán and Sears, 1938). Results using these theories have been given in the context of fish swimming by Lighthill (1970) and Wu (1971a and b).

Three-dimensional aspects of oscillating hydrofoils have been investigated with special reference to aquatic swimmers, and the method used to evaluate the flow are somewhat varied and lead to some differences in the thrust and efficiency estimates. Chopra (1974) used the superposition of periodic, lifting ribbons of infinite span to calculate the performance of rigid rectangular wings undergoing general heave and pitch. The case of large amplitude harmonic oscillation was treated later by Chopra (1976) with an impulse approach, and Chopra and Kambe (1977) used unsteady lifting-surface theory to obtain numerical results for a variety of rigid, swept back wings. Lan (1979) used a *quasi-vortex lattice* method for rectangular wings.

Using an asymptotic method, Cheng (1975) looked at an unsteady lifting-line theory for a wing with curved or swept planform in harmonic oscillation and identified various frequency domains for the influence of unsteadiness on the induced downwash. His analysis is extended by Cheng and Murillo (1982) to account for a broader range of reduced frequencies. Recently, Ahmadi (1980) used linearized unsteady lifting-line theory to calculate the flow about three-dimensional large aspect ratio wings. Ahmadi also investigated the optimum motion of large aspect-ratio wings in heaving and pitching. Inclusion of chordwise flexibility with large amplitude motions was treated by Katz and Weihs (1978). A brief look at these theories gives a helpful understanding of the pertinent parameters on which the thrust and power depend.

Taking a frame of reference moving with speed (U) in the negative x direction, parallel to the mean direction of swimming, the position of any point on the undulating fin can be specified by

$$z = h_1 \cos \omega t - \alpha(x - b)\cos(\omega t + \alpha_{ph}) \qquad \left(-\frac{1}{2} < \frac{x}{C} < \frac{1}{2}\right) \qquad (59)$$

where h_1 is the amplitude of heave, α the amplitude of pitch, b the pitching axis, α_{ph} the phase lead of the pitch relative to the heave, C the wing chord, and ω the radian frequency of the motion. Lighthill (1969) introduced the proportional feathering parameter

$$\theta = \frac{U\alpha}{\omega h_1} \qquad (60)$$

For small amplitude motions, θ is the ratio of the maximum angle (α) the wing makes with the direction of motion and the maximum angle ($\omega h_1 / U$) achieved by the trajectory in space of the pitching axis. For the case of pure heaving motion, $\alpha = 0$ and hence $\theta = 0$. When $\theta = 1$, the wing is always tangent to the trajectory of the pitching axis $x = b$, and the motion is termed *perfect feathering*. In most of these models the phase difference between heaving and pitching is taken as 90 degrees (Lighthill, 1970), and b is taken near the trailing edge. The reduced frequency $\sigma = \omega C / U$ is based on the chord C of the lunate tail. The motion is then fully described by specification of the σ, θ, and h_1.

The various theories have been compared by Ahmadi (1980) and Lan (1978). Ahmadi (1980) finds his method predicts a higher thrust than did Chopra and Kambe (1977), while Lan (1978) finds a 20% lower thrust at high reduced frequencies than did Chopra and Kambe (1977). The efficiency predicted by all three models is in better agreement and varies by only a few percent. Detailed expositions of these methods can be found in the literature, and they generally require some numerical computation. Typical results are taken from Chopra and Kambe (1977) for a wing with $A_R = 8$ and $\alpha_{ph} = 90$ degrees pitching about the trailing edge of the wing at the center and are shown in Figure 6.5.

For the small amplitude theory, the thrust depends on the square of the heaving amplitude, and thus h_1/C is included in the thrust coefficient

$$C_T = \frac{\overline{T}}{\frac{1}{2}\rho U^2 S_t \left(\frac{h_1}{C}\right)^2} \qquad (61)$$

Example Application

Some observations on lunate tail swimmers are available and can be used to estimate thrust and efficiency predicted by these theories. Several relevant

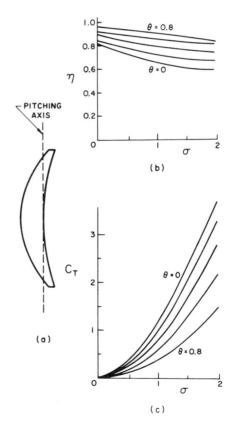

Figure 6–5
The lunate tail planform ($A_R = 8$) is illustrated in (a) with the leading edge to the left and the pitching axis indicated. The efficiency (b) and the thrust (c) are shown for this wing undergoing heaving and pitching with a phase difference of 90 degrees and for values of the feathering parameter in increments of 0.2 between 0 and 0.8. (Adapted from Chopra and Kambe, 1977).

quantities are not reported and are assigned reasonable values based on typical numbers for the particular animal in question. The example is worked with the intent of illustrating the type of data needed and the procedure used in estimating C_T and η, and use of the numerical values should await more refined measurements.

Two sets of data are presented in Table 6-3: the first, for the porpoise (*Lagenorhyncus obliquidens*), is taken from Lang and Daybell (1963); the second, for kawakawa (*Euthynnus affinis*), is taken from Fierstine and Walters (1968) as given by Magnuson (1978). The first column of Table 6-3 contains the observed parameters in their dimensional form, and the second column lists the important nondimensional parameters. The thrust and efficiency are read from Figure 6-5 using the prescribed values of σ and θ.

Figure 6-5 is computed for a wing of aspect ratio 8 and for small amplitude motion. Both these assumptions are in variance with the data, and some explanation of their application is needed. Using the results of Chopra (1976) for large-amplitude motion of an infinitely long, flat plate, Chopra and Kambe (1977) justify the use of their infinitesimal theory up to amplitudes of $h/C = 2$. The effects of aspect ratio indicates that the C_T and η values given in Table 6-3 are overestimations. Neglecting the body will enhance the leading edge suction and should result in further increasing thrust. Thus the values of Table 6-3 should be regarded as upper bounds.

Pitching Axis and Heave-Pitch Phase

For the motion described by equation 59, one of the quantities h_1, α, b, or α_{ph} can be chosen arbitrarily (as long as α does not vanish). Having chosen

Table 6-3
LUNATE TAIL PROPULSION

	PORPOISE[b] (LAGENO- RHYNCHUS OBLIQUIDENS)	KAWAKAWA (EUTHYN- NUS AFFINIS)		POR- POISE[b]	KAWA[c]
U(m · sec^{-1})	5.18	1.88	$A_R = s^2/S_t$	5.5	6.5
L(m)	2.0	0.40	$Re = UL/v$	1.04×10^7	7.52×10^5
C(m)	0.20	0.019	$R_c = UC/v$	1.04×10^6	3.57×10^4
h_1(m)	0.25	0.040	h_1/C	1.25	2.11
s(m)	(0.66)[a]	0.70	$\sigma = \omega C/U$	0.68	0.79
α(radians)	(0.66)[a]	0.70	$\theta = U\alpha/\omega h_1$	0.78	0.42
S_t(m^2)	0.049	2.2×10^{-3}			
S(m^2)	1.56	0.072	C_T (Fig. 6-5c)	0.23	0.50
f(Hz)	2.8	12.5	η (Fig. 6-5b)	0.92	0.80
b/C	(1)[a]	(1)[a]			
α_{ph} (degrees)	(90)[a]	(90)[a]			

[a]not available (assumed value)
[b]Lang and Daybell (1963)
[c]Fierstine and Walters (1968) per Magnuson (1978)

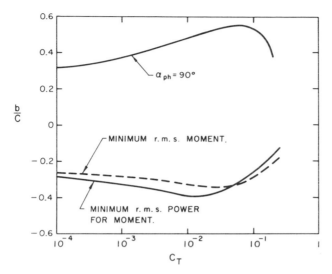

Figure 6-6
The pitching axis b/C that gives a minimum root mean square moment or power for producing moment about the pitching axis is shown as a function of the wing loading. Motion of the wing is taken from the optimum solution of Wu (1971) at minimum leading edge suction (Fig. 6-7).

one, the others can be adjusted to maintain the prescribed motion. Since $\alpha_{ph} =$ 90 degrees is the only possible value of α_{ph} for which perfect feathering can be achieved, Lighthill (1970) and most investigators have taken $\alpha_{ph} = 90$ degrees as a starting point. Lan (1979) shows that the efficiency and thrust are both sensitive to α_{ph}, and the highest efficiency for a fixed pitching axis near the trailing edge of the wing occurs near $\alpha_{ph} = 90$ degrees. Taking $\alpha_{ph} = 90$ degrees, Wu (1971b) found the pitching axis to move aft of the half chord toward the trailing edge as the wing loading increases (Fig. 6-6). These results support Lighthill's (1970) suggestion that the pitching axis should be placed near the three-quarter chord position.

On the other hand, if high thrust is to be achieved, perfect feathering is not expected, and α_{ph} may differ from 90 degrees. Attempting to make the choice of α_{ph} more quantitative, a re-examination of the criteria for locating the pitching axis is undertaken. Large excursions of α_{ph} from 90 degrees, however, are not permitted because they would result in separated flow and reduced performance. Rather than choose α_{ph}, we will consider several criteria for the selection of the pitching axis b. If α_{ph} or b are not chosen arbitrarily, an additional condition must be specified. The fish musculature is especially well adapted for creating forceful undulations of the tail, and the major portion of the power for propulsion is expected to be provided by the heaving motion. Keeping the power for pitching small, the fish may minimize the effort needed to vary the pitching angle of the tail and hence permit easier control of the swimming motion and enhance maneuverability. It thus seems reasonable to investigate the root mean square of the moment about b and the root mean square of that part of the power that goes toward producing moment about the pitching axis.

The optimum motion of a wing described by Wu (1971) is taken as a prescribed motion. This optimum solution is obtained by minimizing the energy wasted in the wake while maintaining a constant thrust. Wu finds the leading edge suction force to have a minimum for any given loading at $\sigma = \sigma_m$ and grows rapidly as σ varies from σ_m. Because large suction forces suggest the likely occurrence of flow separation from the leading edge, the discussion is confined to $\sigma = \sigma_m$.

Using the optimum motion of Wu (1971) at $\sigma = \sigma_m$ and requiring the mean square power used to produce moment to be minimum gives a pitching axis near the quarter chord position (Fig. 6-6). For lightly loaded wings, the reduced frequency σ_m goes to zero (Fig. 6-7), and the pitching axis approaches the quarter chord position as expected from quasisteady theory. As the loading increases the pitching axis moves forward to about the one eighth chord and then moves rearward as the loading increases further. Similar results are obtained if the root mean square of the moment about the pitching axis is minimized (dashed curve in Fig. 6-6).

It should be noted that the thrust coefficient C_T in Figures 6-6 and 6-7 was derived from strip theory and is thus the thrust per unit span. By replacing S_t with $4\pi C$ in equation 61, the appropriate nondimensionalized form of C_T is

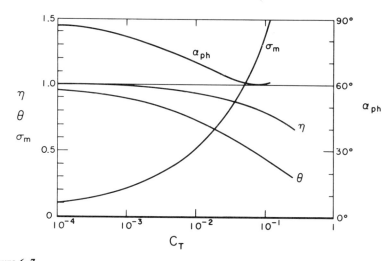

Figure 6-7
For the optimum motion of Wu (1971), the efficiency η and the reduced frequency σ_m at the minimum leading edge suction are plotted against the wing loading. The feathering parameter θ and heave-pitch phase α_{ph} are shown for the pitching axis, which minimizes the power for producing moment.

obtained. Once the pitching axis has been chosen, α_{ph} and θ are determined and are shown in Figure 6-7 for the power for producing moment being minimized. As expected, α_{ph} does not vary greatly from 90 degrees, with the largest difference being about 30 degrees at heavy loading (at the minimum leading edge suction) and poor feathering.

This new look at the pitching axis and heave-pitch phase difference has important morphologic implications not only for fish but for any heave-pitch mode of propulsion. Some support of this new interpretation is offered in that birds have their wing bones positioned near the leading edge of their wings. Control of pitch of the fins of fish, however, is a more complex problem because the muscle groups responsible for controlling pitch and those for producing heave are not clearly distinguished. Observations and measurements aimed at isolating the moment and separating the power into its constituent parts for force and moment warrants further attention in light of this discussion.

SWIMMING POWER AND DRAG

The great difficulties in directly measuring the drag a fish must overcome in swimming forced many early researchers to assume that it is comparable to the drag on an equivalent stretched-straight body (see Chap. 1). Although this assumption leaves considerable room for caution, many attempts have been made to measure the viscous drag of either a mechanical model or a paralyzed fish in steady flow in wind or water tunnels, towing tanks, or water tanks for drop-down tests. Another approach has been to observe the retardation of a fish in glide (for reviews see Gray, 1968; Newman and Wu, 1975; Webb, 1975). Generally speaking, the measured values of the drag coefficient C_D show wide scatter over a range of a few times to tens of times the drag coefficient for turbulent drag on a flat plate at the same Reynolds number; however, some reports (Lang and Daybell, 1963; Webb 1975) indicate that the measured drag is close to that of an equivalent mechanical model predicted by boundary layer theory. Magnuson (1978) has more appropriately and creditably isolated and combined the components of drag on the body and the fins caused by skin friction, form drag, and induced drag. The differences between various results can be attributed to the difficulties in performing such experiments.

In view of the uncertainty associated with direct drag measurements, it is useful to take advantage of the energy balance $C_D = \eta C_P$ (equation 8) discussed under the momentum and energy section. The power input can be determined by measuring the animal's oxygen consumption and by applying standard energy conversion factors. If the standard metabolic rate is subtracted from the measured metabolic rate during active swimming, the power for swimming activities is appropriately identified. Using data collected by Brett (1965a and b) and taking $\overline{P}$ in equation 9 as the metabolic rate for swimming, C_P can be plotted as a function of Re (Fig. 6-8). Including both the muscle and mechanical efficiency in the overall efficiency $\eta = \eta_m\eta_h$, an estimate of the propulsive drag can be made. A typical value of $\eta = 0.2$ would place the estimated C_D line at the maximum activity (not shown in Fig. 6-8) quite close to the turbulent C_D line for a smooth flat plate.

The range of velocities for which this comparison is appropriate is limited by the accuracy with which the oxygen consumption for swimming can be identified. For very slow speeds, C_D is expected to become increasingly smaller than ηC_P owing to possible consumption of power for nonswimming purposes (*e.g.*, maneuvering). At higher burst speeds, the actual biochemical

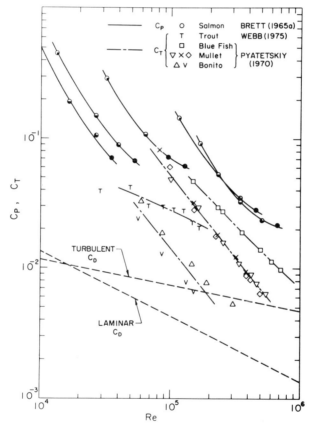

Figure 6-8

Scale effects in the variation of the measured metabolic power coefficient (for swimming) with Reynolds number for five different size groups of sockeye salmon (Brett, 1965a). Solid lines show variation of C_P with various activity levels for each size group. Dash-dot lines illustrate theoretical thrust coefficient C_T computed from equation 62. The drag coefficients of a flat plate for both laminar and turbulent boundary layers are shown for reference (Adapted from Wu and Yates, 1978).

power supplied for muscular activities is recognized to be higher than that measured from the oxygen consumption because most energy is provided by depletion of energy reserve in the anaerobic muscle. It seems reasonable to expect that the corresponding drag coefficient at these higher frequencies of body undulation would increase with increasing speed. The result of this analysis appears to place the slopes of the C_P curves closer to the slopes of the two reference lines in Figure 6-8 for laminar and turbulent C_D of a smooth flat plate.

It is interesting to compare the estimated drag with the theoretically predicted thrust. By elongated body theory (as cited earlier), the mean thrust coefficient has the following approximate expression

$$C_T = \frac{\overline{T_e}}{\frac{1}{2}\rho U^2 S} = \frac{1}{2}\pi\sigma^2 \left(\frac{h_1}{L}\right)^2 \frac{b_L^2}{S} \left(1 - \frac{U^2}{c^2}\right) \tag{62}$$

where $\overline{T_e}$ is taken from equation 31. By making use of the observed data of Pyatetskiy (1970) and Webb (1975) on these quantities, the resulting theoretical values of C_T are plotted versus Re in Figure 6-8 for four groups of fish. The slopes of these C_T lines based on Pyatetskiy's data are qualitatively similar to those of estimated C_P curves derived from Brett's results for sockeye salmon, even though the species do not match and no information about the activity level is available in Pyatetskiy's work. The predicted C_T values are quite comparable to the estimated C_D, albeit no quantitative comparison can be made at this time. Nevertheless, these qualitative results have already made possible the perspective that a consistent explanation is taking hold for a possible, even plausible, account of the power required and power available.

Acknowledgments

I am indebted to Professor T. Y. Wu for his encouragement and discussions throughout this work. The assistance of Dr. Y. X. Su is also recognized especially regarding his work on the vortex sheet interaction between body and caudal fins. The review of this work by Professor S. Corrsin is greatly appreciated. The support of the National Science Foundation Grants CME-77-21236 and PCM-8013473 and Office of Naval Research Contract N00014-76-C-0157 are gratefully acknowledged.

REFERENCES

Ahmadi, A.R. 1980. An asymptotic unsteady lifting-line theory with energetics and optimum motion of thrust-producing lifting surfaces. MIT, Department of Aeronautics and Astronautics Fluid Dynamics Research Laboratory Report 80.2.

Bainbridge, R. 1958. The speed of swimming fish as related to size and to the frequency and amplitude of the tail beat. *J. Exp. Biol.* 35:109–133.

Batchelor, G.K. 1967. *An Introduction to Fluid Dynamics.* Cambridge: Cambridge University Press.

Batty, R.S. 1981. Locomotion of plaice larvae. *Symp. Zool. Soc. Lond.* 84:53-69.

Beamish, F.W.H. 1978. Swimming capacity. In *Fish physiology, vol. VII Locomotion,* edited by W.S. Hoar and D.J. Randall, 101-187. New York: Academic Press.

Blake, R.W. 1980. Undulatory median fin propulsion of two teleosts with different modes of life. *Can. J. Zool.* 58:2116-2119.

Breder, C.M. 1926. The locomotion of fishes. *Zoologica, N.Y.* 4:159-256.

Brett, J.R. 1965a. The relation of size to the rate of oxygen consumption and sustained swimming speeds of sockeye salmon (*Oncorhynchus nerka*). *J. Fish. Res. Board Can.* 22:1491-1501.

Brett, J.R. 1965b. The swimming energetics of salmon. *Sci. Am.* 213:80-85.

Brett, J.R. 1967. Swimming performance of sockeye salmon (*Oncorhynchus nerka*) in relation to fatigue time and temperature. *J. Fish. Res. Board Can.* 24:1731-1741.

Cheng, H.K. 1975. On lifting-line theory in unsteady aerodynamics. In *Unsteady Aerodynamics,* edited by R.B. Kinney, 719-739. Proceedings of a Symposium held at the Univ. of Arizona, March 18-20.

Cheng, H.K., and Murillo, L.E. 1982. Lunate-tail swimming propulsion as a problem of curved lifting line in unsteady flow: 1. Asymptotic theory. University Southern California School Engineering, Department Aerospace Engineering, Report USCAE 139.

Chopra, M.G. 1974. Hydromechanics of lunate-tail swimming propulsion. *J. Fluid Mech.* 64:375-391.

Chopra, M.G. 1976. Large amplitude lunate-tail theory of fish locomotion. *J. Fluid Mech.* 74:161-182.

Chopra, M.G., and Kambe, T. 1977. Hydromechanics of lunate-tail swimming propulsion, Part 2. *J. Fluid Mech.* 79:49-60.

Fierstine, H.L., and Walters, V. 1968. Studies in locomotion and anatomy of scombroid fishes. *Mem. South. Calif. Acad. Sci.* 6:1-31.

Goldspink, G. 1977. Muscle energetics and animal locomotion. In *Mechanics and Energetics of Animal Locomotion,* edited by R. McN. Alexander and G. Goldspink. Chapman and Hall.

Gray, J. 1968. *Animal Locomotion.* London: Weidenfeld and Nicolson.

Hoar, W.S., and Randall, D.J. 1978. *Fish Physiology Vol. VII Locomotion.* New York: Academic Press

Hunter, J.R. 1971. Sustained speed of jack mackerel, *Trachurus symmetricus. Fish. Bull.* 69:267-271.

Hunter, J.R., and Zweifel, J.R. 1971. Swimming speed, tail beat frequency, tail beat amplitude and size in jack mackerel, *Trachurus symmetricus,* and other fishes. *Fish. Bull.* 69:253-266.

Katz, J., and Weihs, D. 1978. Hydrodynamic propulsion by large amplitude oscillation of an airfoil with chordwise flexibility. *J. Fluid Mech.* 88:485-497.

Katz, J., and Weihs, D. 1979. Large amplitude unsteady motion of a flexible slender propulsor. *J. Fluid Mech.* 90(4):713-723.

Lan, C.E. 1979. The unsteady quasi-vortex-lattice method with applications to animal propulsion. *J. Fluid Mech.* 93:747-765.

Lang, T.G., and Daybell, D.A. 1963. Porpoise performance tests in a sea-water tank. NAVWEPS Report 8060; NOTS TP 3063.

Lighthill, M.J. 1960. Note on the swimming of slender fish. *J. Fluid Mech.* 9:305–317.

Lighthill, M.J. 1969. Hydromechanics of aquatic animal propulsion—a survey. *Annu. Rev. Fluid Mech.* 1:413–446.

Lighthill, M.J. 1970. Aquatic animal propulsion of high hydromechanical efficiency. *J. Fluid Mech.* 44:265–301.

Lighthill, M.J. 1971. Large-amplitude elongated-body theory of fish locomotion. *Proc. R. Soc. Lond.* 179B:125–138.

Lighthill, M.J. 1973. Scaling problems in aquatic locomotion. Symposium at Duke University, Durham, North Carolina (unpublished).

McCutchen, C.W. 1976. Flow visualization with stereo shadowgraphs of stratified fluid. *J. Exp. Biol.* 65:11–20.

Magnuson, J.J. 1970. Hydrostatic equilibrium of *Euthynnus affinis*, a pelagic teleost without a gas bladder. *Copeia* 1970:56–85.

Magnuson, J.J. 1973. Comparative study of adaptations for continuous swimming and hydrostatic equilibrium of scombroid and xiphoid fishes. *Fish. Bull.* 71:337–356.

Magnuson, J.J. 1978. Locomotion by scombroid fishes: hydromechanics, morphology, and behavior. In *Fish Physiology VII Locomotion,* edited by W.S. Hoar and D.J. Randall, 239–313. New York: Academic Press.

Magnuson, J.J., and Prescott, J.H. 1966. Courtship feeding and miscellaneous behavior of Pacific bonito (*Sarda chiliensis*). *Animal Behav.* 14:54–67.

Newman, J.N., and Wu, T.Y. 1973. A generalized slender-body theory for fish-like forms. *J. Fluid Mech.* 57:673–693.

Newman, J.N., and Wu, T.Y. 1975. Hydromechanical aspects of fish swimming. In *Swimming and Flying in Nature,* edited by T.Y. Wu, C.J. Brokaw, and C. Brennen, 615–634. New York: Plenum Press.

Pyatetskiy, V.Y. 1970. Kinematic swimming characteristics of some fast marine fish. *Bionika* 4:11–20. (Translation from Russian, Hydrodynamic Problems of Bionics 4:12–23 JPRS 52605, 1971, NTIS.)

Taylor, G.I. 1952. Analysis of the swimming of long and narrow animals. *Proc. R. Soc. Lond.* 214A:158–183.

Theodorsen, T. 1935. General theory of aerodynamic instability and the mechanism of flutter. NACA Rep. 496.

Videler, J.J., and Wardle, C.S. 1978. New kinematic data from high speed cine film recordings of swimming cod (*Gadus morhua*). *Neth. J. Zool.* 28:465–484.

von Karman, T., and Sears, W.R. 1938. Airfoil theory for nonuniform motion. *J. Aeronaut. Sci.* 5:379–390.

Wardle, C.S. 1975. Limit of fish swimming speed. *Nature* 255:725–727.

Webb, P.W. 1971. The swimming energetics of trout. I. Thrust and power output at cruising. *J. Exp. Biol.* 55:489–520.

Webb, P.W. 1973. Effects of partial caudal-fin amputation on the kinematics and metabolic rate of under-yearling sockeye salmon. (*Oncorhynchus nerka*) at steady swimming speed. *J. Exp. Biol.* 59:565–581.

Webb, P.W. 1975. Hydrodynamics and energetics of fish propulsion. *Bull. Fish. Res. Board Can.* 190:1–158.

Webb, P.W. 1978a. Fast start performance and body form in seven species of teleost fish. *J. Exp. Biol.* 74:211–226.

Webb, P.W. 1978b. Hydrodynamics: Nonscombroid fish. In *Fish Physiology, vol. VII Locomotion,* edited by: W.S. Hoar and D.J. Randall, 189–237. New York: Academic Press.

Weihs, D. 1972. A hydrodynamical analysis of fish turning manoeuvres. *Proc. R. Soc. Lond.* 182B:59–72.

Weihs, D. 1973. The mechanism of rapid starting of slender fish. *Biorheology* 10:343–350.

Wu, T.Y. 1961. Swimming of a waving plate. *J. Fluid Mech.* 10:321–344.

Wu, T.Y. 1971a. Hydromechanics of swimming propulsion. Part 1. Swimming of a two-dimensional flexible plate at variable forward speeds in an inviscid fluid. *J. Fluid Mech.* 46:337–355.

Wu, T.Y. 1971b. Hydromechanics of swimming propulsion. Part 2. Some optimum shape problems. *J. Fluid Mech.* 46:521–544.

Wu, T.Y. 1971c. Hydromechanics of swimming propulsion. Part 3. Swimming and optimum movements of slender fish with side fins. *J. Fluid Mech.* 46:545–568.

Wu, T.Y., and Yates, G.T. 1976. Finite amplitude unsteady slender body flow theory. *Proc. 11th ONR Symp. Naval Hydrodynam. Lond.,* 517–528.

Wu, T.Y., and Yates, G.T. 1978. A comparative mechanophysiological study of fish locomotion with implications for tuna-like swimming mode. In *The Physiological Ecology of Tunas,* edited by G.D. Sharp and A.E. Dizon. New York: Academic Press.

Yates, G.T. 1977. Finite amplitude unsteady slender body theory and experiments. Ph.D. Thesis, California Institute of Technology, Pasadena.

Yih, C.S. 1977. *Fluid Mechanics. A Concise Introduction to the Theory.* Ann Arbor, MI: West River Press.

SYMBOLS

A, A_L	area of circle circumscribing the body cross section	C_D	mean drag coefficient
		C_n	constant
A_R	aspect ratio	$C_T, C_{Te}, C_{Tf}, C_{Ti}, C_{To}$	mean thrust coefficient
a, a_L	acceleration		
$b, b_0, b_1, b_2, b_f, b_p, b_L$	dorso-ventral body height	$C_p, C_{Pe}, C_{Pf}, C_{Ph}, C_{Pi}$	mean power coefficient
b	pitching axis	c	wave speed (of propulsive wave)
C	fin chord	D	viscous drag

$D = \left(\dfrac{\partial}{\partial t} + U\dfrac{\partial}{\partial x}\right)$ linear differential operator (total time derivative

D_L lateral viscous drag

E rate of energy loss in the wake

f frequency

g body thickness

H, h, h_0, h_1 amplitude of lateral movements

k wave number

L fish length

$L.$ dorsal-caudal fin separation

L_n, L_a, L_f, L_c section lateral force

m, m_e, m_p, m_s mass of the fish; added mass

n integer

P, P_e, P_f, P_h, P_i power

Re Reynolds number

S wetted surface area

S_t projected planform area

s fin span

T, T_e, T_f, T_i, T_s thrust force

T_L lateral inertial force

t time

$t.$ retarded time

U mean forward swimming speed

$V, V_n, V.$ lateral fluid velocity

V_s fluid velocity tangent to the backbone

W lateral fluid velocity

$x, x_f, x_p, x_o, x.$ position along the fish body

x, y, z spatial coordinates

α amplitude of pitch

α_{ph} pitch-heave phase difference

β coefficient (body thickness effect on the sectional added mass)

$\eta, \eta_e, \eta_h, \eta_m$ efficiency

θ proportional feathering parameter

$\theta.$ parameter (vortex interaction)

λ wave length (of propulsive wave)

υ kinematic viscosity

ρ fluid density

σ, σ_m reduced frequency

ω radian frequency

Chapter 7

MEDIAN AND PAIRED FIN PROPULSION

Robert W. Blake

CONTENTS

INTRODUCTION

The hydromechanics and energetics of fish propelled by undulations of the body and caudal fin are now relatively well understood (see Chap. 6). In contrast, little is known about median and paired fin mechanisms of propulsion, a subject that has only recently been approached using modern methods, and it could be argued that it is rather early to attempt a review of our knowledge in this area. The main purpose of this account is to draw attention to an interesting area for research and to outline some of the approaches that have proved effective so far.

A basic distinction is made between forms propelled by undulatory fins and those propelled by oscillatory fins. The kinematics of swimming in both groups is discussed, and hydromechanical models are outlined. Undulatory fin swimming is discussed in terms of actuator-disc theory and elongated body theory. Oscillatory fin swimming can be divided into two groups on hydromechanical grounds: drag-based swimming and lift-based swimming. A blade-element theory of drag-based propulsion is outlined, a simplified form of which is used in considering the influence of fin shape on pectoral fin rowing. Lift-based pectoral fin propulsion is also analyzed with a blade-element theory. Applications of each of the models are discussed with particular reference to the functional morphology, behavior, and ecology of the forms concerned.

In a general discussion, speed, acceleration, maneuverability, streamlining, and drag in forms propelled by median and paired fins are compared to fish that are propelled by flexure of the body and caudal fin.

OCCURRENCE OF MEDIAN AND PAIRED FIN PROPULSION

Most bony fish swim by means of median and paired fin propulsion at low speeds. Some groups are specialized and use these methods for all of their routine swimming. Four major suborders of marine teleosts are propelled by the action of undulatory median and paired fins: the Balistoidei (triggerfishes, filefishes, tripodfishes), Ostraciodei (boxfishes, cowfishes, trunkfishes), Tetraodontoidei (puffers, porcupine fishes), and Synathoidei (seahorses and pipefishes). The Balistoidei, Ostraciodei, and Tetraodontoidei are coral reef fish, while the Synathoidei inhabit grassy undersea meadows. Of these groups, only the Tetraodontoidei have freshwater representatives (*e.g., Tetraodon fluviatilis*). The Gymnotoidei (electric eels) and Notopteroidei (knifefishes) are the major groups of freshwater undulatory fin swimmers.

Pectoral fin rowing is common among the families Chaetodontidae (*e.g.,* angelfish), Serranidae (*e.g.,* groupers), Scaridae (*e.g.,* parrotfishes), Scorpididae, and Cichlidae. Many of these forms are coral reef fish and inhabit similar niches to those occupied by the undulatory fin swimmers. Most fish that are propelled by the rowing action of pectoral fins are characterized by extreme lateral compression and a fin base that subtends a high angle to the horizontal.

Lift-based propulsion occurs among the suborders Acanthuroidei (tangs, surgeon fishes, unicorns) and Siganoidei (spinefeet, rabbitfishes), and families Labridae (wrasses), Chaetodontidae (*e.g.,* butterflyfishes), Histiopteridae (*e.g.,* boarfish), and Embiotocidae (surf perch). Among the Holocephali, the ratfish (*Hydrolagus*) is propelled by the lifting action of its pectoral fins. Many fish that swim in the lift-based mode are strongly laterally compressed coral reef forms that are characterized by high aspect-ratio fins and a pectoral fin-base that subtends a small angle relative to the horizontal.

KINEMATICS

Undulatory Mechanisms

Breder (1926) originally classified undulatory fin forms on the basis of the number and location of fins that are active. This classification has been reviewed recently by Lindsey (1978), to which the reader is referred for detail.

Breder's classification can be criticized for its lack of any functional basis; instead, a simple classification is suggested based on fin kinematics:

> *Group 1*—Forms that show wave forms of relatively high amplitude, low frequency, and large wavelength (*e.g.,* Tetraodontidae, Diodontidae, Ostraciidae, Gymnarchidae, and some Balistidae)
>
> *Group 2*—Forms with undulatory fins of low amplitude, high frequency, and small wavelength (*e.g.,* Synathidae, Aluteridae, Canthigasteridae, and some Balistidae)

The hydromechanical significance of the two different kinematic styles is discussed in the following section. It should be noted, however, that the above classification identifies the extremes of what may be viewed as a continuum of possible fin motions.

Blake (1977, 1978, 1979c and d, 1980b) has recorded kinematic data from a variety of group-1 forms, including the mandarin fish, *Synchiropus picturatus* (Callionyiidae), *Lactoria cornuta,* and *Tetrasomus gibbosus* (Ostraciidae); and *Odonus niger* (Balistidae). In all of the forms examined, wave-form frequency increased linearly with increasing swimming speed, above speeds of about 1.0 to 1.5 lengths $\cdot$ sec^{-1} (Fig. 7-1). The amplitude of the wave forms is highly variable at low speeds for undulatory fin swimmers; wavelength tends to remain more or less constant over a large range of swimming speeds.

The seahorse (*Hippocampus*) falls into group 2 of the kinematic classification; it is propelled by the action of its dorsal fin. Fin kinematics of the seahorse have been described by Breder and Edgerton (1942) and Blake (1976, 1980b). Breder and Edgerton (1942) recorded a wave-form frequency of 35 Hz for a slow upward movement in *Hippocampus hudsonius*; the phase difference between the dorsal fin rays was about 17 degrees. Blake (1976) observed a frequency of about 32 Hz for a specimen of the same species (length = 12 cm) swimming at about 0.5 lengths $\cdot$ sec^{-1}. The dorsal fin kinematics of *Hippocampus* have been compared with those of *Gymnarchus*, a group-1 form. Mean specific wavelength (mean wavelength of the wave form present on the fin divided by the length of the fin base) was about 75% greater in *Gymnarchus* (0.51) than in *Hippocampus* (0.29). At a similar steady swimming speed (about 16.0 cm $\cdot$ sec^{-1}), wave-form frequency was approximately 41 Hz and 2.5 Hz for *Hippocampus* and *Gymnarchus*, respectively (Blake, 1980b)

Turning maneuvers have been described in a variety of undulatory fin swimmers (*e.g.,* Blake, 1976, 1977, 1978). Many teleosts that are propelled by the undulatory motions of their fins are encased in a protective armor (*e.g.,* Synathidae, Ostraciidae). Consequently, turns cannot be initiated by movements of the body as they are in fish that swim in the carangiform modes (see Weihs, 1972 for an account of turning maneuvers in carangiform swimmers).

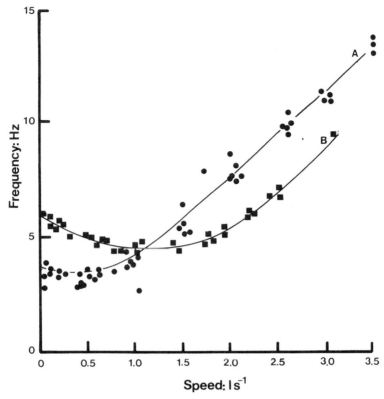

Figure 7-1
Fin-beat frequency is plotted against swimming speed for the dorsal fin of *Rhinecanthus aculeatus* (*A*) and the pectoral fins of *Cymatogaster aggregata* (*B*). (Data from Webb, 1973 and Blake, 1978)

In the seahorse and trunk fishes, the short-based median fins are able to change their long axes relative to that of the body, and parts of the fins may move relative to others. Blake (1976) describes a 180-degree turn to the left in *Hippocampus*, in which the posterior part of the dorsal fin progressively bends to the right until about two-thirds of the length of the fin was deflected. Similar results were found for *Lactoria cornuta* and *Tetrasomus gibbosus* (Blake, 1977).

Oscillatory Mechanisms

Pectoral fin rowing in the angelfish (*Pterophyllum eimekei*) is described by Blake (1979a and b, 1980a). The pectoral fins are the only fins active in steady forward swimming. There is a power stroke when the fins are oriented "broadside on" to the flow at a high geometric angle of attack. The phase difference between the most dorsal and ventral fin rays is small, and the fins rotate as a unit about their base. At the end of the power stroke the fins are "feathered" and move forward. The product of frequency and amplitude is linearly related to speed. At high swimming speeds the pectoral fins are folded against the sides of the body, and the fish is propelled by its caudal fin.

Webb (1973) has described the kinematics of lift-based pectoral fin propulsion in the shiner seaperch (*Cymatogaster aggregata*). The pectoral fins oscillate in an up-and-down motion and at the same time pass a wave back over their length. On the basis of an index relating the length of the wave to that of the trailing edge of the fin, Webb classified the fin movements into two groups, pectoral fin patterns A and B. In pattern A the wavelength was about twice the trailing edge length, resulting in a phase difference of about π between the anterior and posterior fin rays; the phase difference in pattern B movements was only about 0.2π. Pattern A fin movements (illustrated in Fig. 7-2) were observed up to speeds of approximately 2 lengths · sec^{-1}.

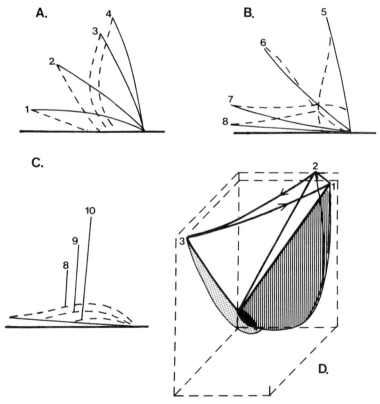

Figure 7–2

Movements of the pectoral fins of *Cymatogaster aggregata* in pectoral fin pattern A (*A* to *C*, the interval between frames is 0.018 sec) and a diagrammatic representation of the fin motion (*D*, arrows indicate the motion of the tip of the trailing edge of the fin; the fin is indicated by shading). (Based on Webb, 1973)

Webb divided the fin-beat cycle in *Cymatogaster* into abduction, adduction, and refractory phases. Abduction and adduction phases were of approximately equal duration; the duration of the refractory phase decreased with increasing swimming speed. In contrast to drag-based mechanisms, lift-based pectoral fin propulsion does not involve a distinct recovery stroke. Fin-beat frequency and amplitude both increase with increasing swimming speed in *Cymatogaster*. The product of frequency and amplitude increases linearly with speed. At swimming speeds greater than about 3.5 lengths · sec^{-1}, pectoral fin propulsion is supplemented by oscillation of the caudal fin.

HYDROMECHANICAL MODELS

Undulatory Fins

ACTUATOR-DISC THEORY

Actuator-disc theory, a special application of the momentum principle, is a fundamental concept in fluid dynamics that is central to the analysis of flow problems involving the determination of forces. The actuator-disc is essentially an idealized device that produces a sudden pressure rise in a stream of fluid passing through it. The pressure rise, integrated over the disc area, gives the thrust associated with the driving mechanism. In this case, the driving mechanism is the undulatory median or paired fin. We assume the following:

1. That the pressure increment and thrust loading are constant over the entire disc.
2. That there are no rotational velocity components in the wake
3. That there is no discontinuity in the velocity across the disc
4. That a definite boundary separates the flow passing through the disc from that outside it
5. That in front and behind the disc the static pressure in and out of the wake is the same as the free-stream static pressure

These assumptions tend, if anything, to underestimate induced power (see Discussion, Assumptions Involved in Hydromechanical Models), to which they therefore give a useful lower bound (see Lighthill, 1975a).

Far upstream of the fin the pressure is p_0, and the water velocity is V, the swimming speed. Just upstream of the fin, the velocity is assumed to have increased to $(V + v_1)$, and in accordance with Bernoulli's theorem the pressure falls to p. Immediately downstream of the fin, the pressure increases by Δp to $(p + \Delta p)$, while the velocity is unchanged. Far downstream of the trailing edge of the fin, the pressure returns to p_0, while the velocity is increased to $(V + v_2)$. Applying Bernoulli's theorem to a region directly in front of the disc, we have

$$p + \frac{1}{2} \rho (V + v_1)^2 = p_0 + \frac{1}{2} \rho V^2 \qquad (1)$$

where ρ is the water density. Similarly, for the region just behind the disc

$$p + \Delta p + \frac{1}{2}\rho(V + v_1)^2 = p_0 + \frac{1}{2}\rho(v + v_2)^2 \qquad (2)$$

Subtracting equation 1 from equation 2 gives

$$\Delta p = \rho v_2 (V + \frac{1}{2}v_2) \qquad (3)$$

The thrust force developed by the fin can be found by multiplying Δp by the disc area S_d

$$T = \Delta p S_d = S_d \rho v_2 (V + \frac{1}{2}v_2) \qquad (4)$$

During hovering (i.e., when $V = 0$),

$$T = \frac{1}{2}\rho S_d v_2^2 \qquad (5)$$

The rate of mass flow through the disc is $\rho S_d(V + v_1)$, and therefore the rate of increase of momentum of the wake is $\rho S_d(V + v_1)v_2$. Thrust equals the rate of change of momentum and

$$S_d \rho v_2 (V + \frac{1}{2}v_2) = \rho S_d v_2 (V + v_1) \qquad (6)$$

so

$$v_2 = 2v_1 \text{ or } v_1 = \frac{1}{2}v_2 \qquad (7)$$

The minimum power necessary to generate the induced velocity, v_2 (induced power) P_{id} is

$$P_{id} = TV = S_d \rho v_2 (V + \frac{1}{2}v_2) \qquad (8)$$

and

$$P_{id} = TV = \frac{1}{2}\rho S_d V v_2^2 \qquad (9)$$

for the case of forward swimming and hovering, respectively; however, the power input P_{in} will be

$$P_{in} = T(V + \nu_1) \qquad (10)$$

From equations 9 and 10 we can define the ideal efficiency of the undulating fin system as

$$\eta = P_{id}/P_{in} = TV/T(V + v_1) = V/(V + v_1) \qquad (11)$$

With good experimental technique it is possible to get accurate measurements of V and S_d; however, although possible, it is relatively difficult to obtain good estimates of the induced velocity over the fins. Local flow velocities can be measured by using flow visualization (Merzkirch, 1974; Blake, 1979c and d) or anemometry (Blake, unpublished). Values for v_1 and v_2 can be determined, however, if the drag of the fish is known.

Defining an inflow factor Ξ as $\Xi = v_1/V$, T becomes

$$T = S_d 2\rho V(V + \Xi V) = 2\rho S_d V^2 (1 + \Xi) \tag{12}$$

In steady swimming thrust and drag must be equal, and therefore

$$C_{D(b)} = D_{(b)}/\frac{1}{2}\rho V^2 S_w = T/\frac{1}{2}\rho V^2 S_w = 2\rho S_d V^2 \Xi (1 + \Xi)/\frac{1}{2}\rho V^2 S_w \tag{13}$$

where $D_{(b)}$ is the swimming drag, $C_{D(b)}$ is the drag coefficient of the body and S_w is the wetted surface area of the fish. From equation 13

$$(S_w/S_d)C_{D(b)} = 4\Xi(1 + \Xi) \tag{14}$$

and

$$4\Xi^2 + 4\Xi - (S_w/S_d)C_{D(b)} = 0 \tag{15}$$

which gives

$$-4 \pm (16 + 16(S_w/S_d)C_{D(b)})^{\frac{1}{2}}/8 = -1(1 + (S_w/S_d)C_{D(b)})^{\frac{1}{2}} \tag{16}$$

Defining v_{sp} as the slipstream velocity

$$v_{sp} = (V + v_1) = V(1 + 2\Xi) = V(1 + (S_w/S_d)C_D^{(b)})^{\frac{1}{2}} \tag{17}$$

and

$$v_1 = (v_{sp} - V), \ v_2 = \frac{1}{2}(v_{sp} - V) \tag{18}$$

Equation 8 can be written

$$P_{id} = TV = 2\rho S_d V^3 \Xi(1 + \Xi) \tag{19}$$

Similarly, equation 10 can be written as

$$P_{in} = T(V + v_1) = 2\rho S_d V^3 \Xi(1 + \Xi)^2 \tag{20}$$

and the ideal efficiency becomes defined as

$$\eta = 2\rho S_d V^3 \Xi(1 + \Xi)/2\rho S_d V^3 \Xi(1 + \Xi)^2 \tag{21}$$

Particle flow visualization techniques have been used to determine the induced flow velocities over the dorsal and pectoral fins of the seahorse (*Hippocampus hudsonius*) and the pectoral fins of the mandarin fish (*Synchropus picturatus*) during steady swimming at a variety of speeds (Blake, 1976, 1979c). Swimming power is plotted against speed for a specimen of *S. picturatus* in Figure 7-3. The induced power falls off as speed increases; however, both the power required to overcome the drag acting on the fins (profile power) and body (parasite power) increase with speed. This results in a U-shaped total power curve. *Synchiropus* is a negatively buoyant demersal fish, and the form of its power curve can be compared to those of helicopters and birds.

The induced power curve is similar in form (see Bramwell, 1976; and Pennycuick, 1968; Rayner, 1979 on helicopters and birds, respectively).

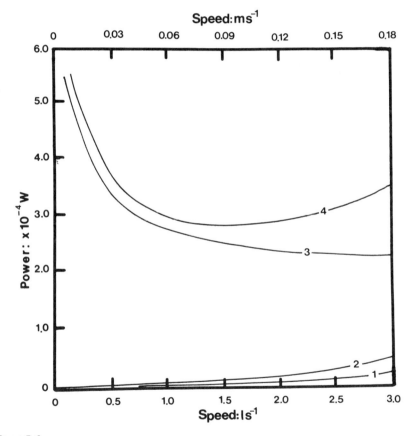

Figure 7-3
Power in relation to swimming speed for *Synchiropus picturatus* (1, parasite power; 2, profile power; 3, induced power; 4, total power; from Blake, 1979c)

Parasite power in birds and helicopters increases rapidly with increasing speed to become the dominant component at high speeds, but parasite power is not an important component of the total power in *Synchiropus*. This is largely because of the low absolute swimming speeds of the fish. The total power curve in helicopters (Bramwell, 1976) and some birds (Pennycuick, 1968; Tucker, 1973; Greenwalt, 1975; Rayner, 1979) is U-shaped with a definite minimum power speed. The total power curve of *Synchropus* is rather flat, and this is consistent with the observation that it does not select a preferred swimming speed (Blake, 1979c).

The modified form of the theory, using the inflow factor Ξ, has been applied to the analysis of forward swimming in *Hippocampus* and the electric fish, *Gymnarchus nilotichus* (Blake, 1980b). Values of η for *Gymnarchus* (of the order of 0.6 to 0.7) are about twice those of *Hippocampus*. *Gymnarchus* falls into group one of the kinematic classification; *Hippocampus* belongs to group 2. Thrust is developed most efficiently when a large mass of water is accelerated to a small eventual velocity, so it can be expected that fish falling into group 1 of the kinematic classification will be characterized by high values of η. *Gymnarchus* is an active carnivore, and a high propulsive efficiency enables it to cruise economically in search of its prey. In contrast, the seahorse is a relatively sluggish fish and feeds on slow-swimming crustaceans. It is probable that the overall energy budget of *Hippocampus* is not greatly affected by the relatively low value of the propulsive efficiency of its dorsal fin; in fact, the high-frequency oscillation of the fin may be viewed as adaptive because it is likely that it operates at a frequency beyond the flicker-fusion frequency of the eyes of most of its potential predators, rendering the fin motion "invisible."

Equation 5 has been used to calculate the thrust force generated by the pectoral fins of *Synchiropus* during hovering at various heights above the ground (Blake, 1979d). The jet produced by the fins spreads out as it impinges on the ground, increasing the effective disc area (S_d) of the system. This enables a given force to be produced at a lower induced velocity than would be required in the absence of a ground plane. Out of the influence of the ground ($J/D > 3.0$, see inset in Fig. 7-4 for definitions of J and D), the thrust produced by the fins must have been equal to the weight of the fish in seawater ($\simeq 6.5 \times 10^{-3}$ N); therefore, each fin must have been producing about 3.25×10^{-3} N of thrust downward. A value of 3.39×10^{-3} N was calculated from equation 5 for $J/D = 3$; the calculated value is within 5% of that expected.

Values of the induced power required to hover decreased in the influence of the ground (*i.e.,* with decreasing J/D). In Figure 7-4, the power required to hover in the influence of the ground is expressed relative to that out of the ground effect for various values of J/D. In captivity at least, *Synchiropus* hovers close to the substrate while feeding. Typically, J/D takes values between 0.25 and 0.5, where savings on induced power of the order of 30% to 60% will occur. It is interesting to note that the ratio of the rotor height to the

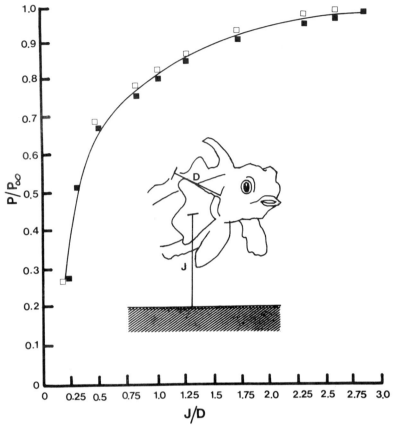

Figure 7–4
The ratio of the total power required to hover at various values of J/D (*see inset*) to that out of ground effect in *Synchiropus picturatus*. The symbols refer to a laminar (■) and a turbulent (□) boundary layer over the fins. (From Blake, 1979d)

distance of the rotor plane above the ground (an index analogous to J/D) in a typical helicopter at takeoff is about 0.3 when a saving on induced power of about 33% is achieved (Bramwell, 1976).

The specific induced power (induced power/weight in water) of *Synchiropus* out of the ground effects (0.075 Wn^{-1}) is low compared to that of hovering insects (*e.g.,* 0.4, 1.71, and 2.1 WN^{-1} for *Tipula Sphinx*, and *Bombus*, respectively; Weis–Fogh, 1973) and birds (*e.g.,* 3 and 2.2 Wn^{-1} for *Columbia livia* and *Archiolochus colubris* from the data of Pennycuick, 1968). The large density difference between air and water ($\rho = 1,000$ kg · m^{-3} and 1.3 kg · m^{-3} for water and air, respectively at 20° C) accounts for this.

It should be emphasized that certain of the basic assumptions underlying actuator-disc theory (*e.g.,* uniform, steady loading and continuous flow across the disc) are probably violated in some applications to the hovering and low-speed swimming of fishes. In some cases, unsteady effects (*i.e.*, time-dependent vortex shedding from the fins) may be important, necessitating new approaches.

ELONGATED BODY THEORY

Elongated body theory mainly results from the work of Lighthill (*e.g.*, 1960, 1970, 1971). It has been successfully applied to the analysis of swimming in fish that are propelled by undulations of the body and caudal fin (Lighthill, 1970, 1971; Webb, 1971a and b; Wardle and Reid, 1977). Blake (1976) points out that elongated body theory should also be applicable to the undulatory motions of the median and paired fins of certain teleosts. The theory emphasizes the inertial forces that are generated between the propulsive surfaces of the fish and a perfect fluid (viscous forces are neglected). The inertial forces depend on the rate of change of the relative velocity of the fish's propulsive parts and the mass of fluid they displace. The theory is discussed further and developed for undulatory fin motions in Chapter 6 of this volume.

Blake (1982b) has used elongated body theory to calculate the swimming thrust, power, and efficiency in six species of electric eel (Gymnotidae) and three species of knifefish (Notopteridae). The study was undertaken in order to answer two questions:

1. What, if any, are the hydromechanical advantages of undulatory median fin swimming over anguilliform and subcarangiform propulsion?
2. Is it possible to offer reasonable functional explanations based on the hydromechanical analysis concerning the morphologic similarities and differences between the fish?

These questions are approached by considering the following criteria:

1. Propulsive efficiency
2. Speed and acceleration
3. Maneuverability
4. Recoil effects during swimming
5. The magnitude of viscous swimming drag

The propulsive efficiency of the nine species using undulatory fins ranged from about 0.7 to 0.9 over a speed range of about 0.2 to 5.0 lengths·sec^{-1}. Webb (1971b) estimated that the propeller efficiency of trout (*Salmo gairdneri*) is high (>0.7) over most of the cruising-speed range of the fish. At low swimming speeds (<0.2 lengths · sec^{-1}), however, the efficiency falls off rapidly to low values. Undulatory fin propulsion in the electric eels and knife fishes can therefore be considered an adaptation for mechanically efficient, low-speed swimming.

Many fish that swim in the anguilliform and subcarangiform modes are capable of high speeds and accelerations. High speed and acceleration are required for the capture of prey and for escape from predators. Most gymnotids and notopterids feed on small slow-swimming fish and therefore do not require high speeds and accelerations for prey capture. It is interesting to note that high-speed swimming (*e.g.,* escape responses) is effected by bodily flexure in the subcarangiform mode (Blake, 1982b).

Figure 7-5 shows two of the gymnotids (*Gymnotus carapo* and *Gymnorhamphichthys hypostomus*; Figs. 7-5*A* and *B*, respectively) and two of the notopterids (*Xenomystis nigri* and *Notopterus notopterus*; Figs. 7-5*C, D*, and *E*, respectively). *Gymnotus* and *Gymnorhamphichthys* rarely execute turning maneuvers. By simply reversing the direction of wave-form propagation on the anal fin, both forms are able to swim as effectively backward as they swim forward. In contrast, *Notopterus* shows the turning behavior characteristic of anguilliform and subcarangiform swimmers (see Weihs, 1972; Blake, 1982b; and Fig. 7-5*E*). *Notopterus* often supplements its undulatory fin motions with a body wave during low-speed swimming.

Notopterus (and to a lesser extent *Xenomystis*) exhibits some of the morphologic traits of subcarangiform fish that are designed to minimize the influence of recoil forces generated during swimming (see Lighthill, 1970, 1971, 1977; Blake, 1982a and b). In particular, both forms have a good depth of section over their center of mass. The variation in the depth of section moving back from the nose is far more gradual in *Gymnotus* and *Gymnorhamphicthys* than in *Xenomystis* and *Notopterus* (compare Figs. 7-5*A* and *B* with *C* and *D*).

For the symmetric movements of the anal fin of most gymnotids the mean time average of the recoil forces generated during swimming will be very small because the lateral components produced by the fin cancel out on either side of the centerline except at the trailing edge. In anguilliform swimmers there is a marked increase in the amplitude of the body wave as it passes posteriorly (Gray, 1933), and this gives rise to a small net recoil force (in addition to that generated at the trailing edge) that tends to "wag" the head. The anal fin of the gymnotiform teleosts does not exhibit the anguilliform pattern of rapid amplitude increase. Fin amplitude increases to a more or less constant value that is maintained over most of the fin length, decreasing close to the trailing edge. The system is essentially symmetrical.

Thrust values calculated from elongated body theory may be used to infer values of the drag coefficient of the body that is being propelled (*e.g.,* Lighthill, 1971; Blake, 1982a and b). The inferred values can then be compared with those to be expected for the given Reynolds number and boundary-layer flow regime for the equivalent rigid body. Following this procedure, various authors (see Webb, 1975b and Blake, 1982b for reviews) have found large differences between the inferred and predicted values of $C_{D(b)}$. Swimming viscous drag may exceed the theoretical rigid-body equivalent by a factor ranging from about 4 to 9 (*e.g.,* Lighthill, 1971; Alexander, 1967). It is thought

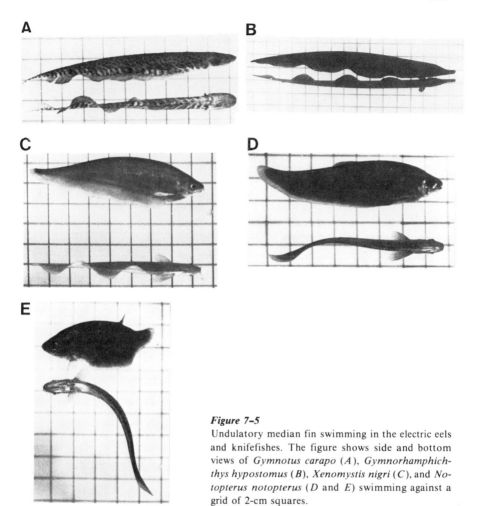

Figure 7-5
Undulatory median fin swimming in the electric eels
and knifefishes. The figure shows side and bottom
views of *Gymnotus carapo* (*A*), *Gymnorhamphichthys hypostomus* (*B*), *Xenomystis nigri* (*C*), and *Notopterus notopterus* (*D* and *E*) swimming against a
grid of 2-cm squares.

that boundary layer thinning in the swimming fish results in an increase in the
viscous drag (Bone, in Lighthill, 1971). The gymnotids and other undulatory fin
swimmers are probably not subject to such large increases in viscous drag
because undulations and therefore boundary layer thinning are restricted to the
fins.

Oscillatory Fins

BLADE-ELEMENT THEORY OF PECTORAL FIN ROWING

Pectoral fin rowing has been analyzed by Blake (1979a and b, 1980a,
1981a); the principle features of the power analysis are outlined below. A more

detailed account including an analysis of the recovery stroke and added mass effects can be found in Blake (1981a).

Figure 7-6 shows a schematic view of a rowing fish. The righthand side of the diagram depicts the fin during successive stages of the power stroke when the fin is oriented "broadside on"to the flow. The normal (v_n), spanwise (v_s), and resultant relative (v_{res}) velocities of the fin during the power stroke are given by

$$v_n(r,t) = \omega r - V\sin\gamma \tag{22}$$

$$v_s(r,t) = V\cos\gamma \tag{23}$$

$$v_{res}^2(r,t) = \omega^2 r^2 + V^2\sin^2\gamma - 2V\omega r\sin\gamma + V^2\cos^2\gamma = \omega^2 r^2 + V^2 - 2V\omega r\sin\gamma \tag{24}$$

where ω is the angular velocity of the fin, γ is the positional angle, and r is the distance from the base of the fin. From this information the hydromechanical angle of attack α can be calculated

$$\tan\alpha = \omega r - V\sin\gamma / V\cos\gamma \tag{25}$$

α and other symbols are defined in Figure 7-7.

It is convenient to divide the fin into a series of arbitarily defined blade elements during the stroke. The normal force (dF_n) and thrust (dT) acting on a given blade element can be calculated from

$$dF_n(r,t) = \frac{1}{2}\rho v_{res}^2(r,t)dA\,C_n \tag{26}$$

$$dT(r,t) = dF_n(r,t)\sin\gamma \tag{27}$$

where dA is the frontally projected area of the element, and C_n is a normal force coefficient that depends, among others on α. The impulse of the thrust force must equal that of the drag force acting on the body, so

$$\frac{1}{2}\rho V^2 S_w C_{D(b)} t_o = 2\int_0^R\int_0^{t_p} dT\,dt \tag{28}$$

where t_p is the duration of the power stroke and t_o is the total fin-beat cycle time; the factor 2 arises because of the operation of two fins.

The rate of working (dP) of an element is

$$dP = \frac{1}{2}\rho dA\,C_n r\omega(\omega^2 r^2 + V^2 - 2V\omega r\sin\gamma) \tag{29}$$

and therefore the mean power produced during the power stroke is given by

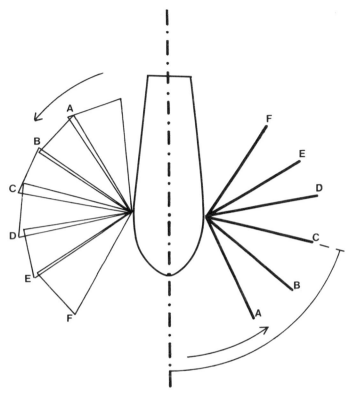

Figure 7-6
Schematic diagram of fin positions during the power and recovery stroke phase of the fin-beat cycle of a rowing fish. (From Blake, 1981c)

$$\overline{P} = \frac{1}{t_p} \int_0^{t_p} \frac{1}{2} \rho \mathrm{d}A\, C_n r \omega (\omega^2 r^2 + V^2 - 2 V \omega r \sin \gamma)\, \mathrm{d}t \tag{30}$$

The power required to drag the body through the water is given by

$$P_b = \frac{1}{2} \rho V^3 S_w C_{D(b)} \tag{31}$$

Dividing this by the total power required for the power stroke gives an expression for the efficiency of the system

$$\eta_p = \frac{1}{2} \rho V^3 S_w C_{D(b)} \Big/ 2 \int_0^R \int_0^{t_p} \mathrm{d}F_n\, \mathrm{d}r\, \mathrm{d}t \tag{32}$$

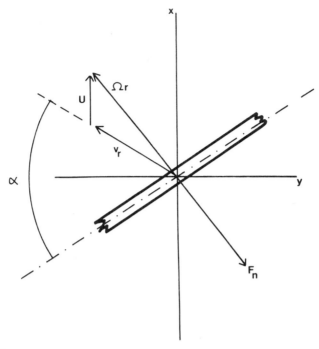

Figure 7-7
A blade element during the pectoral fin power stroke. All notation is defined in the text. (From Blake, 1981c)

The model has been applied to the angelfish, *Pterophyllum eimekei*. Kinematic data on a single specimen (length = 8.0 cm) swimming at about 0.5 lengths · sec^{-1} is summarized in Figure 7-8, which shows that flow reversal and hence negative angles of attack occur at the beginning and end of the power stroke at the base of the fin. Values of v_n and α increase distally. Force and thrust are plotted against time in Figure 7-9. Small amounts of reversed thrust are produced at the base of the fin. The outermost 40% or so of the fin area produces over 80% of the total hydrodynamic thrust force. Equation 28 was used to infer a value for $C_{D(b)}$ of about 0.1.

The various power components associated with the stroke are plotted against time in Figure 7-10. Based on equation 32, a value of 0.26 is calculated for the propulsive efficiency of the stroke. In reality, during its acceleration the fin entrains a mass of water (added mass). Taking into account the energy required to do this, a more appropriate efficiency of 0.18 is calculated. The treatment of added mass in pectoral fin rowing is similar to that outlined in the following section for lift-based mechanisms. This calculation considers only the power stroke. When the energy required for the recovery stroke is also considered (see Blake, 1980a, 1981c), η_p must be further reduced, to 0.16 for this case.

The influence of pectoral fin shape on thrust and drag is discussed by Blake (1981a). A simplified form of the model outlined above was used to derive a shape factor (B). We have

$$\frac{1}{2}\rho V^2 S_w C_{D(b)} t_o = C_n B R^2 A \int_0^{t_{p\,2}} \sin\gamma \, dt \tag{33}$$

For square and rectangular planforms, $B = 0.33$ and is not affected by the height-to-base ratio. For triangular planforms, $B = 0.5$, irrespective of the base-to-height ratio. A value of $B = 0.43$ was measured for the pectoral fins of *P. eimekei*.

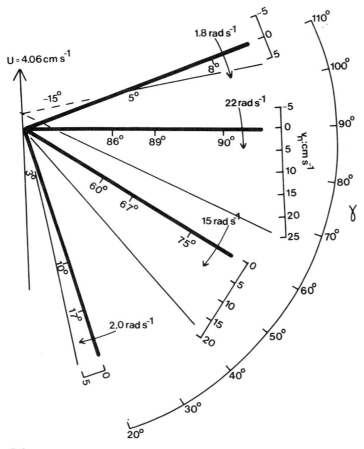

Figure 7-8
Diagrammatic summary of the kinematics of the pectoral-fin power stroke of an angelfish. All notation is defined in the text. (From Blake, 1981c)

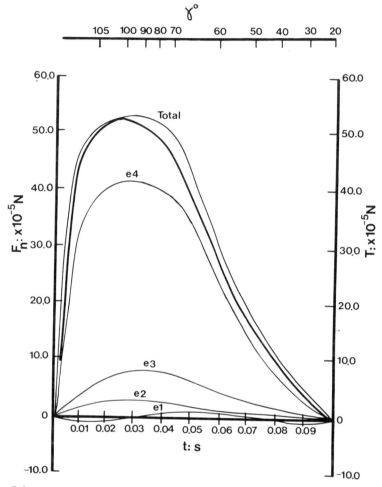

Figure 7-9
Normal force for four arbitrarily defined blade elements (e1 to e4) and thrust (*heavy line*) are plotted against time during the power stroke. (Based on Blake, 1979b)

The influence of pectoral fin shape was further investigated experiment-ally using terminal velocity techniques. Plastic models of angelfish were fitted with square, rectangular, or triangular model fins of equivalent area. Tri-angular fins were always attached to the body at the apex because this is the situation in bony fish. The value of the frictional drag acting on the models was the same for all fin shapes; the pressure drag generated by the square and rectangular fins was found to be about 15% greater than that for the triangular fin forms at the higher velocities. Square fins generated about twice as much interference drag (drag caused by the interference between the flow around the fins with that around the body; see Blake, 1979b, 1981b for further details) as did triangular fins at the same value of V.

On the basis of the results gained from the simple hydromechanical model experiments, it would seem reasonable to suppose that drag-based pectoral fin swimmers would be more likely to have triangular than square or rectangular fins, and this is generally the case.

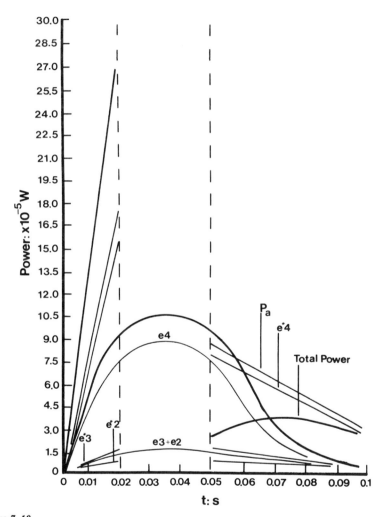

Figure 7-10

The total power required to produce the hydrodynamic thrust force during the pectoral fin power stroke of an angelfish is plotted against time. The contributions to the total of the individual blade elements (e2, e3, e4), the power required to accelerate and decelerate the added mass of the fin and the contributions of the blade elements to this (e*2, e*d, e*4), the total added mass power (P_a), and the total power are shown. (From Blake, 1981c)

BLADE-ELEMENT THEORY OF LIFT-BASED
OSCILLATORY PROPULSION

Oscillatory lift-based mechanisms of propulsion occur in many teleost families (*e.g.*, Embiotocidae, Serranidae, Chaetodontidae). The fin motions of these forms have been likened to the movements of a bird wing in flight (Webb and Blake, 1983); however, currently there is no hydromechanical theory of lift-based pectoral fin propulsion. A preliminary model based on blade-element theory is outlined below.

Assuming that the fin movement is sinusoidal over the downstroke and upstroke

$$\gamma(t) = \overline{\gamma} + \tfrac{1}{2}\Phi\sin(2\pi nt) \qquad (34)$$

where Φ is the stroke angle and n is the fin-beat frequency. The angular velocity of the fin is

$$\omega = d\gamma/dt = \pi n\Phi\cos(2\pi nt) \qquad (35)$$

and therefore the flapping velocity v_f is

$$v_f(r,t) = \omega r = r[\pi n\Phi\cos(2\pi nt)] \qquad (36)$$

The instantaneous resultant velocity $v_{ru}(r,t)$ and $v_{rd}(r,t)$ for the upstroke and downstroke, respectively, is the resultant of the two velocities and the induced velocity v_i and the forward velocity V. The induced velocity is given from actuator-disc theory as

$$v_i = mg/S_d^2\rho \qquad (37)$$

where mg is the weight of the fish in water and S_d is the disc area. Although an important component in the blade element analysis of bird flight (*e.g.*, Pennycuick, 1968), the induced velocity can be neglected in this application because mg is small relative to S_d. Neglecting v_i, the instantaneous resultant velocity for the upstroke v_{ru} and downstroke v_{rd} can be written as

$$v_{ru}(r,t) = [V^2 + v_f^2(r,t) + 2Vv_f(r,t)\cos(\beta + e)]^{1/2} \qquad (38)$$

$$v_{rd}(r,t) = [V_2 + v_f^2(r,t) - 2Vv_f(r,t)\cos(\beta + e)]^{1/2} \qquad (39)$$

where β is the angle of tilt of the stroke plane relative to the horizontal (see Fig. 7-11, for definition of β and other symbols) and e is the downwash angle. The downwash angle is given by

$$e - \tan^{-1}(v_i/V) \qquad (40)$$

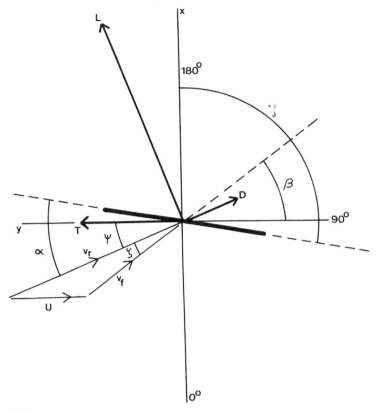

Figure 7-11
A velocity-force diagram for a blade element operating in the lift-based mode.

because v_i is small relative to V, we can neglect e, so

$$v_{ru}(r,t) = [V^2 + v_f^2(r,t) + 2Vv_f(r,t)\cos\beta]^{1/2} \qquad (41)$$

$$v_{rd}(r,t) = [V^2 + v_f^2(r,t) - 2Vv_f(r,t)\cos\beta]^{1/2} \qquad (42)$$

for the upstroke and downstroke, respectively.

The instantaneous lift and drag forces produced by the fin can be written as

$$dL(r,t) = \tfrac{1}{2}\rho v_r'^2(r,t)C(r)r^2drC_L(r,t) \qquad (43)$$

$$dD(r,t) = \tfrac{1}{2}\rho v_r'^2(r,t)C(r)r^2drC_D(r,t) \qquad (44)$$

where C is the chord of the fin, v_r is the resultant velocity in any phase of the fin-beat cycle and $C_L(r,t)$ and $C_D(r,t)$ are the sectional lift and drag coefficients, respectively. Thrust is given by

$$dT = dL\sin\Psi - dD\cos\Psi \qquad (45)$$

The angle Ψ is defined in Figure 7-11. The torque and power associated with the thrust force can be divided into two categories, that associated with profile drag of the fins (*i.e.*, equation 44) and the inertial terms associated with the acceleration and deceleration of the fins and their entrained added mass. The torque associated with the profile drag (dQ_p) is

$$dQ_p = \frac{1}{2}\rho C(r)r^3 dr v_r{}^2(r,t)C_D \tag{46}$$

and the work required is

$$H_P = \int_0^{t_o} Q_p \, d\gamma = \int_0^{t_o} \frac{1}{2}\rho C(r)r^3 dr v_r{}^2(r,t)C_D \, d\gamma \tag{47}$$

The power is given by

$$P_p = n\int_0^{t_o} Q_p \, d = n\int_0^{t_o} \frac{1}{2}\rho C(r)r^3 dr v_r{}^2(r,t)C_D \, dt \tag{48}$$

The term v_r in equations 46 to 48 refers to the resultant relative velocity for both the upstroke and downstroke. The inertial torque associated with the fin mass (dQ_i) is

$$dQ_i = I(d^2\gamma/dt) \tag{49}$$

where I is the moment of inertia of the fin, $I = m(r)r^2$, and so for a sinusoidal motion

$$dQ_i = -2m(r)r^2\Phi\pi^2\sin(2\pi nt) \tag{50}$$

The inertial work (H_i) and power (P_i) are

$$H_i = \int_0^{t_o} Q_i \, d\gamma = \int_0^{t_o} m(r)r^2(d^2\gamma/dt^2) \, d\gamma \tag{51}$$

$$P_i = n\int_0^{t_o} Q_i \, d\gamma = n\int_0^{t_o} m(r)r^2(d^2\gamma/dt^2) \, d\gamma \tag{52}$$

It has already been mentioned that the fin will entrain an added mass of water owing to its unsteady motion. In studies of bird flight, the added mass term is usually neglected because it is small relative to the wing mass. Added mass in pectoral fin swimming, however, can be expected to be significant because of the relatively high density of water compared to that of air. By rotating pectoral-fin blade elements about the median long axis of the fin, a series of cylinders are generated; multiplying the volume of the cylinders by the water density gives the added mass of the elements m_a

$$m_a = \rho\pi(C/2)^2 y \tag{53}$$

where y is the length of a given blade element (measured perpendicular to the chord). The added mass force (dF_a) can be calculated from

$$F_a = m_a(dv_f/dt) = \rho\pi(C/2)^2 y(dv_f/dt) \tag{54}$$

and the torque Q_a is given by

$$Q_a = m_a(dv_f/dt)r' = \rho\pi(C/2)^2 yr'(dv_f/dt) \tag{55}$$

where r' indicates the midpoint of a given blade element.

The total work and power associated with the added mass force (H_a and P_a, respectively) can be written as

$$H_a = \int_0^{t_o} Q_a\,d\gamma = \int_0^{t_o} \rho\pi(C/2)^2 yr'(dv_f/dt)\,d\gamma \tag{56}$$

$$P_a = n\int_0^{t_o} Q_a\,d\gamma = n\int_0^{t_o} \rho\pi(C/2)^2\, yr'(dv_f/dt)\,d\gamma \tag{57}$$

The total hydrodynamic and inertial work H_{tot} and power P_{tot} are

$$H_{tot} = \int_0^{t_o}(Q_i + Q_a) + Q_p\,d\gamma \tag{58}$$

$$P_{tot} = n\int_0^{t_o}(Q_i + Q_a) + Q_p\,d\gamma \tag{59}$$

Equations 47 and 59 can be used to define a dynamic efficiency η_d

$$\eta_d = H_p/H_{tot} \tag{60}$$

The work required to drag the body through the water H_b is

$$H_b = \frac{1}{2}\rho S_w V^3 C_{D(b)} t_o \tag{61}$$

and the propulsive efficiency η_p may be written as

$$\eta_p = H_b / 2H_{tot} \tag{62}$$

The factor of 2 arises owing to the operation of two fins.

Some observations have been made from cinefilms of *Cymatogaster aggregata* (length $= 9.6$ cm; speed $= 23$ cm · sec^{-1}), from which preliminary results have been obtained (R.W. Blake, unpublished observations).

The pectoral fins moved through a stroke plane of about 100 degrees (*i.e.,* $\Phi = 1.74$ rad) moving from a starting position at the top of the downstroke about 80 degrees from the horizontal and dipping about 20 degrees below the horizontal by the end of the stroke. These figures are similar to those given by Pennycuick (1968) on the average arc of travel of the wings of the pigeon during forward flight. The stroke plane of the fins was at an angle of 20 degrees to the horizontal. This corresponds well with the angle that the fin base makes relative to the horizontal. The flapping frequency was about 5.55 Hz, giving a cycle time of 0.18 per second and a mean angular velocity of 9.7 rad · sec^{-1}.

The frequency parameter $\omega \overline{C}/V$ based on chord length ($\overline{C} = 0.65$ cm) can be calculated to be of the order of 0.25. Values of about 0.5 have been calculated for the pigeon and locust in forward flight (Lighthill, 1974). These values are quite low; high values of the frequency parameter indicate that unsteady effects are likely to be an important influence.

On the basis of a respirometric study, Webb (1975a) calculated the power required to swim at a given velocity and compared this to the theoretical minimum drag power required to overcome body drag, assuming a turbulent boundary layer (see Fig. 7-12). Values of η_p of the order of 0.6 to 0.65 were calculated assuming a muscle efficiency of 0.2.

DISCUSSION

Assumptions Involved in the Hydromechanical Models

The advantage of using actuator-disc theory in the analysis of undulatory fin systems is that the model requires a minimum of data concerning the operating mechanism (fin), which is regarded as a "black box." The fin is reduced to an infinitely thin disc with an area equal to that swept out by the fins. Ellington (1978) has pointed out that this black-box approach can be a disadvantage if energy losses in the mechanism are significant in comparison with the kinetic energy of the wake. There are four major sources of energy loss that can be considered:

1. Energy lost in overcoming the frictional drag of the fins
2. Extra energy required because of tip losses

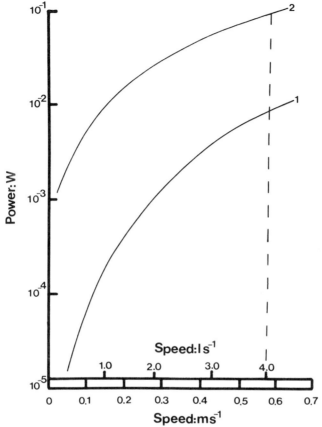

Figure 7–12
The power required to overcome the frictional drag of the body of a specimen of *Cymatogaster aggregata* (curve 1) is compared to the measured aerobic swimming power (curve 2). (From Webb, 1973)

3. Extra energy required because of nonuniform velocity distribution over the disc
4. Losses owing to rotational velocities present in the wake

Weis–Fogh (1973) found that the power required to overcome the drag of the wings in insects in normal hovering (see Weis–Fogh, 1973 for a definition of normal hovering) could be as great as the induced power required and therefore represent a serious loss not accounted for by the model. However, the power required to overcome the frictional drag on the fins of *Synchiropus* in hovering was calculated to be only about 5% of the induced power (Blake, 1979d). The insects are flying in a medium that is about 800 times less dense than water. The flapping velocities of the wings, however, are an order of magnitude greater than those of undulatory fins, and this contributes to the resultant air velocity; power requirements are proportional to the cubed power of the resultant velocity. Because of the lower Reynolds numbers involved, frictional drag coefficients are also higher in insects.

It is difficult to estimate the energy losses caused by tip losses from the fins. Values of about 15% have been determined for helicopter rotors and propellers (Bairstow, 1939; Stewart and Burle, 1950; Bramwell, 1976). Unfortunately, we cannot assume that the data on the flight of helicopters can be directly applied to undulatory fins. Similarly, we cannot evaluate the magnitude of the losses caused by a nonuniform velocity distribution across the disc. Lighthill (1977) notes that a uniform induced velocity distribution will give a minimum value for the induced power. Energy losses caused by rotational velocities in the wake are unknown.

The results of particle visualization (Blake, 1976,1979c and d) and anemometry studies (R. W. Blake, unpublished data) on *Synchiropus* and the seahorse indicate that the flow patterns are in general agreement with actuator-disc flow, with maximum velocities coinciding with the region of maximum wake contraction beneath the fins.

In applying elongated body theory to the action of undulatory fins, the following are assumed:

1. The length of the fin is constant.
2. The fin is of uniform cross-section.
3. Each vertical slice of water perpendicular to the direction of motion is influenced primarily by fin parts close to that slice.

In most cases, none of the above assumptions will be violated when the theory is applied to undulatory fin systems.

The assumptions involved in blade-element theory are the same for drag-based and lift-based mechanisms of oscillatory propulsion:

1. That flow is steady
2. That empirical lift and drag coefficients can be assigned to the blade elements that can be considered as acting independently of each other
3. That the force coefficients are constant along the radius of the fin and in time
4. That spanwise components of the relative velocity can be neglected.

The fundamental assumption of steady-state hydrodynamics is probably reasonable for fast forward swimming, where the reduced frequency parameter ($\overline{C}\omega/V$) is small. At low values of the reduced frequency parameter, freestream convection dominates the flow, and the system may be regarded as steady. Unsteady effects may become important at very low swimming speeds in some forms.

Values of C_L and C_D simply depend on the angle of attack, the relative fluid velocity, and the Reynolds number at which the fin is operating. Mean values of C_D and C_L can be used that satisfy the net force balance (*e.g.,* Weis–Fogh, 1972, 1973, on hovering insects), and this reduces the amount of detailed kinematic data required. Further discussion of the assumptions and limitations of blade-element theory can be found in Ellington (1975, 1980) and Blake (1979a and b, 1982a).

Speed, Acceleration, and Maneuverability

Most pelagic fish use speed and acceleration to capture prey and escape from predators. They swim in the anguilliform and carangiform modes and are characterized by a streamlined body form. Undulatory and oscillatory median or paired fin swimmers spend much of their time foraging at low speeds, and many are incapable of attaining high swimming speeds. Swimming at low speeds releases these forms from the morphologic constraints associated with a streamlined body form. Many undulatory fin swimmers are characterized by unstreamlined body sections (*e.g.,* suborders Ostracoidei, Synathoidei); however, some have retained a streamlined profile (*e.g.,* suborders Balistoidei, Acanthuroidei, Chaetodontidae, and family Labridae).

Low-speed swimming accords the opportunity for precise maneuver. Many undulatory and oscillatory fin swimmers are capable of turning on their own axis with no lateral translation of the body. By reversing the direction of wave-form propagation on their median fins, many Balistidae, Gymnotidae, and Notopteridae are able to move backward almost as well as they move forward. In contrast, many pelagic fusiform fish designed for efficient steady cruising perform relatively poorly in maneuver (*e.g.,* Scombridae). Many slow swimming coral reef fish are herbivorous; others feed on small benthic, slow swimming crustaceans (*e.g.,* Hobson, 1974) and do not require speed and rapid acceleration in order to catch prey.

Webb (1982) suggests that neutral buoyancy is an essential feature of slow swimming and fine maneuver. Negatively buoyant fish have to swim fast enough to generate sufficient dynamic lift to support their weight (Magnuson, 1978; Chap. 5), but many slow-swimming forms capable of fine maneuver are negatively buoyant. The lift forces required to counter excess weight over buoyancy are therefore actively generated by the fins.

Fused bony plates protect the cowfishes and trunkfishes (Ostraciidae) from predators; the Balistidae, Aluteridae, and Tricanthidae are covered in rough scutelike scales and possess retractable dorsal spines; sharp spines characterize the Tetraodontidae and Diodontidae; the flesh of some Aluteridae, Balistidae, and Tetraodontidae is poisonous; the boxfish, *Ostracion lentiginosum*, protects itself from its enemies by releasing a highly toxic substance into the water. Not all oscillatory and undulatory fin swimmers, however, are armored or poisonous. It has been noted that the gymnotids and notopterids are capable of brief bouts of relatively high-speed swimming in the anguilliform mode (Blake, 1982b). Most labriform swimmers are also able to perform rapid escape responses using undulations of the body and caudal fin.

The Ostraciiform Tail

Fish that are designed for good steady cruising performance are characterized by a forked, high aspect-ratio caudal fin (*e.g.,* Carangidae; Scombridae). In contrast, the caudal fin of most slow-swimming teleosts has a low aspect ratio. On the basis of hydromechanical theory, the ostraciiform tail can be expected to have a propulsive (Froude) efficiency of 0.5 (Lighthill, in Blake, 1982b). An experimental study of *Ostracion lentiginosum* swimming in the ostraciiform mode gave values of the order of 0.5 (Blake, 1981b). Anguilliform and carangiform swimmers are characterized by higher propulsive efficiencies in steady swimming. Values in excess of 0.9 have been reported for trout swimming in the subcarangiform mode (Webb, 1971b).

Streamlining and Drag

In Figure 7-13 the experimentally determined drag coefficients of a variety of undulatory and oscillatory median or paired fin swimmers is plotted against Reynolds number. The experimental points can be compared with the minimum frictional drag coefficients possible for the case of either a fully developed laminar or turbulent boundary layer (broken and full curve, respectively). For the Reynolds number range involved (10^3 to 10^5), a laminar boundary layer would be expected; however, many of the forms considered are characterized by substantial roughness elements (*e.g.,* spines) that probably ensure a turbulent boundary layer.

From Figure 7-13 it can be seen that only the points for angelfish and gourami without pectoral fins lie close to the predicted minimum drag curves. The more streamlined *Gymnarchus* shows relatively low values of C_D; values for the seahorse and boxfish are high. Errors in the experimental determination of the rigid-body drag values are likely to mean that most of the points in Figure 7-13 are overestimates of the true values (see Webb, 1975b; Blake, 1982a for a general discussion of the experimental techniques and errors involved in estimating "dead drag").

The results of dead-drag experiments on most undulatory and oscillatory median or paired fin swimmers ought to give reasonable estimates of the actual swimming drag. This is not the case for fish that swim in the anguilliform and carangiform modes, where the rigid body analogy does not apply. In these forms, the actual swimming drag may be many times greater than the equivalent rigid body drag because of the increased viscous drag caused by boundary layer thinning over the flexing body.

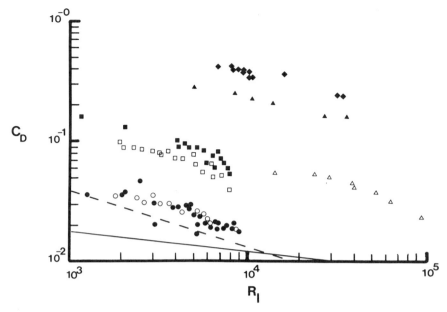

Figure 7-13
The relationship between drag and Reynolds number for a variety of fish that are propelled by median or paired fins. Symbols refer to angelfish and blue gourami with pectoral fins amputated (● and ○, respectively), angelfish and blue gourami with pectoral fins broadside on to the flow (■ and □, respectively), *Hippocampus* (▲), *Ostracion lentiginosum* (◆), and *Gymnarchus* (△). The theoretical curves for the base of a laminar boundary layer (*broken line*) and a turbulent boundary layer (*full line*) are also shown.

REFERENCES

Alexander, R. McN. 1977. Swimming. In *Mechanics and Energetics of Animal Locomotion*, edited by R. McN. Alexander and G. Goldspink. New York: Academic Press.

Bairstow, L. 1939. *Applied Aerodynamics*. London: Longmans.

Blake, R.W. 1976. On seahorse locomotion. *J. Marine Biol. Assoc. U.K.* 56:939–949.

Blake, R.W. 1977. On ostraciiform locomotion. *J. Marine Biol. Assoc. U.K.* 57:1047–1055.

Blake, R.W. 1978. On balistiform locomotion *J. Marine Biol. Assoc. U.K.* 58:73–80.

Blake, R.W. 1979a. *The mechanics of labriform locomotion*. Unpublished Ph.D. thesis. Cambridge: University of Cambridge.

Blake, R.W. 1979b. The mechanics of labriform locomotion I. Labriform locomotion in the angelfish (*Pterophyllum eimekei*): An analysis of the power stroke. *J. Exp. Biol.* 82:255–271.

Blake, R.W. 1979c. The swimming of the mandarin fish *Synchiropus picturatus* (Callionyiidae: Teleostei). *J. Marine Biol. Assoc. U.K.* 59:421–428.

Blake, R.W. 1979d. The energetics of hovering in the mandarin fish (*Synchiropus picturatus*). *J. Exp. Biol.* 82:25–33.

Blake, R.W. 1980a. The mechanics of labriform locomotion II. An analysis of the recovery stroke and the overall fin-beat cycle propulsive efficiency in the angelfish. *J. Exp. Biol.* 85:337–342.

Blake, R.W. 1980b. Undulatory median fin propulsion of two teleosts with different modes of life. *Can. J. Zool.* 58:2116–2119.

Blake, R.W. 1981a. Influence of pectoral fin shape on thrust and drag in labriform locomotion. *J. Zool. Lond.* 194:53–66.

Blake, R.W. 1981b. Mechanics of ostraciiform propulsion. *Can. J. Zool.* 59:1067–1071.

Blake, R.W. 1981c. Mechanics of drag-based mechanisms of propulsion in aquatic vertebrates. In Vertebrate locomotion. *Symp. Zool. Soc. Lond.* 48:29–52.

Blake, R.W. 1982a. *Fish Locomotion.* Cambridge: Cambridge University Press.

Blake, R.W. 1982b. Swimming in the electric-eels and knifefishes. *Can. J. Zool.* (In Press).

Bramwell, A.R.S. 1976. *Helicopter Dynamics.* London: Edward Arnold.

Breder, C.M. 1926. The locomotion of fishes. *Zoologica* 4:159–256.

Breder, C.M., and Edgerton, H.E. 1942. An analysis of the locomotion of the seahorse, *Hippocampus hudsonius*, by means of high-speed cinematography. *Ann. N.Y. Acad. Sci.* 43:145–172.

Ellington, C.P. 1975. The aerodynamics of normal hovering flight: three approaches. In *Comparative Physiology: Water, Ions and Fluid Mechanics,* edited by K. Schmidt-Nielson, L. Bolis, S.H.P. Maddrell. Cambridge: Cambridge University Press.

Ellington, C.P. 1980. Vortices and hovering flight. In *Instationare effekte un schwingenden tierflugeln,* edited by W. Nachtigall. Wiesbaden: Franz Steiner.

Gray, J. 1933. Studies in animal locomotion I. The movement of fish with special reference to the eel. *J. Exp. Biol.* 10:88–104.

Greenwalt, C.H. 1975. The flight of birds. *Trans. Am. Phil. Soc.* 65:1–67.

Hobson, E.S. 1974. Feeding relationships of teleostean fishes on coral reefs in Kona, Hawaii. *Fish. Bull.* 72:915–1031.

Lighthill, M.J. 1960. Note on the swimming of slender fish. *J. Fluid Mech.* 9:305–317.

Lighthill, M.J. 1969. Hydromechanics of aquatic animal propulsion. *Ann. Rev. Fluid Mech.* I:413–446.

Lighthill, M.J. 1970. Aquatic animal propulsion of high hydromechanical efficiency. *J. Fluid Mech.* 44:265–301.

Lighthill, M.J. 1971. Large-amplitude elongated-body theory of fish locomotion. *Proc. R. Soc. Lond.* 179B:125–138.

Lighthill, M.J. 1974. Aerodynamic aspects of animal flight. In *Swimming and Flying in Nature,* edited by T.Y. Wu, C.J. Brokaw, and C. Brennen, vol 2. New York: Plenum Press.

Lighthill, M.J. 1975a. Introduction to the scaling of aerial locomotion. In *Scale Effects in Animal Locomotion,* edited by T.J. Pedley. London: Academic Press.

Lighthill, M.J. 1975b. *Mathematical Biofluiddynamics*. Society for Industrial and Applied Mathematics.

Lighthill, M.J. 1977. Mathematical theories of fish swimming. In *Fisheries Mathematics*, edited by J.E. Steele. New York: Academic Press.

Lindsey, C.C. 1978. Form, function, and locomotory habits in fish. In *Fish Physiology*, edited by W.S. Hoar and D.J. Randall, vol. 7. London: Academic Press.

McCutcheon, C.W. 1975. Froude propulsive efficiency of a small fish measured by wake visualization. In *Scale Effects in Animal Locomotion*, edited by T.J. Pedley. London: Academic Press.

Merzkirch, W. 1974. *Flow Visualization*. London: Academic Press.

Pennycuick, C.J. 1968. Power requirements for horizontal flight in the pigeon *Columba livia*. *J. Exp. Biol.* 49:527–555.

Rayner, J.M.V. 1979. A new approach to animal flight mechanics. *J. Exp. Biol.* 80:17–54.

Stewart, W., and Burle, M.F. 1950. The application of jet propulsion to helicopters. Aeronautical Research Council, Rep. No. 8.

Tucker, V.A. 1973. Bird metabolism during flight: Evaluation of a theory. *J. Exp. Biol.* 58:689–709.

von Mises, R. 1959. *Theory of Flight*. New York: Dover.

Wardle, C.S., and Reid, A. 1977. The application of large amplitude elongated body theory to measure swimming power in fish. In *Fisheries Mathematics*, edited by: J.H. Steele, London: Academic Press.

Webb, P.W. 1971a. The swimming energetics of trout I. Thrust and power output at cruising speeds. *J. Exp. Biol.* 55:489–520.

Webb, P.W. 1971b. The swimming energetics of trout II. Oxygen consumption and swimming efficiency. *J. Exp. Biol.* 55:521–540.

Webb, P.W. 1973. Kinematics of pectoral fin propulsion in *Cymatogaster aggregata*. *J. Exp. Biol.* 59:697–710.

Webb, P.W. 1975a. Efficiency of pectoral fin propulsion of *Cymatogaster aggregata*. In *Swimming and Flying in Nature*, edited by T.Y. Wu, C.J. Brokaw, and C. Brennen. New York: Plenum Press.

Webb, P.W. 1975b. Hydrodynamics and energetics of fish propulsion. *Bull. Fish. Res. Board. Can.* 190:1–159.

Webb, P.W. 1982. Locomotion patterns in the evolution of actinopterygian fishes. *Am. Soc. Zool.* 22:329–342.

Webb, P.W., and Blake, R.W. 1983. Swimming. In *Functional Vertebrate Morphology*, edited by M. Hildebrand. Cambridge, MA: Harvard University Press. (In Press).

Weihs, D. 1972. A hydromechanical analysis of fish turning maneuvers. *Proc. R. Soc. Lond.* 182B:59–72.

Weihs, D. 1974. Energetic advantages of burst swimming of fish. *J. Theoret. Biol.* 48:215–229.

Weis-Fogh, T. 1972. Energetics of hovering flight in hummingbirds and *Drosophilia*. *J. Exp. Biol.* 56:79–104.

Weis-Fogh, T. 1973. Quick estimates of flight fitness in hovering animals, including novel mechanisms for lift production. *J. Exp. Biol.* 59:169–230.

SYMBOLS

R	total fin length	v_f	fin flapping velocity
r	distance out from fin base	v_{sp}	slipstream velocity of fin wake
r'	distance out from fin base to the midpoint of a blade-element	v_i	induced velocity
C	fin chord	v_{ru}, v_{rd}	resultant fin velocities in upstroke and downstroke, respectively of lifting fin
y	length of a blade-element		
S_w	wetted surface area of a fish	v'_r	resultant velocity in any phase of finbeat cycle
S_d	area swept out by fins (disc area)	F_n	normal force component
A	frontally projected area of a fin	T	thrust force
		D	drag force
m	mass	$D_{(b)}$	drag force acting on fish body
m_a	added mass		
t	time	L	lift force
t_p	power stroke duration	F_a	added mass force
t_o	fin-beat cycle time	C_D	drag coefficient
n	fin-beat frequency	$C_{D(b)}$	drag coefficient of fish body
γ	positional angle of fin (angle between the projection of the fin onto the horizontal plane and the median axis of the body)	C_n	normal force coefficient
		C_L	lift coefficient
		I	moment of inertia
		p	pressure
α	hydrodynamical angle of attack	p_o	static pressure
β	angle of tilt of stroke plane	Q_p	torque associated with the profile drag acting on a fin
Φ	stroke angle	Q_i	inertial torque associated with fin
e	downwash angle of fin		
V	forward velocity of fish	Q_a	torque associated with the added mass force acting on a fin
v_n	a normal component of velocity relative to the fin		
v_s	a spanwise component of velocity relative to the fin	H_p	work associated with fin profile drag

H_i — work associated with fin inertia

H_a — work required to move added mass of fin

H_b — work required to overcome body drag

P_{id} — induced power

P_{in} — power input

P_b — power required to overcome body drag

P_p — power associated with fin profile drag

P_i — power associated with fin inertia

P_a — power associated with the added mass of a fin

P_{tot} — total hydrodynamic and inertial power

η — ideal efficiency

η_p — propulsive (Froude) efficiency

η_d — dynamic efficiency

B — a shape factor

Ξ — an inflow factor

J/D — an index of the height of a fin above the ground

ρ — water density

Chapter 8
HEAT TRANSFER
Jeffrey B. Graham

CONTENTS

INTRODUCTION

This chapter considers the mechanisms of heat transfer between a fish and its ambient water, the physical and behavioral circumstances affecting this process, and the cases in which by evolving the capacity to regulate heat transfer, a few species have gained a level of independence for their body temperature (T_b) relative to that of ambient water (T_a).

Close conformity between T_b and T_a found for most fishes made inquiries about heat transfer appear trivial and before 1970 few studies were conducted. Increased recognition of the rapidity, frequency, and magnitude of the T_b changes experienced by many species in the natural environment together with concern about the effects of thermal pollution stimulated heat transfer investigations. Initial work focused on how metabolic heat production affected T_b and on the factors that determined how fast T_b would change following a change in T_a. Evaluation of the relative importance of conduction and convection in nonsteady heat transfer led to the surprising revelation

248

that the gills of fish, long thought to be principal sites of heat transfer, were three to four times less important than the body surface in this process. Current pursuits include determination of physical, temporal, and biotic factors that affect heat transfer and the modeling of these variables in the context of Newton's law to precisely predict rates of T_b change.

Work with endothermic tunas and sharks has progressed from descriptive accounts of $T_b - T_a$ relationships and adaptations for heat conservation to investigation of the factors affecting heat balance and thermoregulation. Endothermy may increase the swimming efficiency of tunas relative to other active fishes. Linkage between the oxygen-delivery and heat-conservation functions of the tuna vascular system place theoretical limits on the aerobic heat production capacity of red muscle, which likely eliminates the potential for overheating. This linkage also permits estimates of the heat-conserving efficiency of retia and speculation about mechanisms for facultative heat production.

WATER HEAT CAPACITY, FISH BODY TEMPERATURE, AND OBLIGATE ECTOTHERMY

Relative to air, water has a four times greater heat capacity ($1 \, cal \cdot g^{-1} \cdot C^{-1}$) and is about 800 times as dense; accordingly, water has about a 3000 times greater heat capacity than air per unit volume. This poses special problems for animals residing in water, which because the potential for heat transfer is so enormous, must either permit their deep (core) T_b to closely conform to T_a or must develop special adaptations (as in the case of marine mammals) to retard heat transfer at the body surface in order to maintain T_b within certain limits.

The vast majority of fishes are ectotherms, and their T_b approximates T_a. They are not able to produce sufficient amounts of metabolic heat to elevate their T_b above T_a or to regulate T_b as T_a changes; because they are immersed in water, fish are unable to use mechanisms for evaporative and radiative energy exchange, which are integral strategies in the thermoregulatory repertoires of terrestrial ectotherms (Schmidt–Nielsen, 1979).

The ability of some fish species to detect thermal gradients and to behaviorally select a preferred T_a in a heterothermal environment has been well documented (Beitinger and Fitzpatrick, 1979; Reynolds and Casterlin, 1979). This thermoregulatory option, however, cannot be exercised in all habitats or by all (or even most) species. Physical restrictions (*i.e.,* optimal T_a may be located beyond the range or it may be part of a large thermal front and drift faster than the swimming capacity of a fish) and ecologic factors (needs for shelter and food) very likely place real limitations on the extent to which behavioral thermoregulation can be used by many fish species. For these reasons virtually all aspects of the life histories of fishes (and many other aquatic ectotherms) are governed by ambient water temperature, which was described by J. R. Brett (1971) as the *master ecological factor.*

BRIEF HISTORY OF FISH THERMOBIOLOGY

Early Investigation of Fish Body and Ambient Water Temperature Relationships

Literature documenting the poikilothermy ($T_b \propto T_a$) of fishes spans 150 years. Summaries and reviews of early papers are found in Clausen (1934), Gunn (1942), and Morrow and Mauro (1950). With the exception of the endothermic fishes (see below), the temperature excess ($T_x = T_b - T_a$) measured for most fishes caught in the field or in an aquarium is usually not greater than 4°C (Stevens and Fry, 1970, 1974).

The early literature reveals concern for the factors that might contribute to erroneous and misleading T_b estimates in the field. These include the early use of mercury thermometers, the site of temperature measurement in the body, and the likely dependence of observed T_b on the size of a fish and on the intensity and duration of its struggle between the time it is hooked and when T_b is measured. Large fishes usually have a sizeable T_x by the time they are decked (Morrow and Mauro, 1950; Lindsey, 1968). Recent T_a history also affects T_b. The actual T_a at the fish's depth before hooking is usually unknown; therefore, comparison of the observed T_b with surface water temperature or even hook-depth T_a often provides no real insight into normal T_b-T_a relationships. Morrow and Mauro (1950) for example found that the T_b of a 122-kg ocean sunfish (*Mola*) was actually 4°C less than the surface T_a (21°C) where it was captured. They concluded that this fish had been swimming at depth (at least 55 m, 16°C) for a considerable time, had just come to the surface, and had not reached thermal equilibrium at the time it was harpooned and decked.

Use of thermocouples in the 1930s led to the first laboratory measurements of T_b-T_a relationships in fishes that were left relatively undisturbed for long periods in aquaria (Clausen, 1934). In addition, conditions could be evaluated for steady state heat transfer

$$\frac{dT_b}{dt} = 0 \tag{1}$$

where the fish is in thermal equilibrium with its ambient temperature, and nonsteady heat transfer

$$\frac{dT_b}{dt} \neq 0 \tag{2}$$

which could be brought about by slight changes in fish activity (metabolic heat production increasing T_b), a change in T_a, or both.

Early thermocouple work involved small fishes that had very small T_x in steady state conditions and that, in nonsteady conditions tended to reach thermal equilibrium rapidly. As in many of the field observations, the T_x measured for small fishes tends to be less than that for larger ones. Gunn (1942) surmised that although smaller fish could be expected to have a higher mass-specific metabolic heat production rates (*i.e.*, metabolism $\propto$ mass$^{-0.2}$) than a larger fish, the smaller mass and larger body surface-to-mass ratio favored more rapid heat loss.

Thermal Adaptation Mechanisms

For the most part and until very recently it would be correct to view investigations of T_b-T_a relationships as the starting point for a broader inquiry into the thermal adaptations of fishes. Documentation of thermally related incidents of natural fish mortality and the linkage between temperature, O_2 availability, and metabolism (Brett, 1956) clearly established the complete dependence of fishes on T_a and led to a largely thermocentric view of fish physiology. Very extensive investigations have included the factors affecting the upper and lower thermal tolerances (Brett, 1956) and thermal preferences of fishes (Beitinger and Fitzpatrick, 1979), the physiological and biochemical mechanisms in temperature compensation including the roles of acclimatization and acclimation, and the importance of temperature in determining the distribution and abundance and metabolic intensity of fishes (Fry, 1971; Brett and Groves, 1979).

The Real World for Fishes: Nonsteady Heat Transfer

During the early 1970s it became increasingly apparent that although fish were generally considered to be stenothermal, the T_b of some species, because of conformity with T_a, was regularly subjected to large and rapid changes. This was instrumental in renewing interest in and changing the status of investigations of fish T_b-T_a relationships and rates of nonsteady heat transfer.

An important force in this transition was Brett's (1971) classic paper describing the role of temperature in the physiology and ecology of sockeye salmon (*Oncorhynchus nerka*) in Babine Lake, British Columbia. While the bulk of the behavioral, physiological, and life history data collected for this species indicated that 15°C was both its optimal and preferred temperature, Brett found its distribution in the lake to be under the combined control of both biotic and abiotic factors such as prey distribution and time of day. The sockeye quickly moved from deeper (5°C) water where it spent daylight hours to near the water surface (15°C to 17°C) at night; thus, large-scale and rapid changes in T_b seemed to be the rule rather than the exception for sockeye living in Babine Lake. This also is the case with many marine mesopelagic species that undergo daily vertical migrations and experience T_a changes of 15°C to 20°C (Childress *et al.*, 1980).

Rising concern about adverse effects of thermal pollution in aquatic ecosystems also stimulated research (Erskine and Spotila, 1977; Spigarelli *et al.*, 1977). Evidence again indicated that large-scale, rapid and frequent T_b changes commonly occurred for some fish species in impacted areas. Numerous reports (literature in Spigarelli *et al.*, 1977; Kubb *et al.*, 1980) suggested that fish dwelling near thermal outfalls might "average" T_b by balancing their time in cool and warm regions of their habitat. Some species were reported to be able to enhance their feeding success (*i.e.*, stored heat increases muscle power; stunned or disorientated prey often occur in the effluent water) by spending brief periods at or above T_a that would prove lethal with longer exposure. It seems very likely that heat transfer—hence the rate of change of T_b—may be of primary importance in governing these behaviors (Crawshaw, 1979).

HEAT TRANSFER PRINCIPLES

Body and Ambient Temperature Relationships: Steady-State Conditions

Fish T_b is determined by the balance between heat production and heat loss and is constant when a fish is in thermal equilibrium with its ambient water, as shown in equation 1. At steady-state conditions, heat (Q) balance is expressed by

$$Q_{gain} - Q_{loss} = 0 \qquad (3)$$

Principal sources of metabolic heat production in a fish are aerobic cell respiration including that associated with the digestion and assimilation of food stuffs (Brett and Groves, 1979; see also Chap. 10). During activity, frictional heat produced in muscle and other elastic elements will also be added as illustrated by Figure 8-1. Heat transfer between a fish and water occurs only by conduction (Q_{cd}) and convection (Q_{cv}) (Sorenson and Fromm, 1976). In terms of equation 3, heat balance for a fish can be written as follows:

$$Q_M - (Q_{cd} + Q_{cv}) = 0 \qquad (4)$$
$$Q_M = Q_{cd} + Q_{cv}$$

where M denotes sources of internal (metabolic) heat production.

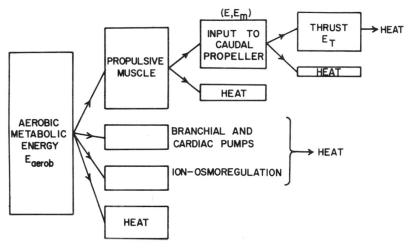

Figure 8-1

Sources of metabolic heat production in a swimming fish. Only thrust heat would not affect T_x. (From Webb, 1975)

Under steady-state conditions there will be an equilibrium body temperature, T_e (Neill and Stevens, 1974), and at thermal equilibrium

$$T_e = T_b = T_a \qquad (5)$$

This implies that the potentials for heat transfer within the body and at the surface vastly exceed the resting heat production rates in these fishes. Some species and many larger fish, however, may have a measurable T_x in steady-state condition

$$T_e = T_b = T_a + T_x \qquad (6)$$

In these cases, metabolic heat is stored. Although the rates of heat loss and heat production are balanced, the thermal gradient needed to drive heat transfer is steeper owing to a thicker body wall and greater body diameter, as in the case of a larger fish (Kubb *et al.*, 1980).

Nonsteady State Conditions

When a fish encounters water of a different temperature than that at which it is in equilibrium, the fish's T_b changes until a new T_e is reached. Periods of vigorous activity may elevate T_b briefly, but heat is gradually lost until T_e is reached (Fig. 8-2). These are examples of nonsteady heat transfer. Two principles regarding nonsteady transfer seem intuitive: the rate of change of T_b is proportional to the magnitude of the change in T_a; the mechanisms for

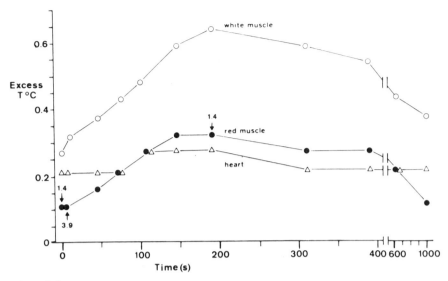

Figure 8-2

T_x in the heart and red and white muscles of a 35-cm Pacific mackerel (*Scomber japonicus*) swimming at speeds from 1.4 to 3.9 body lengths · sec^{-1}. Arrows indicate timing and direction of velocity changes; T_a = 19.5 to 19.6°C. (From Roberts and Graham, 1979.)

heat transfer (conduction and convection) transport heat either into or out of the fish's body depending on the direction of the new thermal gradient. When a fish swims into warmer water, heat gained from the environment is added to the metabolic heat production rate. This implies that for similar step changes in T_a (*i.e.*, increase versus decrease), a fish should heat slightly faster than it cools.

As shall be examined below, experiments contrasting the heating and cooling rates of living and dead fish have been used to estimate the effects of metabolic heat production, to assess the relative importance of various types and internal and external convection and conduction in heat transfer, and to search for mechanisms that may have adaptive significance in permitting certain species to regulate their rates of T_b change.

HEAT TRANSFER MECHANISMS

Thermal Conduction

Conduction is the diffusion of heat from molecule to molecule down the thermal gradient in a solid object. For a fish in thermal equilibrium, conduction transfers metabolic heat produced throughout the body toward the skin. In theory, heat produced at a specific point would diffuse uniformly in all directions; therefore, heat concentrated in the center (core) of a fish is assumed to give a core temperature T_c and produce a small thermal gradient (Fig. 8-3). Heat flow (Q) from the core to the skin can be described by Fourier's equation

$$Q = -KA \frac{\mathrm{d}T}{\mathrm{d}x}$$ (7)

where K is tissue thermal conductivity, A is an area perpendicular to the direction of heat flow, and $\mathrm{d}T/\mathrm{d}x$ is the thermal gradient. Assuming that both heat production and K are uniform at all points in the body (see below, Nonsteady-State Conditions, under Empirical Analyses of Heat Transfer),

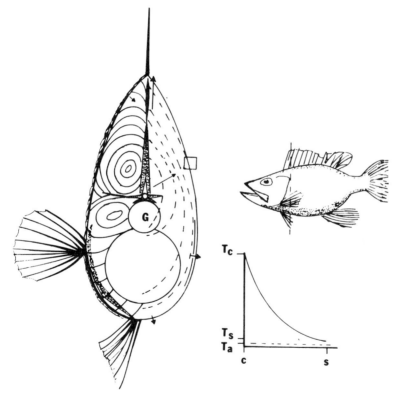

Figure 8-3
Transverse section of a fish slightly posterior of its paired fins, showing relationships between internal and external anatomic features on one side and a set of theoretical thermal profiles established by metabolic heat production and thermal conduction at steady-state conditions. Arrows show direction of conduction and the possible role of body materials in enhancing or retarding heat flow. The graph shows the decrease in temperature from the core (T_c) to the skin (T_s), which is slightly warmer than T_a. (Inset is section shown in Figure 8-4.)

total heat flow to the surface would be the sum of the transfer rates in all coordinates. Because tissues consist of organic and inorganic constituents as well as water, their thermal conductivities are usually assumed to be slightly less than water (about 0.5 watts $\cdot$ m^{-1} $\cdot$ $^{\circ}$C^{-1}; Leyton, 1975; Kubb et al., 1980).

Models of conductive heat transfer in fishes and other ectotherms usually assume that the body is an entity of several compartments, each of which is uniformly contained within a number of concentric outer layers (Spotila et al., 1973; Erskine and Spotila, 1977). These compartments are considered to be isothermal and well mixed by blood circulation. For estimation purposes, uniform values of tissue thermal conductivity (K) are assumed, and heat transfer is considered to occur symmetrically and rapidly throughout the body (Fig. 8-3; Kubb et al., 1980).

Body shape influences the thermal gradient between the core and skin of a fish. For a cylindrically shaped fish, which has the smallest ratio of area to volume, heat flow increases proportionately with the natural logarithm of the ratio of the areas of the core and skin. This can be seen by expressing A in the Fourier equation (7) in terms of the area of a cylinder of radius r and length L ($A = 2\pi rL$) and integrating with respect to temperature and the change in radius

$$Q_{c-s} \int_{r_c}^{r_s} \frac{dr}{2\pi rL} = -K \int_{t_c}^{T_s} dT \tag{8}$$

where subscripts s and c represent surface and core conditions, respectively. Heat flow from core to skin is

$$Q_{c-s} = 2\pi KL \left(T_c - T_s \right) / ln \frac{r_s}{r_c} \tag{9}$$

Temperature will decrease logarithmically toward the skin in this situation (Fig. 8-3).

Convective Heat Transfer

Convection is the transfer of heat by a moving fluid. Within the body of a fish, heat convection occurs principally in the blood (forced internal convection); however, other convective heat-transfer processes, both intracellular (cytoplasmic streaming) and extracellular (active transport linked), no doubt occur (Pettit and Beitinger, 1980; Vogel, 1981). These are difficult to quantify and cannot be readily distinguished from conductive mechanisms to which they seem intimately linked (Pettit and Beitinger, 1980).

FORCED INTERNAL CONVECTION

Within the body of a fish, metabolic heat can be transported from the core toward the edge of the body and eventually to water (via gill or skin) in the blood (forced internal convection). Heat transfer by this means is estimated by

$$Q = f \cdot S \cdot \dot{B} \cdot T_x \tag{10}$$

where f is the fraction of heat lost as blood passes along the surface contacting water, s is the heat capacity of blood (cal $\cdot$ ml^{-1}), $\dot{B}$ is the cardiac output or tissue blood flow rate (ml $\cdot$ min^{-1}), and T_x is the temperature excess measured in the blood where it enters the water-contacting tissue (Stevens and Sutterlin, 1976).

NATURAL CONVECTION

Heat reaching the body surface is transferred to water by natural convection when

$$Q = hA \, (T_s - T_a) \tag{11}$$

where h is an average convective heat transfer coefficient for the entire body surface, A is body surface area, and $T_s - T_a$ is the difference in skin and ambient temperatures. The term h reflects properties of the body surface, the characteristics of water around the body, and also encompasses all the properties (e.g., thermal conductivity, viscosity, density) of water at T_a.

Natural convection describes heat diffusion from a surface into a motionless fluid. This condition rarely exists for a fish; however, in principle, natural convection occurs as heat diffuses from the skin to the layer of water in contact with it. As water is heated its density is lowered, causing it to rise away from the skin and initiating continuous flow parallel to the skin (Fig. 8-4). The thermal gradient from skin to water determines the thickness of the layer of water set in motion—the thermal boundary layer (Leyton, 1975). If the gradient is large, the boundary layer is thin and heat transfer is rapid; if the gradient is small, the boundary layer is broad and heat transfer is slow. All fish movements such as swimming, fin motion, and even gill ventilation propel water along the body surface and establish conditions for forced convection (Fig. 8-4). Water movement reduces the thermal boundary layer and increases heat loss (Leyton, 1975).

The convective heat transfer coefficient, h, is affected by so many factors that it is often impossible to evaluate directly. A practical solution to this problem resides in the combination, through dimensional analysis, of fluid properties that likely affect natural and forced convection rates in the system

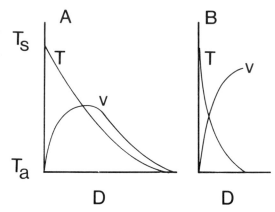

Figure 8–4
Effects of the gradient between T_s and T_a (Fig. 8-3) on the thermal boundary layer. A, Natural convection; water velocity (V) and temperature (T) are less affected with increasing distance (D). B, Forced convection; the boundary layer is narrower, and velocity increases to a maximum with distance. (After Leyton, 1975.)

under consideration. Numerical quantities and their interrelationships have been empirically determined for objects of various sizes, shapes, and orientations at different fluid-flow rates. Because water properties around a fish are not likely to change with velocity, surface heat transfer can be expressed in terms of the dimensionless Nusselt (Nu) and Reynolds (Re) numbers (Kay, 1963). The Nusselt number is a measure of heat transfer; it is analogous to the drag coefficient, which is a dimensionless measure of drag (Vogel, 1981). Nu combines a dimensionless heat transfer coefficient, h, with a typical length of an object, L, and the thermal conductivity, λ, of the fluid.

$$Nu = \frac{hL}{\lambda} \tag{12}$$

Re relates length (L) and velocity (V) and kinematic viscosity of water (see Chap. 6)

$$Re = \frac{VL}{v} \tag{13}$$

It can be shown that the Nusselt number can be described through its empirical relationship with Reynolds number (Kay, 1963; Leyton, 1975; Vogel, 1981).

$$Nu :: Re^a \tag{14}$$

where a is determined by body shape and flow orientation. Erskine and Spotila (1977) calculated the convective heat-transfer coefficient for largemouth bass (*Micropterus salmoides*)

$$Nu = 0.015 \, Re^{0.71} \tag{15}$$

Leyton (1975) elucidates underlying principles of this application. Re is readily calculable, and substitution into equation 14 reveals a solution for h

$$h \frac{L}{\lambda} = \left(\frac{VL}{\nu} \right)^a \tag{16}$$

$$h = V^a \cdot L^{a-1} \cdot \frac{\lambda}{\nu}$$

Erskine and Spotila (1977; see below under Effects of Water Flow on Heat Loss) estimated a heat-transfer coefficient of about $0.8 \, \text{cal} \cdot \text{cm}^{-2} \cdot \text{min}^{-1} \cdot {}^\circ\text{C}^{-1}$ for a largemouth bass in still water. They also found that at water flow velocities greater than about 15 cm $\cdot$ sec^{-1}, the heat-transfer coefficient increased linearly, approaching 3.0 at about 90 cm $\cdot$ sec^{-1} velocity (Fig. 8-5).

EMPIRICAL ANALYSES OF HEAT TRANSFER

The Magnitude of Heat Flow versus the Heat Capacity of Water

For ectothermic fishes a first principle of heat transfer analysis is that the high heat capacity of water together with its complete and continuous contact with the fish body surface ensures that all heat reaching the edge of the body will be instantly dissipated. The thermal boundary layer of a fish in both steady-state and nonsteady-state transfer is effectively nonexistent. Differences between T_s and T_a are undetectable in most if not all ectothermic fish species that have been examined. Endothermic tuna, like most aquatic mammals (Schmidt–Nielsen, 1979), allow T_s to equilibrate with T_a even though the body-core temperature is maintained above T_a by means of vascular specializations (Brill *et al.*, 1978; Stevens and Neill, 1978).

Because the thermal gradient is infinitesimal, external convection is

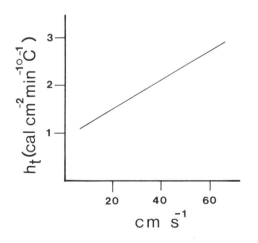

Figure 8-5

Heat transfer and water velocity (cm $\cdot$ sec^{-1}) relationships established for largemouth bass castings by Erskine and Spotila (1977). Equation for line is $h_t = 0.33 \, V + 0.9$.

difficult to quantify. A practical solution for heat transfer problems is to substitute a term that combines conduction and convection into the general heat balance (equation 4)

$$M = h_t \, (T_s - T_a) \tag{17}$$

where h_t is the combined convective and conductive heat-transfer coefficient of water at the body surface and $T_s - T_a$ is the thermal gradient from skin to water (Kubb et al., 1980).

Effects of Water Flow on Heat Loss

Erskine and Spotila (1977) estimated the effects of $T_s - T_a$ (Equation 17) and water flow on the heat-transfer coefficients (h_t) of largemouth bass. The cooling rates of aluminum castings (made from fish weighing between 129 g and 1346 g and heated to exactly 50°C) were monitored in still and flowing water (23, 55, and 67 cm · sec^{-1} flow rates). No effect of temperature difference on h_t was found, but h_t increased with water flow rate (Fig. 8-5); however, experimental results of Kubb and colleagues (1980) showed no significant change in the thermal time constants (time required to reach T_e) for living largemouth bass subjected to 5°C to 7°C step changes in T_a in both still and turbulent waters (Fig. 8-6). These workers concluded that heat transfer occurred so rapidly that increased water flow had no impact; thus the rate of heat flow into or out of a fish experiencing a step change in T_a is limited by heat transfer between its core and outer layers and not at the skin-water interface (Kubb et al., 1980).

Body-Size Effects and Steady-State Body Temperature

The relationship between body mass and T_x discussed by Gunn (1942) was further explored by Stevens and Fry (1974), who compiled all the current

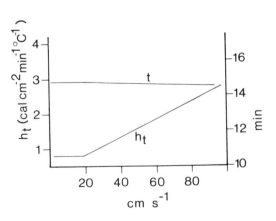

Figure 8-6
Comparison of the heat transfer and water velocity (cm · s^{-1}) relationships calculated for a 1-kg largemouth bass with its predicted equilibrium time constants (t, min) for core T_b. (After Kubb et al., 1980.)

T_c data for different fish species (and marine turtles) for which both body mass and T_a at capture were known. These workers found a linear relationship between T_x at a point deep in the body core and body mass (W).

$$T_x = (C_2/C_1) W^{0.4} \qquad (18)$$

where C_1 and C_2 are constants of proportionality, and W ranged from 0.02 kg to 30 kg. Close agreement between the determined mass exponent (0.4) and the difference in the exponents for weight-specific metabolism ($W^{-0.2}$) and weight-specific heat loss from deep in the body ($W^{-0.6}$; see below) suggested to Stevens and Fry (1974) that the increased body diameter and body-wall thickness of larger fish sufficiently retarded heat flow to give the observed T_x.

Conditions under which data were collected made it unlikely that fish were in thermal equilibrium; thus equation 18 may not be applicable to steady states. In addition, large tuna and skipjack were included in the analysis by Stevens and Fry (1974), but subsequent work has shown that these endothermic fishes can thermoregulate or maintain a specified T_x (Dizon and Brill, 1979; Graham and Dickson, 1981). Additional experiments with other ectothermic fishes revealed no weight-T_x relationship in several species (Spigarelli et al., 1977). In general, the magnitude of T_x has been shown to vary among species (Reynolds, 1977) with the position of measurement (Kubb et al., 1980), and T_x is rapidly affected by exercise and metabolic rate (Spigarelli et al., 1977; Roberts and Graham, 1979). It is therefore unlikely that a predictable relationship between weight and T_x exists for all species.

Nonsteady-State Conditions

Measurements of nonsteady heat transfer have largely focused on determining the relative importance to heat flow of conduction and forced internal convection and on predicting the rate of T_b change following a step change in T_a. There is no evidence suggesting that species can regulate heat flow and thus dT_b/dt.

EFFECTS OF BLOOD FLOW

A surprising finding for most species is that internal body thermal conduction along with intracellular and extracellular convection are the primary mechanisms for heat transfer, and that loss by way of forced internal convection to the gills usually accounts for no more than 10% to 30% of total heat loss. Sorenson and Fromm (1976) and Stevens and Sutterlin (1976) used isolated gill preparations to estimate heat transfer as blood flow rates, gill area, and T_x (see equation 10) were varied. A model developed for rainbow trout (*Salmo gairdneri*) showed that gill heat loss could be raised to 60% of total heat flow, depending on blood flow rate and autonomically controlled vascular dimensions in the gill (Sorenson and Fromm, 1976). In the sea raven (*Hemitripterus americanus*), gill heat loss estimates ranged from 10% to 30%, depending on the amount of heat entering the gill (Stevens and Sutterlin, 1976). Changes in branchial flow rates and perfusion areas are doubtless consequences of activity and responses to physical and sensory stimuli. The above findings clearly indicate that variations in gill blood flow and surface area potentially affect heat transfer rates; however, they do not imply that fishes ordinarily use these mechanisms to regulate heat gain or loss rates (see Rate of Body Temperature Change).

Indirect estimates of internal convection have been made by comparing heating and cooling rates of live and dead fish. Dead fish have 20% to 30% larger time constants, and this is assumed to be caused by the absence of intracellular-intercellular streaming and convective blood flow within the body and forced convection to the gills (Beitinger et al., 1977; Pettit and Beitinger, 1980). The numerous factors likely to affect these indirect estimates were discussed by Kubb and associates (1980). Heat transfer experiments with fishes that ventilate their gills intermittently or not at all when air breathing (*e.g.*, *Lepidosiren paradoxa*, Pettit and Beitinger, 1980) provide an alternative means of estimating gill heat transfer. Pettit and Beitinger (1980) found forced convection accounted for about 18% of the heat transfer of lungfish (*Lepidosiren*) exposed to 6° C step decreases and increases in T_a. This rate is similar to most other fishes; however, lungfish regularly shunt blood flow away from their gills during air breathing. In hypoxic water, lungfish usually take more air breaths and pump less blood to their gills, and when forcibly submerged in normoxic water, gill perfusion increases (references in Pettit and Beitinger, 1980). Examination of the avenues of heat transfer during various modes of breathing may indicate the extent that forced internal heat convection can be modified by branchial blood flow.

THE RATE OF BODY TEMPERATURE CHANGE

Models generally strive to predict heat-transfer time constants of fishes in response to gradual or abrupt T_a changes and oscillating regimes of T_a (Kubb et al., 1980; Fechhelm and Neill, 1982). In natural environments, central processing of rate changes in core and peripheral thermoreceptors is probably important in the detection of thermal gradients (Neill et al., 1976) and in behavioral thermoregulation (Crawshaw, 1979; Beitinger and Fitzpatrick, 1979). Furthermore, time constants for changes in core temperature may influence patterns of fish distribution and abundance (Kubb et al., 1980; see above).

The rate that T_b changes depends on the magnitude of the change in T_a and can be accurately described by Newton's law (Stevens and Neill, 1978)

$$\frac{dT_b}{dt} = k \cdot T(T_e - T_b) \tag{19}$$

where $T_e - T_b$ is the difference between the initial core T_b of the fish and the temperature (T_e) for thermal equilibrium with its new T_a, k is the rate coefficient, and t is time. The rate coefficient k is the instantaneous rate of change in body temperature per unit time per difference in T_e and T_b and is attributable to the combined effects of conductive and convective heat transfer. Empirical estimates of k are obtained by monitoring the rate of change of T_b. The integral of equation 19 with respect to time is

$$ln|T_e - T_b(t)| = ln|T_e - T_b(0)| - kt \tag{20}$$

where $T_b(t)$ is body temperature at time t and $T_b(0)$ is body temperature at $t = 0$ (Stevens and Neill, 1978); therefore, a function expressing $\ln T_e - T_b(t)$ in relation to time has a slope $-k$.

A slight modification of Newton's law was incorporated into a model to predict the T_b of fish exposed to continuous changes in T_a by Fechhelm and Neill (1982). These workers inserted an empirically determined latency term (l) into Newton's equation 19 to correct for the brief interval of time, just after a step change in T_a, when the rate of change in T_b is not exponential (*i.e.*, a constant k does not strictly apply).

$$\frac{dT_b}{dt} = k[T_e(t-1) - T_b(t)] \tag{21}$$

Fechhelm and Neill (1982) found remarkably close agreement between the observed and simulated body temperatures of sunfish (*Lepomis macrochirus*) and two species of *Tilapia* (*T. aurea* and *T. nilotica*) exposed to T_a irregularly cycled between 18°C and 33°C. The mean absolute error between measured and simulated T_b ranged from 0.04°C to 0.24°C in 146-g and 90-g *Tilapia nilotica*; over 90% of their model's prediction errors were less than ±0.3°C.

Other refinements in the estimation of fish heating and cooling rates include dimensional analyses for the effects of water flow (see above, Effects of Water Flow on Heat Loss) and factoring of the effects of body size and shape and metabolic rate. The model developed by Kubb and colleagues (1980; also see Spotila *et al.*, 1973; Erskine and Spotila, 1977) enabled them to closely predict heating and cooling rates of various sizes of largemouth bass subjected to 5°C to 7°C step changes in T_a. Neither fish metabolic rate nor water flow affected heat transfer rate; the thermal time constants varied in different compartments of the body in relation to their remoteness from the body surface. Because of its proximity to the body surface, the heart had a faster time constant than did either the brain or the gut. Thermal time constants determined at anatomically symmetrical positions were found to increase with fish body size for both the brain and gut but not the heart. Morphologic analyses by Kubb and colleagues (1980) revealed that proportional increases in body diameter and body-wall thickness directly contributed to the larger thermal constants of brain and gut in larger fish.

For all fish species that have been examined, general agreement exists for the inverse relationships between heat-transfer rate and body size (Stevens and Fry, 1970, 1974; Spigarelli et al., 1977; Beitinger et al., 1977; Kubb et al., 1980). Specific differences seen in the hierarchies of the thermal time constants of different deep tissues (gut, dorsal muscle mass, and spinal cord) are probably attributable to differences in fish body shape and size and in analytical procedures (Crawshaw, 1977, 1979; Kubb et al., 1980). Finally, slight differences in heating and cooling rates observed for some species are probably without physiological significance (Crawshaw, 1979; Fechhelm and Neill, 1982).

Interspecific comparisons of heat transfer are not at the point where the effects of different morphologic features on thermal conduction and internal convection are known. Such analyses can be expected to show that tissue and whole body conductances are not similar in all species. The value for fish tissue thermal conductivity (K) is usually assumed to be 0.53 watts $\cdot$ m^{-1} $\cdot$ °C^{-1} (references in Kubb et al., 1980); however, this value has been found to vary among species and with body size and shape (Stevens and Fry, 1970; Beitinger et al., 1977; Spigarelli et al., 1977). It is also a function of the site of T_b measurement (Stevens and Fry, 1974; Kubb et al., 1980) and may vary depending on whether T_b is increasing or decreasing in response to the change in T_a (Beitinger et al., 1977; Spigarelli et al., 1977; Fechhelm and Neill, 1982). Heat-transfer rate will likely change for a species with physical condition and season (Kubb et al., 1980). Tissue fat stores, a gas bladder, and thick overlapping scales can be expected to retard heat flow; on the other hand, bony and cartilaginous structures (vertebral spines, ribs, and pterygiophores) lying perpendicular to the body axis may increase conductance. Pterygiophores and paired fin-girdles may focus heat flow to median and paired-fin rays (Brill et al., 1978).

Interspecific comparisons of whole body conductance values have focused attention on the somewhat similar slope values (-0.6) found for the relationship between log K (determined near the core) and log body mass determined for species of fish and other ectotherms (and to some extent, mammals and birds after removal of insulation). Owing to the heat capacity of water, intercept values are higher for fishes than for other aquatic ectotherms, and there are interspecific differences in K. Although a subject of some speculation, the basis for the common relationship between log K and log mass remains unknown (Stevens and Fry, 1974).

ENDOTHERMY: EXCEPTIONS TO THE RULE

Endothermic fishes include the tunas (family Scombridae) and mackerel sharks (Lamnidae), which have a T_x throughout most of their bodies (Carey *et al.,* 1982; Stevens and Neill, 1978), and the swordfishes and marlins (Xiphidae and Istiophoridae), in which a 2°C to 10°C T_x is confined to the brain and adjacent tissues (Carey, 1982). Billfishes have thermogenic tissue located at the base of their skulls that resembles mammalian brown fat, is rich in cytochrome-c, and may function exclusively for metabolic heat production. For mackerel sharks and tunas, which are fast and continuously swimming predators, metabolic heat, a product of constant action by the swimming muscles, is conserved within the body by large vascular retia mirabilia (Carey *et al.,* 1971, 1981).

Retia (Fig. 8-7) are countercurrent heat exchangers that limit forced internal heat convection by transferring heat from warm venous blood, exiting red (slow) muscle, to cool oxygen-laden arterial blood about to enter red muscle after having come into thermal equilibrium with T_a in the gills. Retia lie adjacent to the myotomes, are comprised of arteries and veins (not capillaries), and are in series with the major arterial and venous systemic

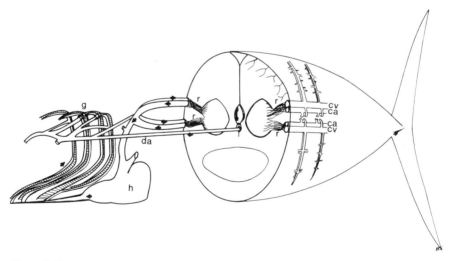

Figure 8-7
Patterns of red and white muscle blood circulation in an albacore. Circulation to red muscle is through lateral retia (r) via cutaneous arteries (ca) and veins (cv). White muscle blood flow, also via cutaneous vessels and smaller segmental vessels and from the dorsal aorta (da), does not pass through retia. Vessels on the right side of the fish are extended anteriorly to show flow to heart (h), through gills (g, only right gill arches are shown), where complete thermal equilibrium occurs, and back to the dorsal aorta and cutaneous arteries.

circulation (Graham and Diener, 1978). In addition to being barriers to forced internal convection at the principal sites of heat production, retia are also positioned at crucial points in the systemic circulation of the fish where if absent, cool arterial blood would penetrate warmed regions and alter heat distribution. All lamnid sharks and a few tunas have retia on some vessels entering the coelom and can elevate gut temperature (Carey et al., 1971, 1981). Billfishes, together with tunas and mackerel sharks, maintain brain T_x with heat-conserving retia. It is unknown whether heat conserved in the brains and viscera of sharks and tunas is produced by local thermogenesis, conducted from body muscle, or both.

Continuous swimming by a tuna requires a high rate of oxygen consumption sustained by a high cardiac output, a large blood volume, a high hemoglobin concentration, and a large respiratory surface area. In a tuna, the magnitude of each of these parameters is much higher than in other fishes and more closely resembles typical values for mammals (Stevens and Neill, 1978). Heat conservation in tunas very likely evolved as a consequence of an elevated metabolic heat production rate and the proliferation of dense bundles of arteries and veins needed to sustain aerobic activity in a deep red muscle mass (see below; Roberts and Graham, 1979). An elevated and relatively constant T_b doubtlessly enhances the metabolic and sensory functions in these fishes and thus contributes to their success as predators (Sharp and Dizon, 1978; Stevens and Neill, 1978).

There appears to be no drag-reducing advantage for endothermy as calculations summarized in Webb (1975) show that as with cetaceans, the rates of surface heat-transfer from endothermic fishes are below amounts required to reduce frictional drag by heating the boundary layer of water. Wardle (1977), however, has suggested that endothermy enables the tuna to maintain its internal physiological functions within an optimal temperature range, permitting them to frequent cooler waters. The kinematic viscosity of water increases with decreasing temperature, thus Reynold's number is reduced (equation 13), which in turn lowers the drag coefficient and may enable large tunas to swim more economically.

Effects of Rete and Locomotor Muscle Position on Tuna Heat Transfer

T_x values of decked tuna are unnaturally high. Depending on species, body size, and T_a, they range from 2°C to 21°C (Stevens and Neill, 1978). The deep T_b maintained by free-swimming thermoregulating bluefin, however, is less than that of a decked fish (Carey and Lawson, 1973; Fig. 8-8). The T_b of albacore quickly dropped from near 30°C at capture to 20°C to 25°C while fish thermoregulated for several hours at water temperatures ranging from 11°C to 17°C (Graham and Dickson, 1981).

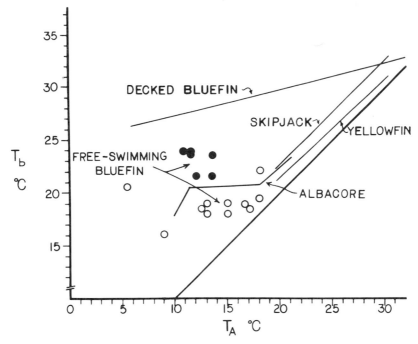

Figure 8-8

T_b-T_a relationships established for four tunas showing the line for thermoregulating albacore and the regulated T_x of skipjack and yellowfin (Dizon and Brill, 1979). Muscle (*dots*) and stomach (*circles*) temperatures of telemetered bluefin are below deep muscle temperatures of decked bluefin (Carey and Teal, 1969; Carey and Lawson, 1973). (From Graham and Dickson, 1981.)

Sources of heat production in tunas are the deeply positioned core of red muscle, which by retia is thermally isolated from T_a and the surrounding layers of white (fast) muscle (Fig. 8-7). Although white muscle is doubtlessly warmed by local heat production and by heat conducted from red muscle, it is not thermally isolated by retia. The locomotor functions and properties of red and white muscle are reviewed by Johnston in Chapter 2. Data for scombrids indicates considerable overlap in the swimming speeds at which both muscles are active (Brill and Dizon, 1979; Roberts and Graham, 1979).

Unlike most fishes including other scombrids, tuna red muscle is located anterior in the body and deep near the vertebral column. This position likely accounts for the rigid thunniform swimming movements described for tunas (Lindsey, 1978). As suggested by measurements of swimming energetics (Gooding *et al.,* 1981 see below, Heat Transfer Efficiency), red muscle position may impart a mechanical advantage to red muscle at faster speeds and by allowing for changes in caudal fin amplitude and frequency, may enhance heat production for thermoregulation (Graham and Dickson, 1981). Studies with scombrids in my laboratory show red muscle amounts range from as little as 4% of total body weight in albacore to as much as 13% in frigate tuna (*Auxis*; Graham *et al.,* 1983); the exponent relating red muscle mass to body mass (red muscle mass = W^b) is significantly larger than 1.0 in two ectothermic scombrids (mackerel and bonito) but 1.0 or less in five endothermic tuna species. These data suggest that endothermic red muscle is more efficient than is ectothermic red muscle. Furthermore, evidence indicates that hydrodynamic factors such as the maximum body size of a species, its buoyancy, and its fin (lift area) dimensions are all related to the amount and position of red muscle (Graham *et al.,* 1983).

The large T_x values measured in both red and white muscle of a decked tuna indicate that red muscle works during intense activity, and heat is conducted to white muscle. If fast, sustained and burst swimming were exclusively powered by white muscle, metabolic heat transfer at the gills and body surface would proceed as in ectothermic fishes and would be enhanced by high blood volumes and flow rates and a large gill area, and the T_x observed for a decked tuna would therefore not be expected to be very much higher than that of other species. For skipjack in nonsteady-state, Brill and associates (1978) calculated that nearly 60% of heat loss occurred through the gills. Without retia, 98% of heat loss by an albacore would occur through the gills (see below). Moreover, forced internal convection to the body surface is greatly facilitated by the blood flow pattern in most species where venous blood exiting white muscle collects at the lateral body surface and flows to the heart in large cutaneous veins (Fig. 8-7; Graham and Diener, 1978).

Affected by both body shape and rete position, thermal conductance establishes temperature profiles within the body that influence surface heat loss (Graham, 1975). Because of the intrusion of cool blood in the dorsal aorta, tunas without central heat exchangers (albacore and bluefin) have relatively cool central cores and warm regions at the center of laterally displaced red muscle packs (Fig. 8-9); in fish with a central rete (skipjacks and yellowfin), red muscle next to the vertebral column is the warmest. Thermal gradients from deep body to skin depend on the size and position of lateral retia. The black skipjack (*Euthynnus*) has no lateral retia, and its lateral thermal gradient (Fig. 8-9) drops abruptly as in an ectothermic fish (Fig. 8-3). A hyperbolic decreases in T_b is seen in skipjack (*Katsuwonus*) that has small lateral retia (Fig. 8-9). For *Katsuwonus*, Brill and colleagues (1978) found that mean surface heat loss rates were lowest along the lateral midline of the body where lateral retia occur and were highest near the dorsal fin.

Factors Affecting Tuna Heat Balance

Conformity between cooling rates observed for some large telemetered tunas and rates predicted by Newton's law (equation 19) suggested that the large T_x values of bluefin tunas were a function of body size and a low but

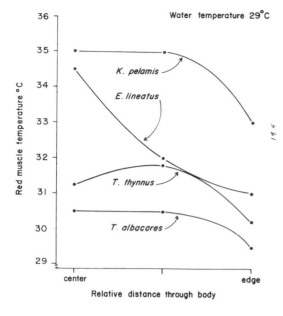

Figure 8-9
Lateral midplane thermal profiles from the center to the edge of the body in four tunas (see also Fig. 8-3). (From Graham, 1975.)

constant thermal conductance afforded by retia (Neill and Stevens, 1974). Subsequent investigations have demonstrated the capabilities of tunas to control rates of both their heat production and loss in order to maintain a constant T_x or to regulate T_b (Fig. 8-8). In addition, these species anticipate and mitigate the effects of T_a and activity on heat balance by rapidly moving from one water temperature to another (Dizon and Brill, 1979; Graham and Dickson, 1981). Assessment of heat transfer in tunas is therefore complicated by the role of behavioral and physiological responses triggered by interactions between T_a and T_b.

Heat production in tunas and mackerel sharks is linked to swimming speed. Surface heat loss by convection is a combined function of water flow rate (swimming speed) and T_x; another significant factor in heat loss is blood flow to the gills. Figure 8-10 illustrates the manner in which swimming speed, T_a, and blood flow may affect heat balance. Calculations for this figure are based on a 90-cm fork length (L) albacore (*Thunnus alalunga*) weighing 10 kg, with an assumed T_x of 10°C ($T_b = 25$°C; $T_a = 15$°C; Graham and Dickson, 1981). Heat transfer values for this fish with a T_x of 2°C are included for comparison.

Experiments in this laboratory have established a heat production rate of 160 cal · min^{-1} for a 10-kg albacore swimming at 1.3 lengths · sec^{-1} in a T_a of 15°C to 18°C (Fig. 8-10). Owing to drag, unit increases in velocity can be assumed to nearly double heat production (*i.e.*, oxygen consumption) in most fishes (Webb, 1975; Brett and Groves, 1979); however, in skipjack tuna the rate of increase in oxygen consumption is much less, possibly because of an increased locomotor efficiency of tunas (Gooding *et al.*, 1981; Stevens and

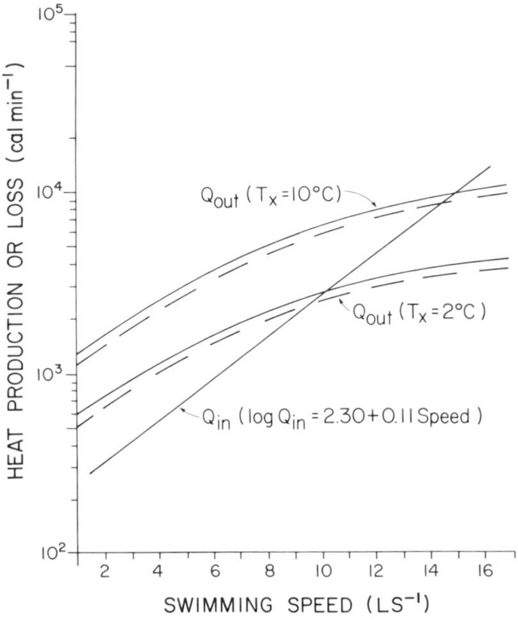

Figure 8-10
Relationship between swimming speed (lengths · sec^{-1}) and heat production (Q_{in}, cal · min^{-1}) and the calculated heat loss (Q_{out}) potential of a 10-kg albacore. Lines for 2°C and 10°C show the effect of T_x on heat loss. Dashed lines are heat loss attributable to forced convection at the gills. Q_{in} line is calculated from Gooding and associates (1981).

Dizon, 1982). A theoretical relationship between oxygen consumption rate and velocity for an albacore (based on the relationship established for skipjack by Gooding *et al.,* 1981) is plotted in Figure 8-10 and represents heat production rate. Convective heat loss by gills at both T_x values was estimated from equation 10 using an empirically determined blood flow rate of 300 ml · min^{-1} at about 1 to 1.5 lengths · sec^{-1} and assuming a linear, sevenfold increase in flow over the velocity range (Jones and Randall, 1978; also see Chap. 4). To obtain a more conservative estimate, the T_x of blood entering the gills (equation 10) was taken to be one-half of body T_x (Neill *et al.,* 1976). For the albacore, combined conductive and convective body surface heat transfer (equation 15) was estimated using the heat transfer term calculated from the relationship between Nu and Re (equation 15; Erskine and Spotila, 1977).

Figure 8-10 succinctly describes heat transfer problems faced by tunas. The gills are clearly the major avenue for heat loss. At typical cruising speeds for a 90-cm albacore (0.5 to 3 lengths · sec^{-1}; Magnuson, 1978; Laurs *et al.,* 1980), the potential for heat loss is much greater than the rate of heat production. A tuna's retia must work efficiently to conserve metabolic heat and maintain a T_x. As speed increases, heat generation rises and ultimately exceeds the combined effects of T_x and velocity on heat dissipation (Dizon and Brill, 1979). As this occurs, T_b begins to rise and the fish probably responds by lowering retia efficiency, reducing activity, swimming to deeper (cooler) water, or all of these. As T_b rises, convective loss increases, but heat loss could be facilitated by behaviorally selecting cooler water.

Figure 8-10 shows that heat production rate does not intersect heat loss rates until a velocity of about 10 lengths $\cdot$ sec^{-1} ($T_x = 2°$C) or 14 lengths $\cdot$ sec^{-1}, ($T_x = 10°$C), speeds that may be briefly sustainable by albacore (Magnuson, 1978). An interesting possibility suggested by Figure 8-10 is that the intersection of the Q_{in} and Q_{out} lines may define the aerobic scope of a tuna. Above this point any heat overflowing the retia and reaching the gills would be lost, and aerobic heat production in red muscle would only be sustained as long as oxygen delivery matched the consumption requirement. If this were true, tunas might through efficient swimming enjoy a larger aerobic scope than do most other species. It also implies that tuna may not run a serious risk of overheating, as suggested in some of the recent literature (reviewed by Dizon and Brill, 1979), because red-muscle heat production and rete heat conservation are both oxygen (blood flow rate) dependent.

Heat transfer principles governing a swimming tuna need refinement and are only generally described by Figure 8-10. The effects of a range of water and body temperatures on the propellor and muscle contraction efficiencies of tunas are simply unknown. Body size and swimming performance differences among tuna species (Magnuson, 1978) also need to be considered. Some species are able to sustain fast speeds for long periods (Magnuson, 1978), and the albacore is probably capable of at least a 16-lengths $\cdot$ sec^{-1} burst speed; at speeds above 1.1 lengths $\cdot$ sec^{-1}, however, the Reynolds number of a 90-cm tuna exceeds 10^6 (Vogel, 1981). Even though these fishes are highly streamlined, turbulent flow along the body surface should reduce swimming economy and by altering the Nu-Re relationship, should affect heat transfer (Kay, 1963). Turbulent heat transfer could be two orders of magnitude greater than laminar heat transfer.

Finally, the heat balance relationships depicted by the $2°$C T_x line in Figure 8-10 illustrates to some extent the plight of ectothermic fishes in nonsteady heat transfer. The potential for heat loss from ectothermic fish with a $2°$C T_x is large, and even if it has a high metabolic rate, it will be unable to conserve heat because it lacks the circulatory specializations present in tunas. It remains somewhat paradoxical that in view of the lesser role played by gills in the heat transfer of ectothermic fishes, heat conservation by endothermic fishes would be impossible were it not for vascular retia that limit forced convective heat transfer to gills.

Rete Efficacy in Heat Conservation

SIZE AND GEOMETRY

Tuna retia contain greater numbers of arteries than veins, but because they have larger diameters, veins constitute about 75% of rete volume (Stevens *et al.*, 1974). Large flow resistances posed by serial blood flow through gills to rete arteries, capillaries, and back to rete veins probably account for the high blood pressures in tuna (Graham and Diener, 1978). Rete flow characteristics have not been examined, but large surface areas (12 to $30 \, cm^2 \cdot g^{-1}$ red muscle) ensure ample contact and long residence times for blood. Because arterial and venous rete flow is very likely a closed loop through red muscle (Fig. 8-7), prevailing arterial and venous pressure, the number of vessels, and differences in their diameters and wall thicknesses all affect heat transfer efficiency (Stevens *et al.*, 1974; Graham and Diener, 1978).

Heat exchanged in the rete is a function of the temperature change (ΔT) and heat capacities (S) of blood in each flow path

$$Q = \Delta T(S) \tag{22}$$

where S is the product of blood mass flow and specific heat. (Mass flow depends on transmural pressure in arterial and venous flow and on vessel number and diameters as determined by Poiseuille's law.) Changes in blood flow rate and surface area modify rete efficiency, but the extent that tunas through autonomic effectors can regulate heat conservation has not been determined. Heat exchange can also be altered by vascular shunts that reduce artery and vein contact. A venous shunt has been found in the suprahepatic retia of lamnid sharks (Carey *et al.*, 1981), but shunts have not yet been detected in muscle retia. Observations that the T_b of thermoregulating albacore rises in T_a above $18°C$ (Fig. 8-8) suggest that a fixed minimum heat exchange efficiency is inherent to retia design (Graham and Dickson, 1981).

HEAT TRANSFER EFFICIENCY

The effectiveness of retia as barriers to heat loss was elegantly demonstrated by Stevens and Neill (1978), who applied a brief heat pulse (jet of warm water) to gill blood of a restrained skipjack and found that heat was promptly and completely reflected by the retia, as evidenced by a subsequent (15-sec) rise in the temperature of blood returning to gills in the ventral aorta. The T_x measured in the ventral aortas (hearts) of decked tuna are very low ($<0.5°C$), indicating that even when red-muscle T_x is high, excessive thermal overflow does not occur (Carey *et al.*, 1971). In restrained skipjack, the T_x of ventral aorta blood equals about 10% of red-muscle T_x (Neill *et al.*, 1976), and assuming that 60% of venous blood passes through the retia, Stevens and Neill (1978) calculated a retial efficiency of about 97%.

Close coupling of the oxygen-transport (heat production potential) and heat-transfer functions of blood flowing through retia and the closed loop circulation in capillaries (Fig. 8-11) permit examination of the scope of rete heat-transfer efficiency. A revealing analysis by Carey and colleagues (1981) indicated that for the visceral temperature of a mackerel shark to remain $8°C$ above T_a, the actual quantity of heat present in a unit volume of blood entering the tissue, together with the increment of metabolic heat represented in its

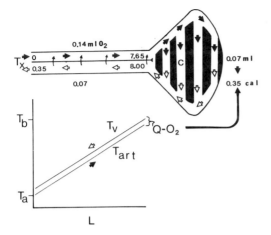

Figure 8-11

Relationship between heat conservation and oxygen delivery in the suprahepatic rete of a mackerel shark. Diagram shows blood flow through capillary bed (c) and intimate contact of venous (v) and arterial (a) rete beds. Graph shows temperature change in arterial (T_{art}) and venous (T_v) blood along rete length (L). To ensure heat balance, T_{art} must be heated from T_a to near T_b so that the increment of heat released by O_2 consumption ($Q\,O_2$) will equal heat loss in venous blood.

store of oxygen, would have to equal the unit heat content of respiring tissue. Referring to Figure 8-11, if each milliliter of arterial blood (0.14 ml O_2) surrendered 0.07 ml O_2 to respiring tissue, a 0.35-cal thermal increment would result (assuming as these workers did that a 5-cal·ml$^{-1}O_2$ was consumed). With a heat capacity of 1.0 cal/ml and thermal equilibrium in the capillaries, venous blood would have a T_x of $8°$C, and the T_x of entering arterial blood would have to be $7.65°$C; therefore, the amount of permissible heat loss through the rete is equivalent to $0.35°$C, a required heat-transfer efficiency of 95.6% ($1 -$ [$0.35/8$]). If tissue thermal conduction dissipated 50% of the metabolic heat increment, transfer efficiency would have to increase to 97.8%.

A similar analysis for red-muscle retia in a 10-kg albacore demonstrates the combined effects of blood flow, red muscle activity, and T_a on heat transfer efficiency (Fig. 8-12). Remarkably good agreement is found between the probable metabolic rate of this tissue during slow speed swimming and oxygen delivery rate. A 10-kg albacore has 410 g of red muscle that receives a blood flow of 108 ml·min^{-1} (36% of cardiac output; F.C. White, unpublished observation). Because each milliliter of arterial blood contains nearly 0.2 ml O_2 (Stevens and Neill, 1978), oxygen delivery is about 0.053 ml·min^{-1}·g^{-1}. Assuming red muscle metabolism is about 0.124 cal·min^{-1}·g^{-1} (Stevens and Neill, 1978) and an oxycalorific equivalent of 4.7 cal·min^{-1}, 0.026 ml·min^{-1}·g^{-1} O_2 would be required at slow speeds—about 50% of oxygen delivery. If total red-muscle heat production is 50.8 cal·min^{-1} (0.124×410), a metabolic heat increment of 0.47 cal·ml^{-1} would be applied to capillary blood ($50.8/108$), and assuming 50% heat conductance to white muscle and a typical T_x of $10°$C, a 97.7% efficiency is needed to maintain T_b.

Efficiency requirements change with T_x (Fig. 8-12) and with oxygen utilization. If 85% of available oxygen was consumed (Fig. 8-12B), red-muscle heat production would rise to 81.2 cal·min^{-1}, and the rise in thermal increment ($81.2/108 = 0.75$) allowing for 50% conductance to white muscle, would require retia efficiency to drop slightly (96.3%) to maintain a 10°C T_x. Some capacity to increase heat production without changing blood flow may enable an albacore on encountering cooler water to compensate for an initial drop in retia efficiency imposed by a larger T_x by increasing its metabolic heat increment. Clearly, a fish could not sustain a tenfold increase in red muscle metabolism (508 cal · min^{-1}, equivalent to increasing speed to about 5 lengths · sec^{-1}) without increasing blood supply. Assuming an 85% maximum utilization, the minimum blood flow requirement at this speed is 627 ml · min^{-1}, and the red muscle thermal increment (508/627 = 0.81), assuming 50% conduction to white muscle, still requires 96.0% efficiency. Even if increased heat production by white muscle at faster speeds stopped all thermal conduction from red muscle, efficiency would only need drop to 92% to maintain heat balance. Close linkage in the circulatory system between the heat production and transfer potentials of red muscle therefore ensures that increased activity will not require marked adjustment of retia efficiency.

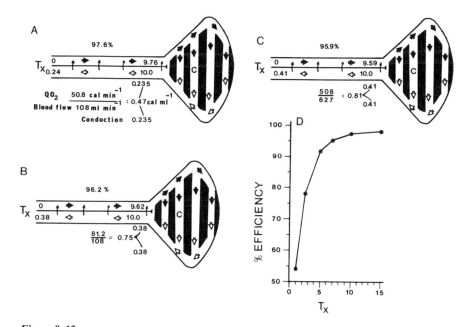

Figure 8–12
Effects of red muscle O_2 utilization (heat production) on the level of retia heat conservation efficiency needed to maintain a constant temperature in red muscle. Increased utilization from 50% to 85% without altering blood flow (*A* vs *B*) requires a drop in efficiency. *C*, A tenfold increase in O_2 uptake, when accompanied by the nearly sixfold increase in blood flow needed to keep utilization at 85%, does not greatly affect efficiency. *D*, Effect of T_x on requisite retia efficiency in case A, above.

RECAPITULATION: SUGGESTIONS FOR FUTURE RESEARCH

This review documents our ignorance about various types of heat transfer mechanisms occurring within fishes and their relative magnitudes. Increased understanding of these would result from an investigation of heat transfer in which gill perfusion and ventilation and cardiac activity (hence forced interval convection) were modified by factors controlling respiration such as hypoxia and hyperoxia as well as vasoactive drugs administered *in situ*. Tests using air breathers, which interrupt branchial blood flow at regular intervals, seem particularly valuable for such an investigation (Pettit and Beitinger, 1980). Additional contrasts of heat-transfer time constants over different temperature ranges and thus at different kinetic energy states would also be useful. This chapter also reveals the paucity of available information for intertissue and interspecific variations in the constant for thermal conductivity K, which is a crucial factor in most heat transfer analyses (reviewed and Fechhelm and Neill, 1982). A wealth of questions related to heat transfer await investigators interested in fish endothermy.

Telemetric tracking of large species such as done by Carey and associates (1982) permits estimation of nonsteady heat-transfer rates in natural settings. This work also suggests that the heat production rates of all endothermic fishes may not be exceedingly high. Tracking of albacore shows they can spend from 50% to 90% of their time in water as cold as 9°C to 12°C (probable T_x values are 13°C to 16°C). The preliminary analyses of heat production and heat loss relationships defined for albacore in this study, and the quantification of linkages between the heat production potential and heat conservation capacity of the vascular system attempted here for albacore and for endothermic sharks by Carey *et al.* (1981) all can be improved. The essential component for my analysis of heat conservation efficiency in albacore was the recently obtained value for cardiac output to the red muscle. Further insight will come from definition of relationships between the oxygen consumption swimming velocity of this species. Given the as yet rather diverse relationships seen among the 13 species of tunas for red muscle quantity and position and heat exchanger size and efficiency, it seems likely that further studies of heat transfer that also incorporate swimming velocity and T_a variables will prove useful.

Acknowledgments

In writing this paper I have had the benefit of illuminating discussions with Drs. Frank Carey, Ted Hammel, Martha Heath, Dick Taylor, and Fred White. Kathryn Dickson critically reviewed this paper and made numerous suggestions for its improvement as did an anonymous reviewer. This work was partially supported by NSF DE79-12235.

REFERENCES

Beitinger, T.L., and Fitzpatrick, L.C. 1979. Physiological and ecological correlates of preferred temperature in fish. *Am. Zool.* 19:319–329.

Beitinger, T.L., Thommes, M.M., and Spigarelli, S.A. 1977. Relative roles of conduction and convection in the body temperature change of gizzard shad, *Dorosoma cepedianum. Comp. Biochem. Physiol.* 57A:275–279.

Brett, J.R. 1956. Some principles in the thermal requirements of fishes. *Q. Rev. Biol.* 31:75–87.

Brett, J.R. 1971. Energetic responses of salmon to temperature, a study of some thermal relations in the physiology and freshwater ecology of sockeye salmon (*Oncorhynchus nerka*). *Am. Zool.* 11:99–113.

Brett, J.R., and Groves, T.D.D. 1979. Physiological energetics. In *Fish Physiology,* edited by W.S. Hoar, D.J. Randall, and J.R. Brett, vol. *8,* 279–352. New York: Academic Press.

Brill, R.W., and Dizon, A.E. 1979. Red and white fiber activity in swimming skipjack tuna, *Katsuwonus pelamis* (Linnaeus). *J. Fish. Biol.* 6:665–670.

Brill, R.W., Guernsey, D.L., and Stevens, E.D. 1978. Body surface and gill heat loss rates in restrained skipjack tuna. In *The Physiological Ecology of Tunas,* edited by G.D. Sharp, and A.E. Dizon, 261–276. New York: Academic Press.

Carey, F.G. 1982. A brain heater in the swordfish. *Science* 216:1327–1329.

Carey, F.G., and Lawson, K.D. 1973. Temperature regulation in free-swimming bluefin tuna. *Comp. Biochem. Physiol.* 44A:375–392.

Carey, F.G., and Teal, J.M. 1969. Regulation of body temperature by the bluefin tuna. *Comp. Biochem. Physiol.* 28:205–213.

Carey, F.G., Teal, J.M., and Kanwisher, J.W. 1981. The visceral temperatures of mackerel sharks (Lamnidae). *Physiol. Zool.* 54:334–344.

Carey, F.G., Teal, J.M., Kanwisher, J.W., Lawson, K.D., and Beckett, J.S. 1971. Warm-bodied fish. *Am. Zool.* 11:137–145.

Carey, F.G., Kanwisher, J.W., Brazier, O., Gabrielson, G., Casey, J.G., and Pratt, H.L., Jr. 1982. Temperature and activities of a white shark, *Carcharodon carcharias. Copeia* 1982:254–260.

Childress, J.J., Taylor, S.M., Cailliet, G.M., and Price, M.H. 1980. Patterns of growth, energy utilization, and reproduction in some meso and bathypelagic fishes off southern California. *Marine Biol.* 61:27–40.

Clausen, R.G. 1934. Body temperature of fresh-water fishes. *Ecology* 15:139–144.

Crawshaw, L.I. 1977. Physiological and behavioral reactions of fishes to temperature change. *J. Fish. Res. Board Can.* 34:730–734.

Crawshaw, L.I. 1979. Responses to rapid temperature change in vertebrate ectotherms. *Am. Zool.* 19:225–237.

Dizon, A.E., and Brill, R.W. 1979. Thermoregulation in tunas. *Am. Zool.* 19:249–265.

Erskine, D.J., and Spotila, J.R. 1977. Heat-energy-budget analysis and heat transfer in the largemouth blackbass (*Micropterus salmoides*). *Physiol. Zool.* 50:157–169.

Fechhelm, R.G., and Neill, W.H. 1982. Predicting body-core temperature in fish subjected to fluctuating ambient temperature. *Physiol. Zool.* 55:229–239.

Fry, F.E.J. 1971. The effect of environmental factors on the physiology of fish. In *Fish Physiology,* edited by W.S. Hoar and D.J. Randall, vol. 6, 1–98. New York: Academic Press.

Gooding, R.M., Neill, W.H., and Dizon, A.E. 1981. Respiration rates and low-oxygen tolerance limits of skipjack tuna, *Katsuwonus pelamis. Fish. Bull.* 79: 31–48.

Graham, J.B. 1975. Heat exchange in the yellowfin tuna, *Thunnus albacares,* and skipjack tuna, *Katsuwonus pelamis,* and the adaptive significance of elevated body temperatures in scombrid fishes. *Fish. Bull.* 73:219–229.

Graham, J.B., and Dickson, K.A. 1981. Physiological thermoregulation in the albacore *Thunnus alalunga. Physiol. Zool.* 54:470–486.

Graham, J.B., and Diener, D.R. 1978. Comparative morphology of the central heat exchangers in the skipjacks *Katsuwonus* and *Euthynnus.* In *Physiological Ecology of Tunas,* edited by G.D. Sharp and A.E. Dizon, 113–133. New York: Academic Press.

Graham, J.B., Koehrn, F.J., and Dickson, K.A. 1983. Distribution and relative proportions of red muscle in scombrid fishes: Consequences of body size and relationships to locomotion and endothermy. *J. Fish Biol.* In press.

Gunn, D.L. 1942. Body temperature in poikilothermal animals. *Biol. Rev.* 17: 293–314.

Jones, D.R., and Randall, D.J. 1978. The respiratory and circulatory systems during exercise. In *Fish Physiology,* edited by W.S. Hoar and D.J. Randall, vol. 7, 425–501. New York: Academic Press.

Kay, J.M. 1963. *An Introduction to Fluid Mechanics and Heat Transfer.* Cambridge: Cambridge University Press.

Kubb, R.N., Spotila, J.R., and Pendergast, D.R. 1980. Mechanisms of heat transfer and time-dependent modeling of body temperatures in the largemouth bass (*Micropterus salmoides*). *Physiol. Zool.* 53:222–239.

Laurs, R.M., Dotson, R.C., Dizon, A., and Jemison, A. 1980. Observations on swimming depth and ocean temperature telemetered from free-swimming albacore. In *Proceedings of the 31st Tuna Conference,* edited by A. Wild, 33–34. La Jolla, CA: Inter-American Tropical Tuna Commission.

Leyton, L. 1975. *Fluid Behaviour in Biological Systems.* Oxford: Clarendon Press.

Lindsey, C.C. 1968. Temperature of red and white muscle in recently caught marlin and other large tropical fish. *J. Fish. Res. Board Can.* 25:1763–1774.

Lindsey, C.C. 1978. Form, function, and locomotory habits in fish. In *Fish Physiology,* edited by W.S. Hoar and D.J. Randall, vol. 7, 1–100. New York: Academic Press.

Magnuson, J.J. 1978. Locomotion by scombrid fishes. In *Fish Physiology,* edited by W.S. Hoar and D.J. Randall, vol. 7, 239–313. New York: Academic Press.

Morrow, J.E., Jr., and Mauro, A. 1950. Body temperatures of some marine fishes. *Copeia* 1950:108–116.

Neill, W.H., and Stevens, E.D. 1974. Thermal inertia versus thermoregulation in "warm" turtles and tuna. *Science* 184:1008–1010.

Neill, W.H., Chang, R.H., and Dizon, A.E. 1976. Magnitude and ecological implications of thermal inertia in skipjack tuna, *Katsuwonus pelamis* (Linnaeus). *Environ. Biol. Fish.* 1:61–80.

Pettit, M.J., and Beitinger, T.L. 1980. Thermal response of the South American lungfish, *Lepidosiren paradoxa*. *Copeia* 1980:130–136.

Reynolds, W.W. 1977. Thermal equilibrium rates in relation to heartbeat frequencies in largemouth blackbass, *Micropterus salmoides*. *Comp. Biochem. Physiol.* 56A:195–201.

Reynolds, W.W., and Casterlin, M.E. 1979. Behavioral thermoregulation and the "final preferendum" paradigm. *Am. Zool.* 19:211–224.

Roberts, J.L., and Graham, J.B. 1979. Effect of swimming speed on the excess temperatures and activities of heart and red and white muscles of the mackerel, *Scomber japonicus*. *Fish. Bull.* 78:861–867.

Schmidt-Nielsen, K. 1979. *Animal Physiology: Adaptation and Environment*. New York: Cambridge Press.

Sharp, G.D., and Dizon, A.E. eds. 1978. *Physiological Ecology of Tunas*. New York: Academic Press.

Sorenson, P.R., and Fromm, P.O. 1976. Heat transfer characteristics of isolated-perfused gills of rainbow trout. *J. Comp. Physiol.* 112:356–357.

Spigarelli, S.A., Thommes, M.M., and Beitinger, T.L. 1977. The influence of body weight on heating and cooling of selected Lake Michigan fishes. *Comp. Biochem. Physiol.* 56A:51–57.

Spotila, J.R., Lommen, P.W., Bakken, G.S., and Gates, D.M. 1973. A mathematical model for body temperatures of large reptiles: Implications for dinosaur ecology. *Am. Naturalist* 107:391–404.

Stevens, E.D., and Dizon, A.E. 1982. Energetics of locomotion in warm-bodied fish. *Ann. Rev. Physiol.* 44:121–131.

Stevens, E.D., and Fry, F.E.J. 1970. The rate of thermal exchange in a teleost, *Tilapia mossambica*. *Can. J. Zool.* 48:221–226.

Stevens, E.D., and Fry, F.E.J. 1974. Heat transfer and body temperatures in non-thermoregulatory teleosts. *Can. J. Zool.* 52:1137–1143.

Stevens, E.D., Lamb, H.M., and Kendall, J. 1974. Vascular anatomy of the countercurrent heat exchanger of skipjack tuna. *J. Exp. Biol.* 61:145–153.

Stevens, E.D., and Neill, W.H. 1978. Body temperature relations of tunas, especially skipjack. In *Fish Physiology*, edited by W.S. Hoar and D.J. Randall, vol. 7, 315–359. New York: Academic Press.

Stevens, E.D., and Sutterlin, A.M. 1976. Heat transfer between fish and ambient water. *J. Exp. Biol.* 65:131–145.

Vogel, S. 1981. *Life in Moving Fluids*. Boston: Willard Grant Press.

Wardle, C.S. 1977. Effects of size on the swimming speeds of fish. In *Scale Effects in Animal Locomotion*, edited by T.J. Pedley, 229–313. London: Academic Press.

Webb, P.W. 1975. Hydrodynamics and energetics of fish propulsion. *Bull. Fish. Res. Board Can.* 190:1–158.

SYMBOLS

T	temperature	S	blood heat capacity
T_b	body temperature	$\dot{B}$	cardiac output or tissue blood flow rate
T_a	ambient (water) temperature		
T_x	excess body temperature	h	average convective heat trans-
T_c	core body temperature		fer coefficient for the entire body surface
T_e	equilibrium body temperature		
T_s	skin surface temperature	Nu	Nusselt Number
Q	heat quantity	λ	fluid thermal conductivity
Q_{cd}	heat transfer by conduction	v	water kinematic viscosity
Q_{cv}	heat transfer by convection	Re	Reynolds number
Q_m	metabolic heat production	h_t	combined convective and con-
K	tissue thermal conductivity		ductive heat transfer coeffi-
L	body length		cient of water at the body sur- face
A	body surface area		
f	fraction of heat lost from blood across a surface contacting water	W	body mass
		k	rate of coefficient for instan- taneous temperature change

Chapter 9
FOOD CAPTURE
George V. Lauder

CONTENTS

INTRODUCTION

The capture of energy is a process of fundamental importance to the growth, reproduction, and maintenance of physiological function in organisms. Energy is the focus of many physiological analyses that seek to determine how energy use is distributed among various body functions and the metabolic costs of locomotion, breathing, or reproduction. Energy is often the currency used to compare alternative life-history strategies, and it provides a common denominator for optimality models of behavior and ecology (see Chap. 11).

Despite the important role of energy use in discussions of fish mechanics and ecology, we are just beginning to understand the actual processes by which energy is acquired: the biomechanical pathways and mechanisms underlying the capture of prey items. The feeding apparatus provides an especially interesting problem in fish mechanics. The cranial musculoskeletal system is an extremely complex multilinkage system with over 30 movable bony elements controlled by more than 50 muscles. Furthermore, movements of this complex feeding apparatus may occur extremely quickly, and fishes are known to possess the most rapid feeding mechanisms in vertebrates: prey capture can occur in 0.012 sec (Grobecker and Pietsch, 1979).

The primitive method of prey capture in vertebrates was probably suspension feeding (Mallatt, 1981). Suspended matter in the water column or organic material on the bottom were filtered by the branchial apparatus or mucus in the pharynx. Many extant fish species capture prey by combining a high-velocity attack with rapid mouth opening to trap prey in the oral cavity, and both predator body velocity and jaw movements are important components of feeding behavior. Sustained high-velocity attacks used to overtake prey is the capture method used by many elasmobranchs and appears to be primitive for ray-finned fishes.

In teleost fishes suction feeding is the dominant aspect of food capture. Body velocity during the strike may contribute less to the capture of prey than does rapid high-volume water flow entering the mouth cavity. Suction feeding (or inertial suction feeding) involves rapid mouth cavity expansion that causes an intraoral pressure reduction relative to the surrounding water. This results in water flowing rapidly into the mouth carrying in the prey. During suction feeding, prey tend to be drawn toward the predator by water entering the mouth cavity. The major structural modifications relating to high-speed suction feeding are found first in the halecomorph fishes (*e.g., Amia*) and have been retained in most teleost lineages. One key aspect of the teleost radiation is the structural and functional diversification in the feeding mechanism (Marshall, 1971), and the primitive suction mechanism of teleosts has been modified greatly in relation to different prey and habitat types.

This chapter analyzes the biomechanics of suction feeding in teleost fishes, the mechanics of intraoral prey manipulation and transport following initial capture, and certain evolutionary and ecologic aspects of feeding mechanics. Filter feeding has evolved independently in many teleost clades and will be discussed as a contrast to suction-feeding mechanisms.

MECHANICS OF SUCTION FEEDING

Suction feeding may be divided into a number of discrete phases each having distinct kinematic, electromyographic, and pressure attributes (Table 9-1). The preparatory phase occurs before mouth opening and involves buccal and opercular cavity compression that forces water out and reduces mouth volume. The expansive phase, defined for convenience by mouth opening movements, begins as the jaws first open and lasts until peak gape has been reached. The compressive phase extends from peak gape to closure of the jaws, while the recovery phase is the time after mouth closure in which skeletal elements return to their initial position. The expansive phase can be explosively rapid (from 10 to 50 msec in most high-speed suction feeding fishes) and is usually 20% to 50% shorter than the compressive phase.

The buccal cavity is defined as that portion of the mouth cavity lying anterior to the gill arches, medial to the suspensory apparatus, and posterior to the buccal valve. The opercular (gill) cavity is bounded laterally by the operculum, posteriorly by the pectoral girdle and body wall, anteriorly by the

Table 9-1
PHASES OF PREY CAPTURE IN GENERALIZED PERCOMORPH FISHES

PHASES	MAJOR ATTRIBUTES		
	Pressure	Electromyographic	Kinematic
Initial Strike			
Preparatory	Buccal cavity positive	Adductor arcus palatini, adductor mandibulae, geniohyoideus, pharyngohyoideus muscles active	Hyoid and suspensorium protracted
Expansive	Buccal and opercular cavities negative	Levator operculi, sternohyoideus active	Mouth opens; hyoid retracted
Compressive	Buccal cavity positive; opercular cavity negative	Adductor mandibulae, geniohyoideus muscles active	Mouth closes; opercular abduction
Recovery	Buccal cavity negative → ambient; opercular cavity positive → ambient	Adductor operculi, adductor mandibulae, geniohyoideus active	Opercular adduction; hyoid protraction
Buccal Manipulation	Similar to initial strike	Sternohyoideus, hypaxialis, levator operculi active; no preparatory phase	Similar to initial strike without the preparatory phase
Pharyngeal Manipulation	_____[1]	Sternohyoideus inactive; hypaxialis and branchial musculature active	Pectoral girdle retraction; abduction of pharyngeal jaws
Transport	_____[1]	Rhythmic activity in pharyngeal muscles; no activity in sternohyoideus, epaxialis, or hypaxialis	Alternate protraction and retraction of the upper and lower pharyngeal jaws

[1]No available data.

gill filaments and arches, and ventrally by the branchiostegal rays. It is extremely important to realize that the buccal and opercular chambers form functionally distinct units and cannot be treated as one in considering suction dynamics.

The anatomic basis of suction feeding will not be described in detail here, and the reader is referred to Liem (1970, 1978), Lauder and Liem (1980), Osse, (1969), and Tchernavin (1953) for anatomic descriptions. Suffice it to note that buccal expansion is achieved by abduction of all four sides of the cavity: hyoid depression and cranial elevation in the ventral and dorsal aspects, lateral movement of the suspensory apparatus, and anterior extension of the upper jaw bones (maxilla or premaxilla). The opercular cavity is expanded primarily by lateral movement of the gill cover and ventral expansion (abduction) of the branchiostegal rays. Posterior rotation of the pectoral girdle on the skull may also contribute to opercular cavity volume increase.

Kinematics and Muscle Mechanics

During high-speed suction feeding there is extensive overlap in the timing of electrical activity between the different cranial muscles, particularly during the expansive phase (Fig. 9-1). The preparatory phase, usually of much longer duration than the expansive phase (up to 0.5 sec), shows less synchrony. The major preparatory phase muscles include the adductor mandibulae (part A2/3) and the geniohyoideus, which together cause hyoid protraction, and the adductor operculi and adductor arcus palatini, which compress the mouth cavity laterally. Interestingly, several branchial muscles are also active during the preparatory phase (Fig. 9-1). The pharyngohyoideus protracts the entire branchial basket, while the levatores externi (parts 3 and 4) draw the upper gill arch elements (pharyngobranchials and epibranchials) forward. Just as the expansive phase begins, the branchial apparatus may be moved posterioventrally by activity in the pharyngocleithralis internus and externus.

During the expansive phase, both buccal and pharyngeal muscles are active to rapidly expand the mouth cavity (Fig. 9-1). The expansive muscles of the buccal cavity have short duration bursts ($<$50 msec) and may only lead the compressive phase muscles by 5 minutes (Lauder, 1980b). Rapid mouth opening and closing results in increased synchrony of abductor and adductor muscle activity. In slower jaw movements, overlap in activity period is less marked.

Three musculoskeletal linkage systems are active during the expansive phase (see Figs. 9-2 and 9-3). The epaxial muscles cause upward rotation of the neurocranium on the vertebral column. A complex ventral coupling is active to mediate mandibular depression. This musculoskeletal coupling involves synchronous activity in the ventral body muscles (which retract the pectoral girdle) and in the sternohyoideus muscle, resulting in a posterioventral rotation of the hyoid apparatus (visible in Fig. 9-2) that causes mandibular depression via the mandibulohyoid ligament. The opercular series rotates posteriodorsally (Fig 9-3), causing the mandible to abduct (Liem, 1970). These three mechanisms are critical elements of the expansive phase in all teleost fishes.

Just before the end of the expansive phase, electrical activity is observed in the adductor mandibulae, which initiates adduction of the lower jaw, and a second burst of activity occurs in the geniohyoideus muscle, initiating the return of the hyoid to its rest position, a movement not completed until well into the recovery phase (Figs. 9-1 and 9-3).

One important aspect of the kinematic profile that appears to be extremely consistent in teleosts is the delay in lateral expansion of the operculum. Although opercular abduction is often held to contribute to negative pressure generation in the mouth cavity (*e.g.,* Osse, 1969; Osse and Muller, 1980), the kinematic data do not corroborate this assumption (see Fig. 9-3). Lateral movement of the gill cover does not begin until the compressive phase or late

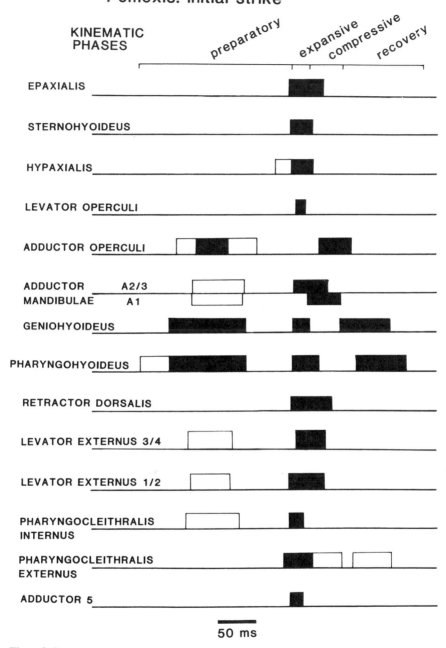

Pomoxis: initial strike

Figure 9–1
Summary of the electromyographic activity in the mandibular, hyoid, and pharyngeal muscles during the initial strike by *Pomoxis annularis* (Centrarchidae). Black bars indicate consistent muscle activity; white bars indicate that the muscles were active in fewer than 50% of the observations. A preparatory phase is not observed in all strikes. Note the occasional activity of three sets of branchial muscles during the preparatory phase (pharyngocleithralis internus and levatores externi muscles) and the consistent activity of a fourth, the pharyngohyoideus. For definitions of the kinematic phases see text and Table 9-1.

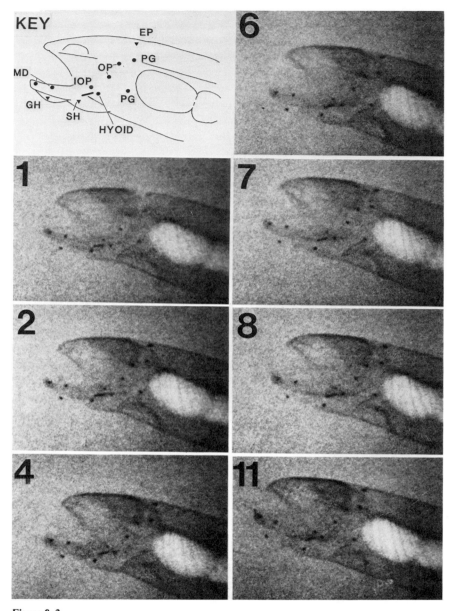

Figure 9-2

Frames 1, 2, 4, 6, 7, 8 , and 11 from a high-speed x-ray film (180 frames per second; unretouched) of prey capture in *Hoplerythrinus* (Erythrinidae). Small metal markers have been implanted in the skull bones and muscles to permit direct visualization of bone movement as indicated in the key. Note the changing relationship between the sternohyoideus marker and the short wire implanted along the ceratohyal. (Dots indicate screws in bones; triangles indicate small lead pellets imbedded in heat musculature; EP, epaxial marker; GH, geniohyoideus marker; hyoid, screw, and short wire located in the ceratohyal; IOP, screw in the interoperculum; MD, two screws in the dentary; OP, two screws in the operculum; PG, two screws in the cleithrum; SH, sternohyoideus marker.)

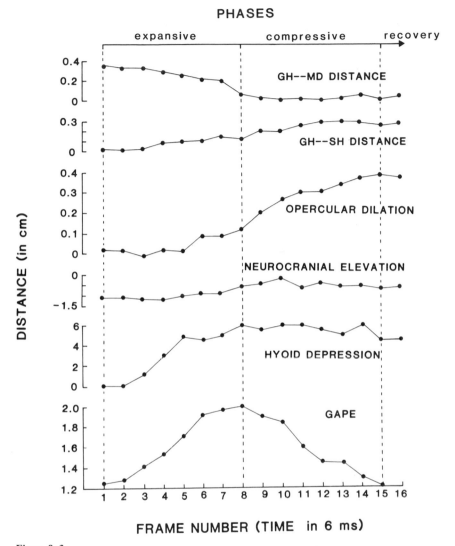

Figure 9–3

Kinematic events measured from a high-speed x-ray film of initial prey capture in *Hoplerythrinus*. Note the onset of hyoid depression synchronously with the increase in gape and the maintenance of hyoid depression into the recovery phase. Opercular dilation begins late in the expansive phase. GH, SH, and MD distances refer to the changing lengths between the markers shown in Figure 9-2.

expansive phase, often after the mouth has begun to close. Indeed, measurement of opercular abduction and branchiostegal expansion in sunfishes (Lauder, 1980a) showed that in many cases water does not begin to exit the opercular cavity to the exterior until the mouth has nearly closed.

Alexander (1969) calculated the tension that could be produced by the dilator operculi of the golden orfe (*Idus idus*) assuming that fish muscle at 20° C can generate 25N/cm² cross-sectional area. He showed that the dilator operculi could generate a moment about the anterior opercular articulation of about 0.3N/cm, sufficient to abduct the gill cover against a negative pressure of −7 cm of water. This negative pressure is far exceeded during the expansive phase and most of the compressive phase (see below), so it is not surprising that there is a delay in opercular abduction. The moments of other muscles were considerably higher: sternohyoideus—5.0N/cm; levator arcus palatini—1.0N/cm.

Branchial muscle activity during the initial strike usually occurs in both expansive and compressive phases (Fig. 9-1). The retractor dorsalis, levatores externi 3 and 4, and pharyngocleithralis internus and externus are all active to abduct the pharyngeal jaws as the mouth opens. This contributes to reducing the pressure within the buccal cavity and greatly expands the posterior portion of the mouth cavity. One consequence of branchial expansion is that small prey items may be sucked directly into the stomach. In *Hoplias* (Lauder, 1979) and *Antennarius* (Grobecker and Pietsch, 1979), high speed films reveal a significant distention of the stomach just after the prey has entered the mouth. Both a considerable mass of water and the prey item appear to be transported directly into the anterior portion of the stomach. Constriction of the esophageal sphincter then traps the prey, and the water is released over the next several seconds.

Three aspects of the mechanics of initial prey capture have received considerable attention in recent years: the function of the geniohyoideus muscle, the kinematics of the levator operculi mouth opening system, and the mechanisms governing premaxillary protrusion.

The geniohyoideus muscle of teleosts has been of special interest because it shows two different patterns of electrical activity. Either the muscle is electrically active during the expansive phase as in cichlids (Liem, 1978), percids (Elshoud-Oldenhave and Osse, 1976), and *Hoplias* (Lauder, 1981), or there is a considerable delay after mouth opening (up to 100 msec) as in *Salvelinus* and most centrarchids before the muscle is active. An important feature of the geniohyoideus is that in at least some fishes (*Hoplias; Gymnocephalus*) the mandible may either be adducted or abducted by the geniohyoideus depending on its line of action. If the line of action is above the quadratomandibular articulation, then contraction will adduct the mandible and protract the hyoid; if it is below, the mandible will be abducted. Complicating this picture further is the observation that in several species, the line of action changes during the feeding sequence. At present there is no clear understanding of the functional diversity in the geniohyoideus muscle (Lauder, 1981).

The mechanical roles of two mechanisms operating during the expansive phase, the hyoid apparatus and opercular series couplings, have been modeled as a four-bar linkage system by Anker (1974) and Barel and associates (1977).

The four bars of the opercular linkage system are the suspensorial bar, the opercular bar, the interopercular bar, and the mandibular bar (Liem, 1980a). A mathematical relationship between these elements can be derived that expresses the degree of mandibular depression as a function of the input rotation of the gill cover. A ratio, the kinematic transmission efficiency of opercular rotation (K) is given by q/r where q is the perpendicular distance from the operculohyomandibular articulation to a horizontal line drawn through the mandibular insertion of the interoperculomandibular ligament and the articulation between the suboperculum and interoperculum, and r is the perpendicular distance from the quadratomandibular joint to the same horizontal line. The reciprocal, $F = r/q$, indicates the force transmission efficiency. Barel and colleagues (1977) suggested that high-speed suction feeding fishes have K ranging from 2 to 4, while particle and small invertebrate eaters have K values of 10 or higher. Liem (1980a) tested this model and showed that while this rough pattern seemed to hold in some fishes, it seriously failed in others. The small invertebrate pickers *Eretmodus* and *Spathodus* (Liem, 1979) had K values of 2.5 to 4 while several piscivores had values of up to 17. The hyoid apparatus, when modeled in the same fashion, is revealed to have high K and low F values (Barel *et al.*, 1977), emphasizing the relative kinematic inefficiency of this coupling but its high force transmission capability.

JAW PROTRUSION

Jaw protrusion, extension of the premaxilla and maxilla toward the prey, is one of the most prominent features of prey capture mechanisms in acanthopterygian fishes, but there is relatively little understanding of the diversity of mechanisms by which protrusion occurs (Lauder and Liem, 1981). Jaw protrusion has evolved independently several times in teleosts, and there appear to be at least three major structural and functional systems governing this function. In cyprinids, protrusion of the premaxilla has been proposed to occur by contraction of the superficial divisions of the adductor mandibulae muscle, which pull the maxilla ventrally (Alexander, 1966). As the maxilla slides ventrally, it causes the kinethmoid bone to rotate anteriorly causing premaxillary protrusion (Ballintijn *et al.*, 1972). Protrusion can thus be accomplished independently from lower jaw depression.

In acanthopterygian fishes at least two protrusion mechanisms occur. One, first proposed by Alexander (1967a), depends on the presence of an articular process of the premaxilla that abuts a premaxillary process on the maxilla. As the mandible abducts, the maxilla is pulled ventrally and rotates about its long axis. This rotation causes the premaxillary process to move laterally and press against the articular process of the premaxilla; in a camlike action, the premaxilla is forced anteriorly. Protrusion of the upper jaw is closely linked to lower jaw depression. Alexander (1967a) demonstrated this mechanism in *Gasterosteus* and *Pterophyllum*, but many other acanthopterygian fishes lack the requisite maxillary and premaxillary processes for the cam action.

Liem (1970) has shown experimentally in nandid fishes that the degree of upper jaw protrusion is closely coupled with mandibular depression. By surgically eliminating selected anatomic pathways by which protrusion could be effected, he showed that reducing the degree of mandibular depression consistently reduced the amount of upper jaw protrusion. More recently, Liem (1979) has suggested another system by which the jaws are protruded. This "decoupled model," originally proposed for cichlids, also appears to be true for centrarchids and may have wide applicability to advanced teleosts. If the mandible is held in a fixed, partially depressed position by activity in the geniohyoideus, levator operculi, and/or sternohyoideus, activity in the epaxial muscles would elevate the neurocranium causing the premaxilla to protrude. The degree of protrusion could be modulated by varying the amount of cranial elevation. Films and synchronous electromyograms reveal that protrusion does indeed occur by this mechanism, which seems to be particularly important during prey manipulation in the buccal cavity (Table 9-1).

The function of the protrusible upper jaw of teleost fishes has been the subject of more speculation than probably any other aspect of the feeding mechanism. Only one point is clear: no single explanation will serve for all species. Lauder and Liem (1981) reviewed the various proposed functions for jaw protrusion and noted that one species, *Luciocephalus pulcher*, refutes all hypotheses. *Luciocephalus* possesses one of the most protrusible jaws known to teleosts, the premaxilla extending anteriorly a distance of 33% of the head length; however, feeding occurs exclusively by surrounding the prey with an open mouth cavity and using the forward speed of the predator, not by suction. Peak gape and maximum jaw opening are reached well before the prey enters the buccal cavity.

The most commonly hypothesized function of jaw protrusion is that the "added velocity" obtained as the jaws move toward the prey increases the efficiency of suction (Nyberg, 1971; Gosline, 1971; Alexander, 1967b). This explanation receives indirect support in the recent model of suction feeding proposed by Weihs (1980), showing that forward movement by a fish can increase the distance from which prey can be sucked in by over 60%. Protrusion of the jaws may significantly contribute to this effect, especially when protrusion velocities may exceed body velocity during a strike by 50 cm·sec^{-1} or more.

JAW MUSCLES

One final aspect of the mechanics of the teleost musculoskeletal system concerns physiological properties of jaw muscles. Remarkably little work has been done, and even the most basic attributes of the jaw musculature, such as time to peak tension for twitch and tetanic stimuli and fusion frequencies have yet to be published. Preliminary experiments on the adductor mandibulae of *Lepisosteus*, a fish in which mouth opening and closing can be accomplished in 20 msec, showed that time to peak tension for a twitch stimulus averaged 34 msec and that tetanic stimuli of 300 Hz resulted in peak tensions after about 150 msec, although 50% of peak tension was achieved in about 40 msec (the experiments were conducted at 20°C). These values compare favorably with those from locomotor muscle (Johnston, 1980), where the time to half peak tension at 15°C ($t_{1/2}$) for cod white myotomal muscle averaged 15.4 msec, with a peak twitch tension of 10.4 g/cm^2.

These values are of interest in the light of the rapid jaw movements occurring during feeding and are consistent with the "peripheral control" hypothesis of Thexton and associates (1977). It is not necessary for the central nervous system to precisely preprogram both the sequence of muscle activity and the force of contraction in order to generate a precision movement such as mouth opening and closing. Both opening and closing muscles may be maximally activated within 5 to 20 msec of each other, and the opening muscles may have a considerably greater mechanical advantage in the rest position than do the closing musculature. As the mandible is depressed, the mechanical advantage of the opening muscles steadily decreases, and shortening reduces the amount of force generated per unit length change. Continuing activation of the closing muscles during the expansive phase generates a lengthening contraction that can produce 15% more force in one-fifth the time, compared to a normal isotonic contraction (Hill, 1970). Thus, at some point toward the end of the expansive phase, jaw opening begins to slow as a result of the increasing mechanical advantage of the closing muscles. Jaw closure may occur considerably more rapidly than might be expected on the basis of *in vitro* twitch or tetanic shortening times because of the marked change in physiological response when a quick stretch precedes active shortening.

Complicating the analysis of physiological properties in fish muscles is the lack of comparative and quantitative information on jaw muscle-fiber types. The perch, (*Perca*) is the only species for which published information is available (Akster and Osse, 1978; Barends, 1979), and there appear to be a number of differences from myotomal fiber types. Akster and Osse (1978) distinguished four main types, two of which were "white" and two "red." While the physiological properties of these fibers are unknown, only the red-fiber component of the adductor operculi muscle (showing both high adenosine triphosphatase [ATPase] and lactate dehydrogenase [LDH] reactions) was electrically active during quiet respiration. In the adductor mandibulae, the most medial (A3) fibers are highly vascularized, have a small diameter ($\bar{x} = 0.002$ mm^2), and show mainly oxidative metabolic properties (Barends, 1979); this portion of the muscle is active during respiration. In contrast, the lateral adductor divisions consist of large fibers ($\bar{x} = 0.015$ mm^2) with fewer mitochondria, a reduced vascular supply, and high LDH activity and are not active during quiet respiration.

Hydrodynamics

The study of fluid flow through the mouth cavity of fishes during prey capture poses a considerable number of technical problems in that the process of prey capture is dynamic, and unsteady flows require measuring devices of high frequency response; the mouth cavity is not uniform throughout its length, rendering simplistic geometric models of the mouth cavity inaccurate; key resistances within the mouth cavity (such as the gills) vary during the feeding cycle; and feeding is noncyclical and can be considerably more difficult to elicit than repetitive locomotor movements.

BUCCAL AND OPERCULAR PRESSURE CHANGES

In part because of these difficulties, investigators (with one exception) have until recently attempted to deduce the patterns of pressure change in the buccal and opercular cavities from the pattern of bone movement and muscle activity. The one exception is the work of Alexander (1969, 1970), who trained fishes to suck small pieces of food from the end of a pressure transducer cannula suspended in an aquarium. Alexander found that pressures as low as -400 cm H_2O could be generated in the buccal cavity, but this technique did not allow opercular cavity pressures or buccal pressure waveforms to be determined.

Elshoud–Oldenhave and Osse (1976), on the basis of a kinematic analysis, proposed a model of suction feeding consisting of three phases: phase I, the buccal and opercular cavities are expanded with the mouth closed, generating an initial negative pressure; phase II, mouth opening occurs with rapid expansion of both cavities and a peak in negative pressure; phase III, mouth closure and compression of the buccal cavity create a positive pressure and force water out over the gills. While this proposed sequence of events is inconsistent with the kinematic data presented earlier, the hydrodynamic predictions have only recently been tested. Four key predictions about fluid flow and pressure may be derived from the work of Elshoud–Oldenhave and Osse (1976), Osse (1969), Liem (1970, 1978), Alexander (1969, 1970), Nyberg (1971), and Osse and Muller (1980):

1. The opercular and buccal cavities are not functionally distinct, and both can be treated as one large cavity.
2. Flow is unidirectional through the mouth cavity.
3. The buccal and opercular cavity pressure waveforms and magnitudes are similar.
4. The lateral expansion of the operculum contributes to the pressure drop in both the buccal and opercular cavities.

The most important implication of these statements is that the gill bars and filaments can be neglected as an element resistant to flow during feeding (*i.e.,* the "gill curtain" does not form an important resistance to flow).

Recently, experimental tests of these predictions have been conducted in bluegill sunfish (*Lepomis macrochirus*) by implanting pressure transducer cannulae in the buccal and opercular cavities and recording the pressures simultaneously with a film at 200 frames per second to record the pattern of bone movement (see Lauder, 1980a and c for procedures and results). The results from a similar set of experiments on *Ambloplites rupestris*, the rock bass, are shown in Figures 9-4 and 9-5*A*.

The expansive phase of prey capture is characterized by an immediate pressure drop in the buccal cavity as the mouth begins to open, whereas the pressure in the opercular cavity increases (Fig. 9-4). This pressure increase is caused by adduction of the gill cover against the side of the head. At the end of the expansive phase, there may be up to a 400-cm H_2O pressure differential across the gill arches. Pressures measured at the very back of the buccal cavity, as close to the anterior face of the gill arches as possible, confirm that the pressures here are equal to or slightly more negative than in the front of the buccal cavity (Lauder, 1980a, p. 56). Peak negative pressures are reached in the buccal cavity 5 to 15 msec before the opercular cavity, and the ratio of peak buccal to opercular pressure averages 6:1 in *Lepomis* and 2:1 in *Ambloplites*. The maximum negative pressure recorded to date is -790 cm H_2O in the buccal

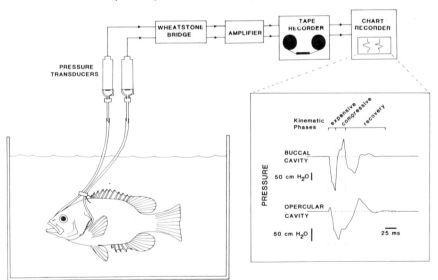

Ambloplites rupestris: mouth cavity pressure recordings

Figure 9–4
Pressure recordings from the mouth cavity of *Ambloplites rupestris* during high-speed suction feeding (on the right) and a diagrammatic view of the methods and apparatus used to obtain these traces (left and top). The pressure transducers are fluid-filled Statham P23 Gb units; calibration, cannula implantation procedures and difficulties with this method are discussed in Lauder (1980a). See text for discussion of pressure traces.

A :Ambloplites

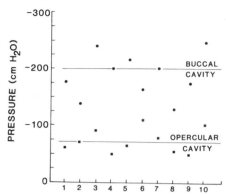

B :Lepomis

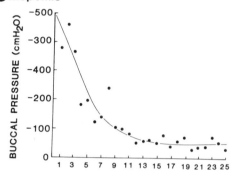

NUMBER OF PREY ITEMS EATEN

Figure 9-5
Satiation curves for *Ambloplites rupestris* (*A*) and *Lepomis macrochirus* (*B*). *Ambloplites* possesses a highly stereotyped feeding pattern, and suction pressure does not vary with the number of prey items eaten (increasing satiation). In contrast, as prey are fed to bluegill (*Lepomis*), suction pressure declines in a roughly exponential fashion, showing that the process of prey capture is modulated in response to satiation. The buccal and opercular pressures for each prey item in *A* were recorded simultaneously.

cavity of *Lepomis macrochirus*; and the peak opercular cavity pressure is -185 cm H_2O.

Buccal pressure rises rapidly to ambient pressure during the compressive phase (Fig. 9-4), and opercular pressure follows at a slower rate of pressure decrease. During high-speed suction, the buccal pressure trace then undergoes a characteristic second decrease after being above ambient pressure for 10 to 50 msec. Opercular pressure is usually positive during this stage and slowly returns to ambient pressure (Fig. 9-4).

An interesting difference occurs between the satiation curves for *Lepomis* and *Ambloplites* (Fig. 9-5). In *Lepomis,* as prey are sequentially fed to a hungry individual, the magnitude and velocity of buccal cavity pressure decrease in a roughly exponential fashion (Fig. 9-5*B*). In contrast, *Ambloplites* shows a highly stereotyped pattern of pressure change that does not vary with prey number (Fig. 9-5*A*). Prey are consumed with the same pattern and ratio of buccal-to-opercular cavity pressure regardless of the number previously eaten.

The difference between the modulated prey capture of *Lepomis*, in which the pattern of jaw movement can be varied in response to satiation, prey type, and prey location, and the stereotyped prey capture of *Ambloplites* is also present in the kinematic and electromyographic pattern. Highly stereotyped prey capture indicates a very consistent motor outflow from the central nervous system to the peripheral jaw structures and that this outflow is not modified by visual, lateral line, or other input from the prey. Each cycle of mouth opening and closing is the same. The implications of the modulated versus stereotyped methods of capturing prey for fish ecology and evolution are discussed below.

Based on the measurement of water pressure in the buccal and opercular cavities of fishes, a fluid flow pattern through the mouth cavity may be proposed that is testable by the direct measurement of velocity magnitude and direction with hot-wire anemometers. At the start of the expansive phase, the gill covers are adducted sharply, and water is forced both anteriorly between the gill bars into the buccal cavity and laterally between the pectoral girdle and the operculum; thus there may be a brief posterior-to-anterior flow. As the buccal cavity expands, water enters the mouth establishing the anterior-to-posterior flow pattern. Water does not begin to flow through the opercular cavity until the jaws have nearly closed. The rapid closure of the jaws (within 25 msec) and the high-velocity flows that can be created by rapid mouth cavity expansion (up to 12 m/sec; Osse and Muller, 1980) suggest an explanation of the second negative phase in the buccal pressure waveform (Fig. 9-4) in terms of the water-hammer effect.

Rapid closure of a valve on a stream of fluid moving through a pipe results in a sharp pressure decrease on the downstream side of the valve and a pressure increase on the upstream side. A high-pressure wave is propagated upstream, causing the banging in old pipes that gives this effect its name. During high-speed suction, the mouth may act like a valve. If the stream of water moving through the mouth cavity is analogous to flow through a pipe, when the mouth closes, the second negative phase of the buccal waveform is produced because of the downstream pressure decrease caused by fluid inertia.

CAVITATION

In addition to the water-hammer effect, a second phenomenon of fluid mechanical interest involved in suction feeding is cavitation. Cavitation of water occurs when the pressure is reduced sufficiently to cause water vapor to come rapidly out of solution in the form of small vapor-filled cavities (as behind a rapidly rotating propeller; Blake, 1949a). The pressure at which fluids cavitate depends on the size of minute air bubbles already suspended in the fluid (Blake, 1949b; Birkhoff and Zarantonello, 1957). Aquarium water normally contains many bubbles in the 0.01-mm size range, and the tensile strength of water is about 0.7 atm when bubbles of this size are present. Small cavitation bubbles collapse within 1 to 30 msec after formation (Strasberg, 1959), and a characteristic sound spectrum is associated with the bubble collapse (Mellen, 1954; Haddle and Skudrzyk, 1969).

At least one fish, the bluegill (*Lepomis macrochirus*), seems to be capable of cavitating water during rapid suction-feeding. Pressures as low as 0.7 atm have been measured with pressure transducers, and this is likely to be a considerably smaller pressure difference than can be produced under unrestrained conditions. In addition, during high-speed suction a sharp sound can be heard as the mouth opens, possibly caused by the collapse of cavitation bubbles. Alexander's calculations (1969) of the tensile strength of fish muscles show that fish muscle is easily capable of generating forces in the range of $70 \text{N}/\text{cm}^2$, a tension sufficient to cause cavitation in aquarium water. Cavitation of water during aquatic feeding appears to set a practical limit on the capture of prey by the use of suction. At least one species of fish appears to have reached this limit.

Finally, the gill cover appears to play little or no role in generating negative opercular and buccal pressures in fishes feeding by high-speed suction. Four pieces of evidence lead to this conclusion: the calculations of Alexander (1969) show that the dilator operculi muscle can generate only sufficient force to abduct the gill cover against a 10 cm H_2O pressure differential, considerably less than that present during feeding; the consistent delay in the onset of opercular abduction indicates that opercular cavity expansion does not even begin in many cases until the mouth is closing; the role of the gill arches as a resistance in the mouth cavity; and a strain-gauge analysis of opercular deformation patterns, which reveals that the operculum is being flattened laterally against the side of the head and twisted during the expansive phase.

Solid Mechanics

The importance of the operculum in controlling mouth opening and in preventing fluid inflow into the opercular cavity suggested that this bone might be a good subject for an analysis of bone strain and loading patterns (Lauder and Lanyon, 1980), and indeed the operculum is the only element of the feeding mechanism that has been analyzed within a solid mechanics framework.

By bonding a rosette strain-gauge to the operculum of the bluegill (*Lepomis macrochirus*), Lauder and Lanyon (1980) showed that this bone, during rapid-feeding, is deformed at a rate that far exceeds strain rates reported for normal functional activity in other vertebrates. A peak strain of $-615 \times 10^3 \ \mu\epsilon/$ sec and peak principal compression of $-1800 \ \mu\epsilon$ on the lateral surface of the operculum was recorded. These strains were viewed as the result of opercular deformation caused by the pressure decrease in the opercular cavity (of up to -145 cm H_2O). The rapid pressure decrease flattens the laterally convex gill cover against the side of the head, causing the center of the operculum to be subjected to predominantly compressive strains. A twisting moment is also produced by contraction of the levator operculi and adductor operculi muscles and the resistance of the lower jaw to movement. This twisting causes the principal strain axis on the operculum to be displaced anteriodorsally from the purely vertical and horizontal planes. The gill cover is thus being twisted at a 45-degree angle to the two prominent orthogonal bony struts on the medial opercular surface.

Much of the interest in this data lies in the comparison of deformation patterns with other vertebrates and in the properties of fish bone as they relate to strain rates (see Chap. 3). The bone of advanced teleost fishes is acellular in structure—the osteoblasts are not surrounded and embedded in growing bone. The osteoblasts remain on the surface of the bone, and thus acellular teleost bone is not capable of undergoing internal remodeling to repair microfracture damage. This is of special interest in that the peak strain rates recorded on the operculum exceed by a factor of nearly ten the highest *in vivo* strain rates previously recorded in vertebrates (-76×10^3 $\mu\epsilon$/sec; Lanyon and Rubin, 1980). The high physiological strain rates on the operculum may, however, result in less potential disruption of the bone matrix than the same strain magnitude imposed at a lower rate. It is a general property of vertebrate bone that high strain rates increase the fracture strain and that higher absolute compressive strain magnitudes are thus possible (Robertson and Smith, 1978). It may be that the dynamic nature of the imposed loads during suction feeding considerably increases the maximum possible strain for a given permitted level of fracture damage to the head bones.

MECHANICS OF INTRAORAL MANIPULATION AND DEGLUTITION

Three major classes of kinematic and electromyographic patterns following initial prey capture are discernable in generalized teleosts (Table 9-1): buccal manipulation, pharyngeal manipulation, and pharyngeal transport. It is important to realize that these three processes are characterized by unique patterns of muscle activity and bone movement because failure to distinguish between them can lead to the conclusion that intraoral manipulatory patterns are highly modulated and variable, when in fact there are three distinct stereotyped patterns.

Buccal Manipulation

Buccal manipulation (Fig. 9-6) is similar to the electromyographic pattern during the initial strike (compare Fig. 9-6 to Fig. 9-1) except that a preparatory phase is lacking. Both pharyngeal, mandibular, and hyoid arch muscles are active to create suction and move the prey from the anterior buccal cavity (between the parasphenoid and basihyal) back to the pharyngeal jaws. A key

Micropterus: buccal manipulation

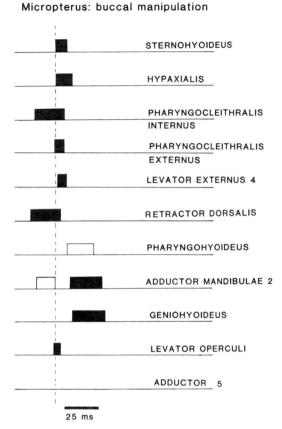

STERNOHYOIDEUS

HYPAXIALIS

PHARYNGOCLEITHRALIS
INTERNUS

PHARYNGOCLEITHRALIS
EXTERNUS

LEVATOR EXTERNUS 4

RETRACTOR DORSALIS

PHARYNGOHYOIDEUS

ADDUCTOR MANDIBULAE 2

GENIOHYOIDEUS

LEVATOR OPERCULI

ADDUCTOR 5

25 ms

Figure 9-6
Summary of the pattern of electromyographic activity in branchial and selected hyoid arch muscles during buccal manipulation in *Micropterus salmoides*. Note the similarity to muscle activity patterns during the initial strike (Fig. 9-1; Table 9-1). A preparatory phase is never present. Black bars indicate consistent activity; white bars activity in less than half of the observed cases. No activity is observed in the fifth branchial adductor. Dashed line indicates the onset of sternohyoideus activity.

feature by which buccal manipulation may be distinguished from pharyngeal manipulation (at least in centrarchids) is the nearly synchronous activity in the sternohyoideus and obliquus inferioris (hypaxial) muscles (Fig. 9-6). By causing a rapid depression of the hyoid, anterior-to-posterior water flow is created, which carries the prey back to the pharyngeal jaws. Repeated cycles of manipulatory movements may also be used to position irregularly shaped prey, such as crayfish, for swallowing.

Pharyngeal Manipulation

Pharyngeal manipulation (Table 9-1) is distinct from buccal manipulation in generalized percoids because the dominant mandibular and hyoid arch muscles used to create suction are not active. The ventral body muscles are active in conjunction with the pharyngocleithralis externus and internus (see Fig. 9-7 for a diagrammatic illustration of the major pharyngeal muscles and

PHARYNGEAL APPARATUS: MUSCULOSKELETAL COUPLINGS

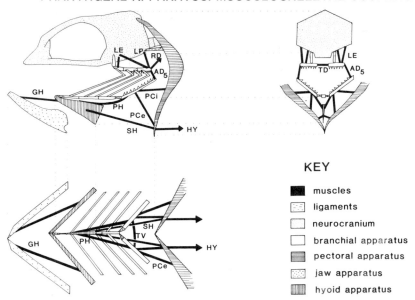

KEY

▦ muscles
▦ ligaments
□ neurocranium
□ branchial apparatus
▤ pectoral apparatus
▦ jaw apparatus
▥ hyoid apparatus

Figure 9-7
Diagrammatic view of the major musculoskeletal couplings in the pharyngeal apparatus involved
in pharyngeal manipulation and transport of prey items. The structural pattern depicted is that of
a generalized percomorph. Intrinsic gill arch muscles have been omitted. (AD5, adductor arcus
branchialum 5; GH, geniohyoideus; HY, hypaxialis; LE, levatores externi muscles; LP, levator
posterior; PCe, pharyngocleithralis externus; PCi, pharyngocleithralis internus; PH, pharyngohyoideus; RD, retractor dorsalis; SH, sternohyoideus; TD, transversus dorsalis; TV, transversus ventralis.) Origin of the retractor dorsalis is from the ventral surface of the first few
vertebral bodies.

their lines of action) to move the lower pharyngeal jaw posterioventrally, and
the sternohyoideus is inactive. At the same time, the retractor dorsalis and levatores externi (Fig. 9-7) elevate the upper pharyngeal jaw. Prey are thus positioned
and manipulated in the pharynx before deglutition. If extensive intraoral
manipulation of awkwardly shaped prey occurs, buccal manipulation will
usually alternate with pharyngeal manipulation. In these cases, a reverse flow
(posterior to anterior) may occur, and prey may be sucked anteriorly from
between the pharyngeal jaws, repositioned in the buccal cavity, and then moved
back between the pharyngeal jaws for swallowing.

Pharyngeal Transport

Transport of prey from the pharynx into the esophagus and stomach
involves the coordinated action of the upper and lower pharyngeal jaws (Table
9-1). In teleosts with relatively generalized pharyngeal jaw structure, the
movements occur primarily in the anterioposterior plane as the prey is raked
into the esophagus (Fig. 9-7; Liem, 1970).

Five main musculoskeletal couplings are involved in pharyngeal transport (this is a considerable simplification). (1) Protraction of the lower pharyngeal jaw occurs by the combined action of the pharyngohyoideus, geniohyoideus, and occasionally the adductor mandibulae (Figs. 9-7 and 9-8). The actual protraction of the lower pharyngeal jaws relative to the branchial basket is rather small, and the pharyngohyoideus also pivots the lower pharyngeal jaws laterally because of its line of action (Fig. 9-7). (2) Ret action of the lower jaw occurs by contraction of the pharyngocleithralis internus (Figs. 9-7 and 9-8). During transport, the ventral body musculature and (usually) the pharyngo- cleithralis externus are inactive. (3) Retraction of the upper pharyngeal jaws occurs by activity in the retractor dorsalis muscle (Figs. 9-7 and 9-8), which also has a dorsal (elevating) component to its line of action. (4) Protraction of the upper pharyngeal jaws occurs by the levatores externi and levatores interni muscles (Fig. 9-7); usually, the levatores externi 3 and 4 have a significantly greater anterioposterior line of action than the levatores externi 1 and 2 or the anterior levatores interni. (5) Finally, the adductor arcus branchialum 5

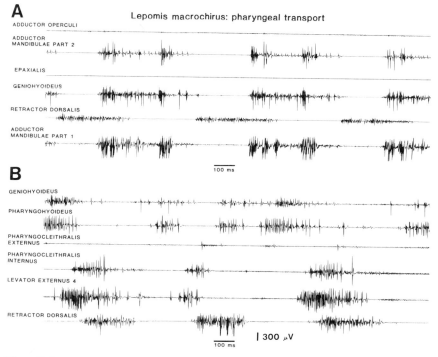

Figure 9-8

Pattern of muscle activity during the pharyngeal transport phase of feeding (see Table 9-1) in *Lepomis macrochirus*. Note the rhythmic pattern of activity and the greatly expanded time scale compared with either the initial strike or buccal manipulation. *A* and *B*, Two sets of six simultaneous recordings of pharyngeal muscle activity during transport of prey into the esophagus. (See text for discussion of activity patterns.)

adducts the lower pharyngeal jaw towards the upper (Fig. 9-7), squeezing the prey between the posterior portion of the toothed pharyngeal jaws.

The electromyographic pattern during pharyngeal transport in centr- archids shows that the upper and lower jaws move synchronously in raking the prey into the esophagus (Fig. 9-8; Lauder, 1982): the upper and lower pharyngeal jaws are protracted and retracted together. While there is con- siderable overlap between activity of the levator externus 4 and the retractor dorsalis, levatores externi 1 and 2 alternate cleanly with the retractor dorsalis. The lower jaw couplings show relatively little overlap between protractive and retractive muscle activity. The pharyngohyoideus and geniohyoideus are usually synchronously active and do not significantly overlap with the pharyngocleithralis internus (Fig. 9-8B). During transport, the sternohyo- ideus, ventral body musculature, epaxialis, and most of the mandibular and hyoid arch muscles show no activity. Not all electromyographic patterns during swallowing are symmetrical. Occasionally, asymmetrical activity between the right and left sides of the pharynx occurs to rotate the jaws around a sagittal axis. Presumably this orients the prey for transport.

At present there is very little data on the mechanics of the pharyngeal apparatus of teleosts, and the available comparisons are limited. Preliminary analysis reveals that the synchronous pattern of upper and lower pharyngeal jaw movement occurs in other acanthopterygian fishes also. Sponder and Lauder (1981) found in *Periophthalmus* that both the upper and lower jaws are protracted and retracted together, and Liem (1970) found this to be true of nandids. In both *Periophthalmus* and the centrarchids analyzed here, the upper pharyngeal jaw plays the dominant role in raking the prey into the esophagus. The lower jaw, while it does have some independent mobility, is constrained by its anterior attachment to the branchial basket. *Esox* and *Perca* also use synchronous movements of the upper and lower pharyngeal jaws during prey transport. In *Esox,* as in all non-neoteleostean fishes, a retractor dorsalis muscle is absent. Retraction of the upper pharyngeal jaws occurs by the levator externus 1 and levator internus 2, which have a posterodorsally inclined line of action (Lauder, 1982). This contrasts with the protractive effect of these muscles in neoteleostean fishes (*e.g.,* Fig. 9-7). Retraction and posterior rotation of the lower pharyngeal jaw about its anterior attachment to the basibranchials occurs by the pharyngocleithralis internus as in neoteleostean fishes.

The only other experimental studies on pharyngeal jaw mechanics have been on the Cichlidae (Liem, 1973, 1978; Liem and Osse, 1975). Cichlids provide an interesting comparison with the morphologically generalized Centrarchidae. The cichlid upper pharyngeal jaw is relatively immobile in the anterioposterior direction because of its articulation with the base of the skull (Fig. 15 in Liem, 1978). The upper jaw pivots on the pharyngeal apophysis, and the lower jaw provides the primary transport movement. Cichlid fishes have an extremely complex pharyngeal manipulation phase of intraoral food processing that involves prey maceration via two power strokes of the upper and lower pharyngeal jaws.

In power-stroke one, the upper jaw pivots anteriorly, and the lower jaw is adducted against it, crushing the prey. A transitional stroke follows as both jaws move posteriorly, and finally power-stroke two occurs with the jaws in the retracted position. Power-stroke one involves a "bite" between the anterior teeth of the pharyngeal jaws, while in power-stroke two the bite is between the posterior jaw teeth. The electromyographic pattern of chewing differs significantly from that of centrarchids in that the sternohyoideus is active during pharyngeal manipulation, and a protracted pharyngeal transport phase appears to be absent. A comparative experimental analysis of several taxa at different phylogenetic levels will be necessary before any more general conclusions about the evolutionary mechanics of the pharyngeal apparatus can be formulated; this is a key task for future research on the mechanics of food capture.

MECHANICS OF FILTER FEEDING

Filter feeding as a mode of food capture in fishes is distinct from suction feeding. In filtering small particles from the water column, the selection of prey to be swallowed occurs at the filter itself after the potential prey items have entered the mouth. Food value thus plays little role in determining which particles enter the mouth, and mechanical attributes of the particles such as size, shape, and density as well as mobility may regulate capture (Jorgensen, 1966). In suction feeding, prey selection usually occurs before the mouth is opened, and the visual system plays a major role in the initiation of feeding (Confer et al., 1978; Durbin, 1979).

The theoretical mechanisms by which particles may be removed from a flowing fluid have been considered within the context of aerosol theory by Rubenstein and Koehl (1977), who identified seven possible mechanisms by which suspended particles can be filtered, one of which is sieving. Most vertebrate and invertebrate suspension feeders use other methods of particle capture such as direct interception by filter fibers and mucus or gravitational deposition onto the filter surface (Rubenstein and Koehl, 1977; Jorgensen, 1966), and sieving appears to occur relatively rarely.

In fishes, however, sieving is the dominant filtration mechanism. If a sieving mechanism is being used by suspension-feeding fishes to remove food particles from the water, then no particles on the downstream side of the filter should be larger than the pore size of the sieve. Conversely, the food particles found in fish stomachs should in theory be equal to or larger than the pore size of the filter. Because flow streamlines might bypass the filter pores (passing between the tips of adjacent gill rakers for example), one might expect to find a few large particles downstream of the filter, but no particles smaller than the mesh size should be captured.

A number of studies have confirmed these expectations. Durbin and Durbin (1975) studied filter feeding in menhaden (*Brevoortia tyrannus*). They suggested that the gill rakers have a mean pore size of less than 80 μ and measured capture efficiencies of 20-μ particles at 2%, 80-μ particles at 21%, and 1200-μ particles at 68%. Magnuson and Heitz (1971), Galbraith (1967), and Leong and O'Connell (1969) have all noted that prey sizes in the stomachs of filter-feeding fishes invariably exceed the estimated mesh size of the gill raker filter.

Rosen and Hales (1981), in an excellent study of particle filtration in the paddlefish (*Polyodon spathula*), measured a mean mesh size of 0.06 mm to 0.09 mm in the gill filter. They showed that particles strained from the water were at least 0.2 mm long and 0.1 mm wide, and that while smaller particles did occur in the water column, they were not retained by the filter. These results confirm a sieving model of prey capture for filter-feeding fishes, as the particle size distribution in relation to filter pore size is not consistent with other filtration mechanisms (Rubenstein and Koehl, 1977). Rosen and Hales (1981) also showed that all particles of the appropriate size, regardless of food value, were filtered from the water. Detritus and sand particles constituted 50% of the stomach content volume.

The actual mechanism by which particles are held on the gill filters and subsequently swallowed has not been investigated. If food is trapped on the lateral surface of the gill rakers as water entering the mouth passes laterally into the opercular cavities, it may be forced by water pressure to the base of the gill rakers and entrapped in mucus covering the gill arches. Mucus strands from the separate arches may be swallowed when the mouth is closed between periods of filtering, and pharyngeal jaw movement probably aids deglutition.

The rate of filtration is varied in fishes by two mechanisms: altering swimming speed and thus the volume flow over the filter and active alterations in the filter mesh size. Changing body velocity in response to food particle concentration is a well-documented phenomenon. Durbin and associates (1981) showed that swimming speed in menhaden increases approximately hyperbolically with increasing particle density, and feeding usually stops below a certain prey-density threshold. Active changes in gill raker spacing are less well documented, but branchial arch musculature could adjust the spacing between adjacent arches and thus influence the flow pattern through the gill rakers.

Most filter feeding fishes can switch to a particulate or suction feeding mode for larger prey, and the process of prey capture occurs by the musculo-skeletal couplings discussed above under Suction Mechanics. Leong and O'Connell (1969) analyzed feeding in the anchovy (*Engraulis mordax*) and found that suction feeding was used for *Artemia* adults from 5 to 10 mm long, but that anchovies switched to filter feeding to capture the 0.6-mm sized nauplii. Filter-feeding individuals usually swim actively and hold the mouth widely open for 2 to 3 seconds. The mouth then closes, locomotion ceases, and a brief glide ensues before the mouth is opened and forward progress resumed; 30 to 50 feeding cycles of this type can occur per minute in an actively filtering fish.

From this brief review of filter feeding dynamics, it is apparent that the hydrodynamics of flow over the gill arches and rakers is poorly understood (see also Chap. 4). Flow patterns over the gill rakers could be examined in a horizontally sectioned head of a freshly dead menhaden, for example, in a flow tank with small hydrogen bubble tracers or even live *Artemia* as prey. This would allow the direct observation of particle entrapment and flow pattern, and the gill rakers and arches could be manipulated to examine the effect on particle capture efficiency at different prey size classes. A second puzzling feature of filter feeding concerns swallowing of the prey. It is not at all clear how prey trapped on gill rakers are ultimately swallowed. Perhaps only pulse feedings with dyed particles will allow determination of the route captured particles take on their way to the esophagus.

FOOD CAPTURE: ECOLOGY, BEHAVIOR, EVOLUTION

Kinematic Modulation

From an ecologic viewpoint, one of the most interesting concepts to emerge from recent investigations on fish feeding mechanics is the distinction between modulating and highly stereotyped feeding behavior in different species (*e.g.,* Liem, 1978, 1979, 1980b). Modulation of feeding is the alteration of kinematic, electromyographic, and pressure patterns during feeding in response to different prey types and locations (Lauder, 1981). Highly stereo-typed feeders show very little variability between feeding sequences even when eating prey of widely differing escape capacity. Of special interest is the fact that modulating and stereotyped feeders can be closely related.

Ambloplites and *Lepomis*, as noted earlier, show radically different satiation curves but are very similar in anatomic design; *Hoplias* and *Lebiasina*, two characoid species studied by Lauder (1981), share many structural features in common but differ greatly in the jaw movement pattern elicited in response to different prey. *Lebiasina*, for example, uses a different pattern of muscle activity and jaw movement in feeding on the bottom than is used in eating the same prey type on the surface. The differences between stereotyped and modulated trophic types can be expressed in terms of the neural control of motor output to the jaw muscles (Fig. 9-9). Both *Lebiasina* and *Hoplias* share the same structural network, but *Lebiasina* possesses a greater number of independent functional units that can be altered to produce any one of three

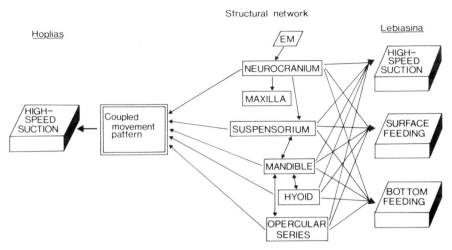

Figure 9-9

Diagrammatic illustration of modulated (*Lebiasina*) and stereotyped (*Hoplias*) feeding patterns
in two fishes with a very similar structural network in the head. Based on data presented in Lauder
(1981). In *Lebiasina*, the various components of the structural network can be linked in a number
of patterns and with different temporal relations to produce varying kinematic outputs during
feeding. This results in at least three statistically definable outputs (three-dimensional boxes). In
Hoplias, movement of the structural network is governed by a "coupled-movement pattern" that
only allows one kinematic sequence of jaw movement regardless of the type or position of the
prey.

motor output patterns (Fig. 9-9). *Hoplias* possesses a "coupled movement
pattern" in that the various functional units of feeding behavior are tightly
associated into a single fixed pattern of motor output (Fig. 9-9).

These findings have major implications for ecologic models of prey
capture (Keast and Webb, 1966; Werner and Hall, 1979). Diversity in the
functional repertoire (*i.e.*, species with an increased number of modulated
patterns) may show a greater breadth of trophic resource utilization than do
highly stereotyped species. Modulated functional patterns are predicted for
species that use a wide range of food resources. In addition, the versatility and
plasticity inherent in nonstereotyped feeders may permit greater adaptibility
to varying trophic conditions (Liem, 1980b), while at the same time con-
founding optimality models of prey capture behavior.

The concept of ecologic specialization takes on new meaning in the light
of differences in fish functional repertoires (Liem, 1980b). Piscivorous species
and "generalized predators" are often considered to represent ancestral
unspecialized types (*e.g.*, Schaeffer and Rosen, 1961), but if these species are
highly stereotyped suction feeders with a single pattern of motor output to the
jaw muscles, they must be considered as specialized when compared to
modulating forms. *Lepomis*, for example, possesses a broad functional
repertoire and is generalized in comparison with the more predaceous but

highly specialized *Ambloplites*. Nonmodulating, high-speed suction feeding is a specialized mode of prey capture that has evolved independently numerous times in ray-finned fishes. Through this type of analysis, the study of fish mechanics can contribute to ecologic investigation and suggest hypotheses for future exploration.

Evolutionary Mechanics of Food Capture

The major feature of the evolution of the feeding mechanism in ray-finned fishes (Actinopterygii) is the increase through time (in a series of discrete stages) of the complexity of the biomechanical pathways governing jaw movement (Lauder, 1982). This increase in complexity is correlated with an increase in the diversity of structural and functional patterns shown in derived actinopterygian clades.

As an example, consider the primitive musculoskeletal apparatus involved in prey capture. The earliest ray-finned fishes retained the mechanism of mandibular depression that is primitive for gnathostomes: posterioventral rotation of the hyoid apparatus mediated by the sternohyoideus and ventral body musculature. The structure of the skull was such that relatively little lateral mobility of the cheek occurred, and ventral depression of the hyoid was limited by the extensive series of closely articulated branchiostegal plates (Jessen, 1968). The buccal volume change that could occur during feeding was thus small, and it is unlikely that negative pressures of less than -100 cm H_2O below ambient pressure could have been generated. The process of prey capture, as inferred from morphology, appears to have been relatively conservative throughout primitive actinopterygians, and this may be reflected in the conservatism of muscle activity patterns in primitive, living actinopterygians (Lauder, 1980b).

The halecostome fishes, including *Amia* and the Teleostei as extant clades plus a number of extinct taxa, are characterized by two mouth-opening couplings. Halecostomes retain the primitive hyoid system for mediating mandibular depression, and an additional system is present: rotation of the operculum causes depression of the mandible via a ventral connection through the interopercular bone and interoperculomandibular ligament. This provides two independent mechanical systems that both control mouth opening; the mechanical relationships of these two systems are such that the opercular coupling is more efficient at translating a small muscular contraction into mandibular depression, while the hyoid apparatus is a more force-efficient system.

The major consequence of this duality in mouth opening mechanisms is an enormous increase in constructional and functional flexibility of the skull, and primitive teleost clades exemplify this by exhibiting a considerable diversity in trophic apparatus. The osteoglossomorph fishes have modified the primitive hyoid coupling into a third set of jaws, the basihyal-parasphenoid bite, and prey are macerated and crushed between the tongue and the base of the skull. This type of structural modification is not possible within the structurally rigid skull framework of primitive ray-finned fishes. Clupeomorph fishes have repeatedly evolved microphagous habits and the concomitant structural and functional modifications in the trophic apparatus.

Within the acanthopterygian fishes, similar evolutionary consequences of biomechanical changes are observable in the mechanism of upper jaw protrusion (Liem, 1980b). Cichlid fishes, for example, have five different mechanical pathways that can be used to produce protrusion of the premaxilla. More primitive acanthopterygians (such as *Perca*) possess four or fewer pathways, and there are tight functional and mechanical linkages between the protrusion systems that constrain directions of evolutionary change in structure and function.

The basic concept underlying this discussion is that independent biomechanical pathways in a structural and functional system promote constructional flexibility in the evolutionary sense, and permit new morphologies and a greater diversity of functional patterns. Clades with fewer pathways of structural control are limited in the direction and amount of evolutionary modification of functional design. The analysis of fish trophic mechanics has thus furnished an excellent example of general properties of biological design and the pathways by which it is transformed.

One final aspect of the evolutionary mechanics of ray-finned fishes that has received relatively little attention is the branchiostegal apparatus. The interopercular bone, noted above as being a key element in the chain of elements transmitting contraction of the levator operculi muscle to the mandible, is generally considered to be homologous to a branchiostegal ray. In *Amia,* the uppermost branchiostegal ray is expanded and has ligamentous connections both with the mandible and hyoid apparatus (Allis, 1897). The dorsal branchiostegal elements may thus have played an important role in the early evolution of the levator operculi coupling by forming a functional linkage between the hyoid, operculum, and mandible. Halecostome fishes possess a branchiostegal apparatus that is considerably reduced in comparison to that of primitive, ray-finned fishes. The individual plates have become more slender, anterioventral elements have been consolidated into gular plates, and there has been a reduction in the number of plates. These modifications may relate to increased mobility of the hyoid in the dorsoventral plane and to the increased role of the branchiostegal apparatus in the halecostome suction-feeding mechanism. The hyohyoideus adductores and abductores muscles (Winterbottom, 1974) that adduct and abduct the branchiostegal rays are hypothesized to be derived from the primitive actinopterygian interhyoideus (Lauder, 1982). These muscles, in permitting finer control over branchiostegal ray movement, may have had an important impact on the nature of respiratory patterns and suction feeding in the early halecostome fishes, but we still lack basic functional data on the branchiostegal apparatus in living forms, and until this badly needed information is obtained, the role of the branchiostegal apparatus in actinopterygian evolution will remain obscure.

CONCLUSIONS AND PROSPECTUS

The last decade has witnessed enormous progress in our understanding of the dynamics of aquatic prey capture in fishes. New experimental techniques have revealed details of the feeding mechanism, and general concepts relevant to fish ecology and the evolutionary biology of complex systems have emerged. Two main topics are in need of considerable future work before a comprehensive understanding of the regulatory processes governing food capture in fishes can emerge. First, the physiological properties of the jaw muscles must be determined. Length-tension curves for opening and closing muscles and the response of these muscles to a quick stretch will aid in interpreting high-speed films and electromyographic data. Second, detailed empirical analysis of feeding hydrodynamics must be extended beyond the current research on mouth-cavity pressures to include the measurement of flow velocities, pressure-velocity relationships for modulated and stereotyped trophic categories, and the effect different patterns of pressure and velocity in the mouth cavity of the predator have on the prey.

Perhaps the area with the greatest potential for experimental and conceptual advance is the relationship between locomotor patterns and feeding behavior. Over the last 10 years, research on the functional morphology of feeding and locomotion has proceeded along separate lines; yet in order to analyze predator-prey interactions and to elucidate patterns of evolution in fishes, the mutual relationships between structure and function in feeding and locomotion need to be considered. Is there a functional relationship between prey capture by high-speed suction and pectoral fin placement? How is the timing of jaw movement modified in ambush predators, and are different locomotor patterns at the strike (Webb and Skadsen, 1980) correlated with differences in jaw movement (Rand and Lauder, 1981)?

Armed with new techniques and a considerable background of experimental data, we now have to consider more general questions and begin to integrate concepts and approaches from feeding and locomotor functional morphology into a synthetic evolutionary framework.

Acknowledgments

Preparation of this paper was supported by a grant from the Andrew W. Mellon Foundation, the Block Fund of The University of Chicago, and NSF DEB81-15048. Thanks go to Dr. William Hylander, who assisted with preliminary contraction-time studies on fish muscle, and to Joan Hives for her most helpful assistance with the manuscript.

REFERENCES

Akster, H.A., and Osse, J.W.M. 1978. Muscle fibre types in head muscles of the perch *Perca fluviatilis* (L.), Teleostei. *Neth. J. Zool.* 28:94–110.

Alexander, R. McN. 1966. The functions and mechanisms of the protrusible upper jaws of two species of cyprinid fish. *J. Zool. Lond.* 149:288–296.

Alexander, R. McN. 1967a. The functions and mechanisms of the protrusible upper jaws of some acanthopterygian fish. *J. Zool. Lond.* 151:43–64.

Alexander, R. McN. 1967b. *Functional Design in Fishes.* London: Hutchinson.

Alexander, R. McN. 1969. Mechanics of the feeding action of a cyprinid fish. *J. Zool. Lond.* 159:1–15.

Alexander, R. McN. 1970. Mechanics of the feeding action of various teleost fishes. *J. Zool. Lond.* 162:145–156.

Allis, E.P. 1897. The cranial muscles and cranial and first spinal nerves in *Amia calva. J. Morphol.* 12:487–772.

Anker, G. 1974. Morphology and kinetics of the head of the stickleback. *Gasterosteus aculeatus. Trans. Zool. Soc. Lond.* 32:311–416.

Ballintijn, C.M., van den Burg, A., and Egberink, B.P. 1972. An electromyographic study of the adductor mandibulae complex of a free-swimming carp (*Cyprinus carpio* L.) during feeding. *J. Exp. Biol.* 57:261–283.

Barel, C., van der Meulen, J.W., and Berkhoudt, H. 1977. Kinematischer Transmissionskoeffizient und Vierstangensystem als Funktionsparameter und Formmodell fur mandibulare Depressionsapparate bei Teleosteirn. *Anat. Anz.* 142:21–31.

Barends, P.M.G. 1979. The relation between fiber type composition and function in the jaw adductor muscle of the perch (*Perca fluviatilis,* L.). *Proc. Konin. Ned. Akad. Weten.* 82:147–164.

Birkhoff, G., and Zarantonello, E.H. 1957. *Jets, Wakes, and Cavities.* New York: Academic Press.

Blake, F.G. 1949a. The onset of cavitation in liquids. *Harvard Univ. Acoust. Res. Lab. Tech. Mem.* 12.

Blake, F.G. 1949b. The tensile strength of liquids: a review of the literature. *Harvard Univ. Acoust. Res. Lab. Tech. Mem.* 9.

Confer, J.L., Howick, G.L., Corzette, M.H., et al. Visual predation by planktivores. *Oikos* 31:27–37.

Durbin, A.G. 1979. Food selection by plankton feeding fishes. *In* Clepper, H., *Predator-Prey Systems in Fisheries Management,* edited by H. Clepper, 203–218. Washington, D.C.: Sport Fishing Institute.

Durbin A.G., and Durbin, E.G. 1975. Grazing rates of the Atlantic menhaden *Brevoortia tyrannus* as a function of particle size and concentration. *Marine Biol.* 33:265–277.

Durbin, A.G., Durbin, E.G., Verity, P.G., and Smayda, T.J. 1981. Voluntary swimming speeds and respiration rates of a filter-feeding planktivore, the Atlantic menhaden, *Brevoortia tyrannus* (Pisces: Clupeidae). *Fish. Bull.* 78:877–886.

Elshoud-Oldenhave, M.J.W., and Osse, J.W.M. 1976. Functional morphology of the feeding system in the ruff—*Gymnocephalus cernua* (L. 1758—Teleostei, Percidae). *J. Morphol.* 150:399–422.

Galbraith, M.G. 1967. Size-selective predation on *Daphnia* by rainbow trout and yellow perch. *Trans. Am. Fish. Soc.* 96:1–10.

Gosline, W.A. 1971. *Functional Morphology and Classification of Teleostean Fishes.* Honolulu: University Press of Hawaii.

Grobecker, D.B., and Pietsch, T.W. 1979. High-speed cinematographic evidence for ultrafast feeding in antennariid angler fishes. *Science* 205:1161–1162.

Haddle, G.P., and Skudrzyk, E.J. 1969. The physics of flow noise. *J. Acoust. Soc. Am.* 46:130–137.

Hill, A.V. 1970. *First and Last Experiments in Muscle Mechanics.* Cambridge: Cambridge University Press.

Jessen, H. 1968. *Moythomasia nitida* Gross und *M.* cf. *Striata* Gross, Devonische Paleonisciden aus dem Oberen Plattenkalk der Bergischen–Gladbach–Paffrather Mulde (Rheinisches schiefergebirge). *Paleontographica* 128A: 87–114.

Johnston, I.A. 1980. Contractile properties of fish fast muscle fibers. *Marine Biol. Lett.* 1:323–328.

Jorgensen, C.B. 1966. *Biology of Suspension Feeding.* London: Pergamon Press.

Keast, A., and Webb, D. 1966. Mouth and body form relative to feeding ecology in the fish fauna of a small lake, Lake Opinicon, Ontario. *J. Fish. Res. Board Can.* 23:1845–1874.

Lanyon, L.E., and Rubin, C.T. 1980. Loading of mammalian long bones during locomotion. *J. Physiol.* 303:72.

Lauder, G.V. 1979. Feeding mechanisms in primitive teleosts and in the halecomorph fish *Amia calva. J. Zool. Lond.* 187:543–578.

Lauder, G.V. 1980a. The suction feeding mechanism in sunfishes (*Lepomis*): An experimental analysis. *J. Exp. Biol.* 88:49–72.

Lauder, G.V. 1980b. Evolution of the feeding mechanism in primitive actinopterygian fishes: A functional anatomical analysis of *Polypterus, Lepisosteus,* and *Amia. J. Morphol.* 163:283–317.

Lauder, G.V. 1980c. Hydrodynamics of prey capture by teleost fishes. In *Biofluid mechanics II,* edited by D. Schneck, 161–181. New York: Plenum Press.

Lauder, G.V. 1981. Intraspecific functional repertoires in the feeding mechanism of the characoid fishes *Lebiasina, Hoplias,* and *Chalceus. Copeia* 1981(1):154–168.

Lauder, G.V. 1982. Patterns of evolution in the feeding mechanism of actinopterygian fishes. *Am. Zool.* 22:275–285.

Lauder, G.V., and Lanyon, L.E. 1980. Functional anatomy of feeding in the bluegill sunfish, *Lepomis macrochirus: in vivo* measurement of bone strain. *J. Exp. Biol.* 84:33–55.

Lauder, G.V., and Leim, K.F. 1980. The feeding mechanism and cephalic myology of *Salvelinus fontinalis:* Form, function, and evolutionary significance. In Balon, *Charrs: Salmonid Fishes of the Genus Salvelinus,* edited by E.K. Balon, 365–390. The Netherlands: Junk Publishers.

Lauder, G.V., and Liem, K.F. 1981. Prey capture by *Luciocephalus pulcher:* Implications for models of jaw protrusion in teleost fishes. *Env. Biol. Fish.* 6:257–268.

Leong, R.J.H., and O'Connell, C.P. 1969. A laboratory study of particulate and filter feeding of the northern anchovy (*Engraulis mordax*). *J. Fish. Res. Board. Can.* 26:557–582.

Liem, K.F. 1970. Comparative functional anatomy of the Nandidae (Pisces: Teleostei). *Fieldiana, Zoology* 56:1–166.

Liem, K.F. 1973. Evolutionary strategies and morphological innovations: Cichlid pharyngeal jaws. *Syst. Zool.* 22:424–441.

Liem, K.F. 1978. Modulatory multiplicity in the functional repertoire of the feeding mechanism in cichlid fishes. I. Piscivores. *J. Morphol.* 158:323–360.

Liem, K.F. 1979. Modulatory multiplicity in the feeding mechanism in cichlid fishes, as exemplified by the invertebrate pickers of Lake Tanganyika. *J. Zool. Lond.* 189:93–125.

Liem, K.F. 1980a. Acquisition of energy by teleosts: adaptive mechanisms and evolutionary patterns. In *Environmental Physiology of Fishes*, edited by M.A. Ali. 299–334. New York: Plenum Press.

Liem, K.F. 1980b. Adaptive significance of intra- and interspecific differences in the feeding repertoires of cichlid fishes. *Amer. Zool.* 20:295–314.

Liem, K.F. and Osse, J.W.M. 1975. Biological versatility, evolution, and food resource exploitation in African cichlid fishes. *Amer. Zool.* 15:427–454.

Magnuson, J.J., and Heitz, G.G. 1971. Gill raker apparatus and food selectivity among mackerels, tunas, and dolphins. *Fish Bull.* 69:361–370.

Mallatt, J. 1981. The suspension feeding mechanism of the larval lamprey *Petromyzon marinus. J. Zool., Lond.* 194:103–142.

Marshall, N.B. 1971. *Explorations in the life of fishes.* Cambridge: Harvard University Press.

Mellen, R.H. 1954. Ultrasonic spectrum of cavitation noise in water. *J. Acoust. Soc. Am.* 26:356–360.

Nyberg, D.W. 1971. Prey capture in the largemouth bass. *Am. Midland Naturalist* 86:128–144.

Osse, J.W.M. 1969. Functional morphology of the head of the perch (*Perca fluviatilis* L.): An electromyographic study. *Neth. J. Zool.* 19:289–392.

Osse, J.W.M., and Muller, M. 1980. A model of suction feeding in fishes with some implications for ventilation. In *Environmental Physiology of Fishes*, edited by M.A. Ali, 335–352. New York: Plenum Press.

Rand, D.M., and Lauder, G.V. 1981. Prey capture in the chain pickerel *Esox niger:* correlations between feeding and locomotor behavior. *Can. J. Zool.* 59:1072–1078.

Robertson, B.M., and Smith, D.C. 1978. Compressive strength of mandibular bone as a function of microstructure and strain rate. *J. Biomechanics* 11:455–471.

Rosen, R.A., and Hales, D.C. 1981. Feeding of paddlefish, *Polyodon spathula. Copeia* 1981(2):441–455.

Rubenstein, D.I., and Koehl, M.A.R. 1977. The mechanisms of filter feeding: some theoretical considerations. *Am. Midland Naturalist* 111:981–994.

Schaeffer, B., and Rosen, D.E. 1961. Major adaptive levels in the evolution of the actinopterygian feeding mechanism. *Am Zool.* 1:187–204.

Sponder, D.L., and Lauder, G.V. 1981. Terrestrial feeding in the mudskipper *Periophthalmus* (Pisces: Teleostei): A cineradiographic analysis. *J. Zool. Lond.* 193:517–530.

Strasberg, M. 1959. Onset of ultrasonic cavitation in tap water. *J. Acoust. Soc. Am.* 31:163–167.

Tchernavin, V.V. 1953. The feeding mechanisms of a deep sea fish *Chauliodus sloani* Schneider. British Museum (Nat. Hist.), London.

Thexton, A.J., Wake, D.B., and Wake, M.H. 1977. Tongue function in the salamander *Bolitoglossa occidentalis*. *Arch. Oral Biol.* 22:361–366.

Webb, P.W., and Skadsen, J.M. 1980. Strike tactics of *Esox*. *Can. J. Zool.* 58:1462–1489.

Weihs, D. 1980. Hydrodynamics of suction feeding of fish in motion. *J. Fish. Biol.* 16:425–433.

Werner, E.E., and Hall, D.J. 1979. Foraging efficiency and habitat switching in competing sunfishes. *Ecology* 60:256–264.

Winterbottom, R. 1974. A descriptive synonymy of the striated muscles of the Teleostei. *Proc. Acad. Nat. Sci. Philos.* 125:225–317.

Chapter 10
ENERGETICS
James F. Kitchell

CONTENTS

INTRODUCTION

Energy budgets and energetics models are an essential requisite to narrowing evolutionary and ecologic questions from the vastly possible to the most likely or most interesting; prediction and experimental test can then follow. Many interesting or novel mechanistic discoveries remain for researchers, but the ultimate value of each may only be known through quantitative tools. Balanced energy budgets and simulation models built from them allow these mechanisms to be evaluated in terms of their quantitative contribution to total adaptiveness (Bock, 1980). Extended to the population level, this approach can be the basis for studies of total fitness and life-history evolution (Ware, 1982). Assemblages of species models represented in energetics terms may be used to study community-level processes such as the impact of predation (Stewart *et al.,* 1981; Kerr, 1979).

Energetics studies are usually initiated at the organismic level; reductionism then focuses on components of the energy-budgeting process (Brett, 1982; Allen and Wootton, 1982). The central questions are the following: "What is important to the survival, growth, and reproduction of a phenotype?" and "How important is this factor or mechanism?" The bulk of today's literature is largely descriptive and usually concludes with some implied or explicit

312

speculation about the relative importance of mechanisms such as selection for higher efficiency or lower mortality or greater reproductive output.

Detailed reviews of the energetics literature are fully presented in several recently published sources (Webb, 1978; Brett and Groves, 1979; Elliott, 1979; Brett, 1982). Fish growth models are excellently and critically reviewed by Ricker (1979). There also exists a substantial and growing literature on conducting rigorous sensitivity analyses of models. This effort stems from the physical sciences and is now being extended to the growing body of ecologic models (e.g., Gardner et al., 1980). As evidenced by the extensive review of Brett and Groves (1979), there are very few laboratory studies of energy budgeting by fishes in which all components of the budget have been independently measured. More typically, one or more of the components is estimated from other studies or by difference in a balanced budget. There are no field studies in which all components of the budget have been measured for any fish species.

The specific objectives of the chapter are to develop the basic precepts of energy budgets for fishes, describe the general ideas presented in energetics models, and evaluate the sensitivity of energetics models and the assumptions they often contain.

BASIC ENERGY BUDGETS

The basic ideas of energetics studies are represented in the form of a balanced energy equation. Symbols used in the equations differ depending on whether the study originates from the biological sciences (e.g., Ricker, 1979; Brett and Groves, 1979) or from the physical sciences (e.g., Webb, 1978; Sharp and Vlymen, 1978). In general, the terms are those of an input-output budget with rates of consumption balanced by output rates that include metabolic expenditures and waste losses plus a long-term energy gain term. A balanced budget would be Energy consumed by feeding (C) = total metabolic outputs + waste losses + energy gain, where total metabolic output (M) = standard metabolism (R) + costs of activity (A) + specific dynamic action (SDA), and waste losses = excretion of soluble wastes (U) + egestion of indigestible wastes (F); and energy gain = somatic growth (ΔB) + gonad growth (G). In symbolic form the budget is

$$C = \underbrace{\underbrace{(R + A + SDA)}_{\text{Maintenance}} + \overbrace{(F + U)}^{\text{Waste}} + \overbrace{(\Delta B + G)}^{\text{Gain}}}_{} \tag{1}$$

where the braces over the terms indicate Total metabolism, Waste, and Gain, and the brace under indicates Maintenance.

The sum of metabolism and waste losses is usually taken as maintenance costs. More properly, maintenance is that level of feeding when net energy gain ($\Delta B + G$) is zero, and C is then the defined maintenance ration. Although maintenance levels are often assumed to be constant, they may be a dynamic function of nutritional state and history. Waste losses ($F + U$) and the calorigenic effect of feeding (SDA) are usually expressed as functions (often simple fractions) of feeding rates. When intensively studied (Elliott, 1976a), waste losses as excreted energy or fecal outputs show complex, nonlinear relations to relative feeding rate, temperature, and fish size. Their sum, however, can be effectively represented as a simple proportion of feeding rate.

The indigestible components (chitin, cellulose, lignins, keratin, etc.) of prey types also alter the relative amount of energy lost in feces. Because much of the digestible portion of most aquatic prey is protein, excretory outputs of nitrogenous waste will vary with prey type; however, the dynamics of feeding rates more substantially affect total energy expended through SDA and a simple proportionality seems both easier and reasonably accurate (Beamish, 1974). In summary, energy outputs to SDA and waste losses will vary primarily as functions of prey type, which is species and size specific. The dynamics of both will closely parallel those of feeding rates. Energy stored as growth or gametes will then vary in proportion to resources available in excess of maintenance costs.

There is no small uncertainty in attempting to develop a "typical" energy budget for a "typical" fish. There are substantial differences between species, test conditions, and measurement techniques used in laboratory environments and of course in the field. Nevertheless, an extensive compilation of energy budgets presented by Brett and Groves (1979) allows a general statement for carnivorous fishes maintained at high rations and amenable temperatures. The average, normalized, balanced energy budget and 95% confidence limits for its components are

C = (total metabolism) + (waste losses) + (energy gain)
  or empirically (as %): $100 = 44 \pm 7 + 27 \pm 3 + 29 \pm 6$.   (2)

Although less studied than carnivores, the data available for young herbivorous fishes offer a general budget of the form

C = total metabolism + waste losses + energy gain
  or $100 = 37 + 43 + 20$.   (3)

Considering the generally greater indigestible component of the herbivore diet, the growth component is remarkably high (Brett and Groves, 1979).

The budgets described above were typically derived from laboratory studies of sub-adult fish fed a single type of natural or prepared food; they are, as stated, dangerously general. It is important to recognize that the range of carnivore growth efficiencies (= energy gain as % of C in the balanced budget) tabulated includes several values near 50% (see Brett and Groves, 1979). Given the vagaries of nature, the proportions for each component will vary as growth rates range from a maximum reflecting optimal environment conditions to the commonly lower and occasionally negative values associated with suboptimal environments.

The Energy Output Hierarchy

Allocation of energy consumed by a fish is presumed to occur in hierarchial fashion. The costs of routine metabolism must be met first and are size- and temperature-dependent. Outputs to specific dynamic action and waste losses represent taxes on consumed energy: these outputs change in proportion to feeding rates. Activity metabolism is a metabolic bet that can yield substantial benefit in located prey or mates or that can prevent the catastrophe of entering another predator's energy budget. The diversity of morphologies and typical swimming modes evident within the fishes offer ample evidence of the many evolutionary responses to complex problems expressed in activity costs and strategies. Only the remainder of consumed energy can be allocated to growth or the longer-term investment in gametes. Which of those storage terms takes precedence is currently a question in life-history studies (see Stearns, 1980; Ware, 1980).

Because it is last in the energetics hierarchy, surplus energy expressed as growth is the most variable budget component. The idea of a single growth constant (von Bertalanffy, 1957) seems inappropriate for most fishes. For example, the empirical growth curve used in fisheries biology is a simple statement of size at age for samples of a fish population; both the means and the variance can differ between years and between populations. Most fishes have indeterminate growth rates and will continue both somatic and gonadal increments until they reach a size that comes to steady state with the available food resources and environmental conditions (Miller, 1979). That size is a complex result of interaction with the ecologic conditions of the habitat; it is highly variable both within and between habitats and most important, is an excellent indicator of both the limiting conditions and selection pressures operating over the recent past. Although there are important and interesting exceptions, selection pressures might often be expected to favor larger size in most fishes: larger individuals can eat larger prey, avoid more predators, find more or better mates, and produce more gametes.

There is not yet a single report of average annual growth rates recorded in natural fish populations that are consistently at or near the maximum possible rates dictated by either the genetic constraints of the species or the abiotic limitations of a native habitat. Although large tunas may be limited by physiological constraints in the face of abundant food (Kitchell et al., 1978) and Brett (1982) feels that sockeye salmon (*Oncorhynchus nerka*) are growing at or near maximum rates in the ocean, growth rates for smaller members of those species are clearly food limited. In other words, the abundance and size distribution of food resources are generally the limiting factors of fish growth. Two general and independent sources of evidence support that generalization: one is the universal report of increased growth accomplished whenever a fish species is brought into aquaculture conditions (although the inevitable news release that follows often claims a miracle of animal husbandry, the growth response observed is in fact little more than the expected result of providing the fish with abundant food in an amenable environment); the second is widely documented as compensatory growth when a fish population is newly-exploited. Released from the density-dependent effects of intraspecific competition, survivors grow more rapidly (Pitcher and Hart, 1982).

Growth curves that can be derived from the scales or bones of fishes contain much of what the "energetics accountant" seeks to know about income, expenditures, accidents, and windfalls. There is a real prospect for misrepresentation or misinterpretation that must be delimited through an understanding of limiting conditions plus ecologic and evolutionary likelihood. Although some biologists view variation in growth rates as confusing, that variability if interpreted using the rules and principles of energetics represents an enormous source of information. As Brett and Groves (1979) concluded, "given a good estimate of growth in a normal population the likely values for the other components of the energy budget can be determined."

ENERGY BUDGETING STRATEGIES

One way to assess differences in energy budgeting strategies is to estimate both the rates and relative apportionment of energy by fishes held at maintenance rations. This provides a comparative measure of minimum energy requisites for survival. A second comparison can be validly made when fishes are at the upper limits of their energetic potential. Apportionment of energy at maximum rations is indicative of the scope for growth (Warren, 1971) or of maximum surplus power (Ware, 1982). Two representative fish species are chosen for comparison of alternative budgeting strategies: a relatively inactive, "sit-and-wait" predator, the largemouth bass (*Micropterus salmoides*), which represents an "energy-saver" strategy, and a highly active "energy speculator" (Stevens and Neill, 1978), the skipjack tuna (*Katsuwonus pelamis*).

Energy budgets for each were determined at maintenance and maximum rations for 1-kg fish at 24°C. Bass energy budgets were taken from an energetics model (Rice *et al.*, 1983) based on the experimental studies of Niimi and Beamish (1974). Energy budgets for skipjack were from estimates made by Kitchell and associates (1978). Both fishes feed on a mixture of fish and

Table 10-1
ESTIMATED ENERGY BUDGETS (J · kJ⁻¹ · day⁻¹) FOR 1-kg LARGEMOUTH BASS AND SKIPJACK TUNA AT 24°C

FISH	RATION	ENERGY BUDGETS ($J \cdot kJ^{-1} \cdot day^{-1}$)						
		C	R_{St}	R_{Act}	SDA	U	F	ΔB
Largemouth Bass	Maintenance	8.1	4.9	0.5	1.1	0.6	0.8	0
Skipjack Tuna	Maintenance	44	13.5	15.5	7	2	7	0
Largemouth Bass	Maximum	31	4.9	0.5	4.4	2.5	3.2	15.6
Skipjack Tuna	Maximum	250	13.5	80–142	38	12	38	7–69

invertebrate prey so that the estimates of specific dynamic action (SDA), excretion (U), and egestion (F) are quite similar as proportions of total energy intake (Table 10-1, Fig. 10-1). The most striking differences between these two species are those evident in the rates of feeding and metabolic outputs. Maintenance rations for skipjack tuna are more than fivefold greater than those for bass. Maximum rations for tuna are approximately eight times greater than those for bass (Table 10-1).

Standard metabolic rates for skipjack tuna are based on the estimates of Gooding and colleagues (1981), which correct for the fact that skipjack are

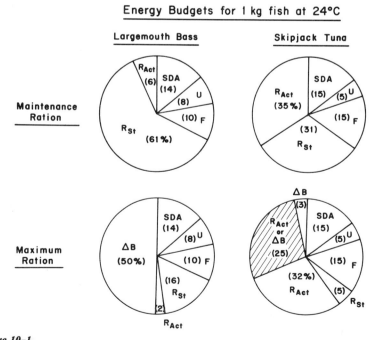

Figure 10-1
Comparison of energy budgets at maintenance and maximum rations for 1-kg largemouth bass and skipjack tuna at 24°C. Symbols correspond to those defined in the text.

continuous swimmers by extrapolating to get metabolic rates at zero swimming speed; even then, skipjack rates are nearly three times those of largemouth bass. Energy expended for active swimming by largemouth bass was estimated from activity profiles of bass tracked by telemetry (Rice *et al.,* 1982). Swimming velocities of 5 cm $\cdot$ sec^{-1} are assumed for both ration levels. By contrast, activity levels for skipjack tuna swimming at minimum sustained speeds required by the hydrodynamics of this negatively buoyant fish are about 60 cm $\cdot$ sec^{-1} (Gooding *et al.,* 1981). As represented by the proportional diagrams of Figure 10-1, largemouth bass are estimated to expend only 6% of total energy output at maintenance rations on activity, while 61% of the total is expended in standard metabolism. Skipjack tuna on maintenance rations expend 31% of total energy output in standard metabolism and 35% of the total as energy required by swimming at minimum sustained velocities. At maximum ration levels, bass expend only 16% and 2% of total energy intake as standard metabolism and activity costs, respectively. Nearly half of total calories consumed can be stored as somatic or gonadal tissue. As stated previously, this remarkable growth efficiency has been confirmed for several fishes by controlled laboratory studies (Brett and Groves, 1979).

Estimates of the energy expended in activity and that stored as growth by skipjack at maximum rations are more debatable. Because the costs of specific dynamic action, waste, and standard metabolism are fixed, there exists a reciprocal interaction of energy for activity and for growth. Growth rates are known only from field studies because no successful laboratory study of growth at maximum ration has been conducted (Kitchell *et al.,* 1978). Tuna activity levels in nature are obviously higher than the minima required for hydrostatic equilibrium because these fish live in one of the most nutritively sparse environments known (Stevens and Neill, 1978). They must actively search for food patches and pursue active prey; thus, a positive feedback is represented in the behavior of these energy speculators. They receive energy rewards in some way generally proportional to their energy output. Skipjack possess a countercurrent heat exchanger. Increased activity elevates body temperatures and presumably, total metabolism. As a result, they have the potential for what is termed *thermal runaway* (Stevens and Neill, 1978). In other words, skipjack tuna represent a condition opposite to that of the conservative strategy of largemouth bass. Skipjack must be active to encounter prey at sufficient frequency to meet or surpass their maintenance demand. Their energy requirements increase as they become more active, which in turn requires that they search even more actively for more prey. Kerr (1982) describes a similar scenario that can be used for estimating the energy budgets of other active predatory fishes.

The minimum estimate of growth represented in Table 10-1 and Figure 10-1 is based on observed growth rates of skipjack in Hawaiian waters are about 7 J $\cdot$ kJ^{-1} $\cdot$ day^{-1}. This growth would be only 3% of total energy consumed at maximum rations, assuming skipjack were very active, and up to 28% of consumed energy if free-living fish swam at rates requiring energy expenditures approximately three times that at minimum sustained speeds.

There are obviously several unknowns in the estimates of energy budgeting by skipjack at maximum rations. Gooding and associates (1981) estimated that optimal swimming speeds (see Chap. 11) would be about 2.1 body lengths $\cdot$ sec^{-1} for a 40-cm, 1-kg skipjack. Interestingly, energy output at the optimal velocity (84 cm $\cdot$ sec^{-1}) would be only 13% greater than that at 60 cm $\cdot$ sec^{-1}, which is the minimum required. It thus seems that the remarkably high minimum energy requirement of skipjack when compared with that of bass is relatively close to that expected from design criteria for maximum transport efficiency. The example of an animal that functions at high rates in a trophically dilute environment provokes many interesting questions. Two key unknowns are the actual levels of energy output by skipjack freely swimming in oceanic waters plus the frequency and success with which they encounter prey. One of these must be measured before their interaction can be better resolved.

Bass can grow nearly twice as efficiently as skipjack (50% versus 28%), but that should not be taken as evidence of advantage or superiority for the energy-saver strategy. The potential absolute growth and gamete production rates by skipjack on maximum rations would be substantially greater than those for bass (69 versus 15.6 J $\cdot$ kJ^{-1} $\cdot$ day^{-1}). If these strategies were in direct competition, the swift would win because more tuna flesh and gametes would be produced per unit of time. That these strategies do co-exist (*e.g.,* tuna are sympatric with the energy-saver strategies of many sluggish ocean fishes such as the ocean sunfish (*Mola mola*) and largemouth bass, with members of very actively foraging taxa such as members of the genus *Morone*) is the object of continuing interest in studies of evolution, ecology, and behavior (*e.g.,* Ware, 1978, 1980, 1982).

GROWTH AS A MARKOV PROCESS

Because most fishes have diel physiological and ecologic cycles that govern daily energy budgeting, fish growth is a Markov process (Bailey, 1964). If each diel feeding cycle is independent of the preceding cycle, it is equally possible each day that a fish will gain or lose weight. More properly, fish growth is a bounded Markov process: size on day $t + 1$ is a function of size on day t; the change in size is described by a probability distribution bounded by physiological and ecologic constraints. Any possible intermediate can exist between maximum growth rate and total starvation. The assumption that most fishes grow on average says that all possibilities are not equally probable. The absolute amount of maximum growth or weight loss is a function of food availability, food quality, temperature, fish size, activity level, and so on. The process has a closed set of possibilities dictated by existing conditions and the constraints of phenotype and genotype.

This concept of Markovian growth is different from that embodied as an assumption in many growth models. These models are little more than statistical expressions of growth curves derived from annual data (*e.g.*, von Bertalanffy, 1957; see review by Ricker, 1979) and do not reflect underlying growth processes or laws. That distinction is important because the repetitious use of growth constants in various kinds of population models reinforces the assumption that growth rates are fixed. Expressing growth as a constant is a sometimes necessary statistical convenience (Pitcher and Hart, 1982) and a potentially misleading conceptual error.

As developed in a previous section, *growth is a variable,* the most sensitive variable in the energy-budgeting hierarchy. Although the boundary conditions of maximum ration and metabolic rates are genetically fixed, actual feeding and metabolic rates change rapidly in a variable environment such as that represented whenever seasonality occurs. Temperatures can change, food availability can change, and the changing size of the fish also causes changes in the size-determined boundaries of feeding and metabolism. These highly dynamic interactions are not easily viewed as constant; in fact, very little of the observed variance in growth is genetic. Heritability of growth rate in teleost fishes is low compared to that in domestic animals and birds (Pitcher and Hart, 1982). The dramatic responses of growth rate and age at maturity to selective mortality such as that imposed by fishing are best viewed as primarily environmental.

Cumulative Effects

Small differences in growth rates are cumulative and are the most sensitive expression of changing interactions between a predator, its abiotic environment, and its food resources. As evidence of this cumulative effect, Kitchell and associates (1977) have used a simulation model of fish growth based nominally on the energetics of percid fishes to demonstrate the magnification of daily energy budgets for hypothetical forms having slightly different temperature optima (Kitchell, 1979). All components of the energetics model were the same except that three different temperature optima for feeding were specified at $21°C$, $22°C$, and $23°C$, respectively. Each hypothetical fish had an initial mass of 100 g and began its simulated growth on 1 January in a temperature habitat with a maximum midsummer temperature of $22°C$. This thermal environment is similar to that of many large temperate-zone lakes and coastal ecosystems. In the first simulation, each fish could feed at 0.33 of maximum ration (C_{max}), which was temperature- and size-dependent (Kitchell *et al.*, 1977). In the second simulation the effect of stochastic variation in food resources was represented by a 30-day increase to $C_{max} = 1.0$

during the equivalent of an early spring month but held at $C = 0.33\ C_{max}$ for the period before and after the spring pulse. These conditions are represented graphically in Figure 10-2. Winter temperatures were set at 2°C for both simulations, and no growth was recorded until temperatures began to increase by day 90. Growth continued until day 360 when temperatures dropped to 2°C.

Based on previous simulations of the relationships between optimum temperatures for feeding and maximum midsummer temperatures (Kitchell *et al.*, 1977), the *a priori* expectation was that the fish with an optimum temperature for feeding closest to the maximum midsummer temperature of 22°C would grow most rapidly. Instead, greatest total growth in both scenarios was achieved by the fish with the lowest optimum temperature. The spring pulse of food resources amplified the growth differences. At $C = 0.33$ C_{max}, the fish with a 21°C optimum for feeding grew to be 40% larger than that with a 23°C optimum. Although all forms responded dramatically to the spring pulse of food, the 21°C fish grew nearly 50% more than the 23°C fish (Fig. 10-3). The 21°C fish began growth earlier in the year, maintained greater growth rates at all temperatures except those during the warm summer months, and continued growth longer into the end of the annual thermal cycle.

The object of this example is to demonstrate the cumulative effect of modest differences in energy budgeting processes when integrated by total annual growth. The growth advantage evidenced should quickly translate through reproductive advantage into numerical dominance by the fish that

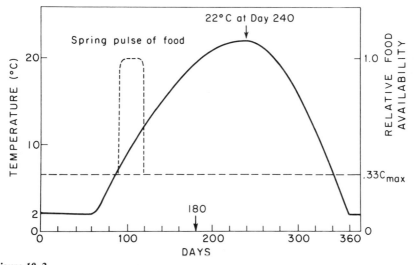

Figure 10-2
Temperature and ration conditions used in simulating growth for three hypothetical fishes. See text for details of assumed conditions.

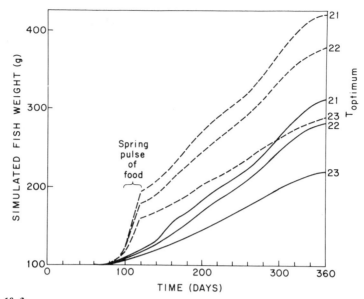

Figure 10-3

Simulated growth of fishes with different temperature optima for feeding. A spring pulse of food availability is represented by unlimited rations for 30 days preceded and followed by feeding at 0.33 of maximum rations.

began growth earlier and stopped later in the annual temperature cycle. In a temporal sense, the scope for growth was greatest for the fish that could establish a positive energy budget at the lowest temperature.

Tradeoffs, however, may counterbalance the accrued advantage. Optimum temperatures for feeding and growth and upper lethal temperature are highly correlated (Magnuson *et al.*, 1979; Crowder and Magnuson, 1982). A fish capable of growth at lower temperatures would have a reduced advantage if rations were lower than 0.33 C_{max} or if maximum summer temperatures were higher than 22°C. The advantage of higher temperature optima would increase as maximum temperatures increased until the fish with highest temperature optimum exhibited greatest relative growth (see Kitchell *et al.*, 1977, Figs. 9 and 10). Further, a midsummer pulse of available food would be most effectively used for growth by that fish with the highest temperature optimum.

Again, the opportunity for multiple strategies emerges as an alternative in a seasonal environment where there may be substantial variability in food resources. Temporal partitioning of food resources translated differentially into seasonal differences in growth allows maintenance of high trophic overlap among species exhibiting slightly different energetic optima. Theoretical evidence exists; many predator-prey models are very sensitive to the rapidly changing thermal conditions of spring and fall (Gardner *et al.*, 1980).

The cumulative nature of growth processes and the Markovian nature of daily energy budgeting combine to allow coexistence of multiple adaptive strategies. This logic leads to the expectation that species cohorts within a species should exhibit thermal habitat partitioning in heterothermal environments. Assuming *ceteris paribus* for food availability, prey capture efficiency, susceptibility to predators, and so on, species and cohorts that have slightly different optima should segregate on a temperature axis; field and laboratory studies confirm that expectation (Magnuson *et al.*, 1979; Crowder *et al.*, 1981). The importance of seasonal partitioning among competitors remains unknown.

SENSITIVITY OF MODELS AND THEIR ASSUMPTIONS

Parameter Sensitivity

Given that any equation or model of energy-budgeting processes has several variables and an even greater number of parameters, the adequacy of that model is dictated by its construction, its assumptions, and the empirical precision of constants or coefficients used to implement it. Because models are simplifications, they should be evaluated in terms of their predictions and assumptions. Of primary concern are the equifinality problems: "right" answers may derive from wrong reasons; the same answer may be right for each of several different questions.

An initial approach in evaluating these problems is to step through each of the parameters independently in a quantitative analysis of its effects on the outcome of model simulations, a technique called *ordinary sensitivity analysis* (Majkowski and Waiwood, 1981). The reference in most cases is a calculated result with all parameters set at their "best-guess" values. This process helps to identify those components most sensitive to error (*i.e.*, those most important to know well) and gives obvious guidance to future research priorities.

Although few models are exactly the same, the laws of thermodynamics cause energetics models for fishes to have many features in common. An attempt is made to generalize their form in the following. The primary variables considered are those dealing with fish size, temperature effects, and activity levels. The allometry of mass (W) effects on feeding (C) and routine metabolic (R) rates are usually described by a power function.

$$Y = aX^b \tag{4}$$

where $Y = C$ or R, $X = W$, and a and b are species-specific, temperature-dependent constants. Temperature (T) effects on C or R are often expressed as simple exponentials

$$Y = ae^{bT} \tag{5}$$

Power functions and exponentials are features common to many models of processes that include size or temperature dependence. Elliott (1976a) also derived a power function to represent the effects of temperature on energy losses to egestion (F) and excretion (U).

The form of any particular model will strongly influence the sensitivity of that model's parameters. One way to identify important individual parameters is to set up a simple criterion: does the change in result exceed the error in input? For example, if a 10% error in the value of any parameter is formally used in model simulations, sensitive parameters would be those that cause $\geq 10\%$ change in the output, and that margin of error is usually within the variance of a measured value. Brett and Groves (1979) report the value of the mass exponent (b) for standard metabolism to have a mean value of 0.86 with standard error of the mean as 0.03 or 0.04. Using the sample size given ($N = 25$) yields an estimate of 0.20 for one standard deviation; thus, an error of $\pm 10\%$ is well within the confidence intervals of the data. The asymmetry of error can be evaluated by overestimating and then underestimating the parameter by the same proportion (*e.g.*, $\pm 10\%$), the interactions of terms within the energy budget equation can be evaluated by specifying the same result and then allowing the interacting terms to vary as the energy budget is satisfied. For example, total annual growth can be specified, allowing an assessment of the sensitivity of estimates for total food consumed or total metabolic output.

Kitchell and associates (1977) conducted a single-parameter sensitivity analysis of an energetics model for yellow perch (*Perca flavescens*). The annual growth of age I + perch in the western basin of Lake Erie was used as the nominal condition. Each of the 21 parameters of the model was varied $\pm 10\%$, and the resulting growth normalized as percent change from the nominal simulation. Details of the full equation series are presented in Kitchell and associates (1977) and need not be repeated here. The most sensitive parameters are those that change the result by more than the normalized error (*i.e.*, more than 10%). A qualitative summary of that analysis is given in Table 10-2, with the components arranged in descending order of sensitivities $> 10\%$.

Although other parameters such as activity coefficients or optimum temperatures for feeding also had sensitivities $> 10\%$, they are less sensitive than the constants (a) used in allometric functions of mass. These parameters are dealt with more effectively as assumptions and are described in a subsequent section of this chapter.

Majkowski and Waiwood (1981) conducted a more sophisticated sensitivity analysis of an energetics model developed for cod (*Gadus morhua*). Their model was adapted from that developed by Ursin (1979), which is quite

Table 10-2
RELATIVE SENSITIVITIES TO ±10% CHANGE OF PARAMETER
VALUES USED IN ENERGETICS MODELS (SEE TEXT FOR
DESCRIPTION OF ASSUMPTIONS)

PARAMETER	SENSITIVITY (%)
Constant (a) for allometry of feeding, C, where $C = aW^b$	30–40
Constant (a) for allometry of routine metabolism (R), where $R = aW^b$	20–30
Mass coefficient (b) for C	20–30
Slope coefficient (b) for temperature dependence of feeding, metabolism, and excretion	15–20
Mass coefficient (b) for R	10–15

similar to that derived for yellow perch (Kitchell *et al.*, 1977). The application developed by Majkowski and Waiwood is closely akin to that done in development of the lake trout model (Stewart, 1980) described in the next section. As with the other models, Majkowski and Waiwood found the constants (*a*) used in allometric functions to be among the most sensitive of components and the exponents for mass dependence of feeding and respiration rates (*b*) to be of significant but lesser sensitivity. Intermediate in sensitivity were parameters for the functional equivalents of SDA and waste losses.

The general conclusion to be drawn from these analyses is that any power function or exponential form such as those used to represent the allometric effects of mass or those used as estimators of temperature dependence in feeding and respiration rates are very sensitive components of most energy-budgeting processes. A nontrivial psychological component may also come to bear in that exponents and constants are traditionally printed in both lower case notation and smaller script than are variables.

Big Effects from Small Errors

Variables common to many components of a model can by their multiplicative interaction assume critical significance. For example, most hydrodynamics and energetics models use mass and length of the fish in several components and use a common length-mass function throughout. The basic power equation (Webb, 1975) is

$$P = (0.5 \cdot \rho \cdot S \cdot U^3 \cdot C_d)/\eta \qquad (6)$$

where P is thrust power (ergs · sec^{-1}), ρ is water density (gm · cm^{-3}), S is fish surface area (cm^2), U is velocity (cm · sec^{-1}), C_d is drag coefficient, and $\eta =$ Froude efficiency.

The estimate of surface area is usually calculated from fish length (L) as S = $0.4L^2$ (Magnuson and Weininger, 1978). The drag coefficient is also dependent on fish length and is estimated as of the order of

$$C_d = 10 \cdot \left(\frac{\rho L U}{\mu}\right)^{-0.5} \tag{7}$$

where μ is water viscosity and the term in parentheses is the Reynolds number (Gooding *et al.*, 1981).

In the simplest of hydrodynamics models (Sharp and Francis, 1976), length is used at least three times; thus, any error in estimate of length is elevated to the third power in the models' sensitivity. In energetics models, the realities of independence of mass and length dynamics must be considered. Fish can lose mass yet remain at constant length; they can gain energy in fat deposits yet remain of similar length. This becomes of major importance when fish density changes in relation to that of the aqueous medium. Length-mass functions are valid for only limited data sets. Extrapolation is often necessary but should be done with at least the cautious recognition that where b has values of ~ 3.0, it is a potentially sensitive component of $W = aL^b$.

Guidelines for Future Research

Another objective of sensitivity analyses is to identify areas for future research. One of the common ironies of model building is that although vast amounts of data are often available for a fish species, few research programs have been directed to those experimental conditions of greatest value to models. Models are often built to represent the dynamics of variables based on their initial, optimal, and limiting conditions. The values of parameters such as the constant (a) in size or temperature-dependence functions requires measures of rate processes at small size, low temperatures, or optimal temperatures. For obvious logistic reasons, studies are too rarely conducted on small or large animals, and in the case of temperature studies, are usually designed to test rates at regular arithmetic increments (*e.g.*, 5°C) rather than over the geometric scale of exponential increase (*e.g.*, at 50% increments) or at the fine scale necessary to identify thermal optima. Brett's work with salmon is an important exception; that it is an exception proves the rule that most models will be heavily dependent on extrapolation procedures in developing parameter estimates.

In a sensitivity analysis of the yellow perch energetics model, Kitchell and associates (1977) attempted a qualitative assessment of the need for future research by combining the empirical estimate of parameter sensitivity with a subjective judgement of the availability of data required to estimate parameters of that model. Again, the constants *a* and *b* of power functions used in feeding, metabolic, and excretion calculations appeared as prominent candidates for future research. Majkowski and Waiwood (1981) also estimated the proportion of total variance in model output that may be assigned to uncertainty in the input parameters. Again, the constants (*a*) of allometric functions and those for SDA and waste losses were of greater significance than the coefficients (*b*) of allometric functions for feeding or metabolic rates. Other poorly studied yet sensitive parameters were those used to estimate the proportionality constants required to estimate levels of feeding and active metabolism of fishes in nature. In general, these parameters may be measured in the laboratory but are poorly known and highly variable under natural conditions; they are also subject to the bias of "flask effects" in the laboratory environment (Bock, 1980; Wightman, 1981).

Two important lessons can be learned from these analyses: first, as suspected, the dangers of extrapolation exist because estimates of constants such as those for allometric functions (*a*) are usually derived from regression analysis; second and perhaps more important is the possible bias imposed by measurements made in the laboratory. Too few experimentalists test for the effects of a favorite apparatus and replicable technique. Although widely used and in fact the basis of most fish energetics studies (Brett and Groves, 1979), laboratory respirometry seems the most likely source of systematic bias (Wightman, 1981).

HYPOTHESES DERIVED FROM MODELS

Other chapters of this book detail the elements of hydrodynamics models for fishes (Chaps. 6 and 7); however, an example of the role that sensitivity analyses can play in developing ideas for future research emerges from the analysis of a model for minimum sustained swimming speed (Magnuson and Weininger, 1978) and the ecologic implications of the whole-animal energetics view of fishes as predators.

Magnuson (1970) developed a modification of aerodynamic models as the basis for estimating minimum sustained swimming speed in continuously swimming tunas. An ordinary sensitivity analysis of that model (Magnuson and Weininger, 1978) revealed that parameters used to estimate densities of the fish and its aqueous medium were very sensitive. A 1% change in either density resulted in 8% to 9% changes in estimated minimum swimming velocities. Similarly, a 1% change in either density had remarkable effects on estimates of total drag experienced by active fish: a change in fish density from 1.09 g/cc to 1.08 g/cc decreased total drag by 14.5%. This interaction is a potentially important component of swimming energetics for negatively buoyant, highly active fishes such as many of the tunas and sharks. Ontogenetic or seasonal changes in energy density will correlate with relative fat and oil contents of the body; thus, a positive feedback develops; fish successful as predators may deposit more high-energy lipid reserves that because of their lower specific density increase buoyancy and reduce the drag costs of sustained swimming. Negative energy budgets cause a reversal, also with positive feedback: starving fish are forced to mobilize energy reserves, become more dense, and must swim both faster in order to maintain hydrostatic equilibrium and at greater cost per unit distance. Fishes capable of buoyancy regulation through passive means such as swimbladder regulation are obviously not subject to these interactions.

From the above it follows that highly migratory, negatively buoyant fishes should where possible take advantage of the density gradients offered by different salinities and temperatures of a stratified water column. When migrating, these fish should orient to strata of densities closest to that of their bodies if oxygen requirements can be met and thermal limits not exceeded (Gooding *et al.*, 1981). Positive feedback also occurs if lower temperatures reduce basal metabolic demand. Even those fishes with countercurrent heat exchangers would benefit because they are not wholly independent of ambient water temperatures (Neill *et al.*, 1976; Stevens and Neill, 1978). These interactions have not yet been fully evaluated. The migratory patterns and cruising depths chosen by active, pelagic species such as skipjack tuna (*Katsuwonus pelamis*) or albacore tuna (*Thunnus alalunga*) (Sharp and Dotson, 1978) offer interesting prospects for hypothesis testing.

A second interesting dichotomy develops from considerations of benefits accrued to an effective predator versus costs incurred by an actively swimming migrant in, for example, pelagic habitats of stratified seas. Surface waters offer more prey for diurnal, visual predators yet have the costs of high temperatures and lower density. Assuming the presence of an oxygen minimum layer at or below the thermocline, deeper waters offer the reduced costs of lower temperature and greater density but lower relative prey densities owing to reduced visual effectiveness. It follows that the depth-versus-time profile for an animal optimizing this interaction should be bimodal. The relative proportion of time expressed in each mode will depend on the strength of density stratification, prey availability, and where applicable, considerations of predator avoidance. Hypotheses derived from modeling can thus be tested with appropriate yet modest field observations.

Simplifying Assumptions

Simplifying assumptions are a necessary requisite of model building. Assumptions made will reflect ignorance of the processes or absence of appropriate data. Although the assumptions are often stated at the outset and sometimes tested during the course of a modeling study, they are rarely dealt with in a quantitative fashion. The example described in the following section is an interesting exception. Stewart (1980) developed an energetics-based population model for lake trout (*Salvelinus namaycush*) in Lake Michigan. His objective was to estimate the impact of predation by trout on their forage base. The basic parameters of an energy-budget model such as that for yellow perch (Kitchell *et al.*, 1977) were available from laboratory studies (Rottiers, 1978; Rottiers *et al.*, 1978) and a miscellany of field studies on food habits, distribution, migration, growth, and mortality (Stewart *et al.*, 1983).

Stewart's sensitivity analyses of the model included a series of incremental changes in the estimates of total energy consumed, total metabolism, and growth efficiency over the 8-year life of a typical lake trout in Lake Michigan. Growth rates were fixed as determined from known sizes at each age. In other words, Stewart fitted the model to observed growth data and by adding incremental improvements over simplifying assumptions made in the original version, determined the quantitative changes necessary in the energy budget to maintain the observed growth pattern.

Initial assumptions made and tested were those used by Weininger (1978) in an earlier study and are similar to those made in many studies:

1. All ages and sizes of lake trout have equivalent energy densities $(J \cdot kg^{-1})$.
2. Energy densities $(J \cdot kg^{-1})$ of prey species are constant over time.
3. All prey were fish and have equivalent energy densities to that of lake trout.
4. Based on field studies, swimming speeds of all lake trout are 0.46 body lengths $\cdot$ sec^{-1} at temperatures $>5°C$ and 0.33 body lengths $\cdot$ sec^{-1} at $<5°C$ (*i.e.*, only temperature effects are important).

Stewart then "improved" the simplifying assumptions based on available data and incremented complexity:

1. Implementing an ontogenetic increase in energy density from $6.0 \times 10^6 J \cdot kg^{-1}$ for juvenile trout to $12.0 \times 10^6 J \cdot kg^{-1}$ for adults (Rottiers and Tucker, 1978)
2. Assuming a seasonal change in $J \cdot kg^{-1}$ for alewife prey which varied from approximately $5.3 \times 10^3 J \cdot kg^{-1}$ to $9.1 \times 10^3 J \cdot kg^{-1}$ over the year (Yeo, 1978)
3. Developing an ontogenetic shift in diet from largely invertebrate prey for juvenile trout to predominately adult alewife prey for adult trout
4. Developing an optimal swimming speed model for lake trout that incorporates mass, temperature-dependence, and their interaction

In short, Stewart treated as variables several of those factors previously assumed as constant; his results are summarized in Table 10-3 and Figure 10-4.

Table 10-3

CONPARISON OF TOTAL ENERGY CONSUMED, TOTAL METABOLISM
AND GROWTH EFFICIENCY OF A LAKE TROUT AS MODELED FOR
INCREMENTAL CHANGES IN ASSUMPTIONS (STEWART 1980). (SEE
TEXT FOR DISCUSSION OF PROCEDURES AND ASSUMPTIONS)

STEP	ASSUMPTION CHANGES	ENERGY CONSUMED K Joules ($\times 10^5$)	ENERGY CONSUMED % change per step	TOTAL METABOLISM K Joules ($\times 10^5$)	TOTAL METABOLISM % change per step	GROWTH EFFICIENCY %	GROWTH EFFICIENCY % change per step
0	Original	2.00	0	1.44	0	11.6	0
1	Energy density of lake trout	2.67	+34	1.54	+7	25.8	+122
2	Energy density of prey	2.69	+1	1.55	+1	25.6	−1
3	Diet composition	2.69	0	1.55	0	25.2	−2
4	Constant swimming speed	2.54	−6	1.42	−8	27.1	+8
Total Change (%) Steps 1-4:		+25		−2		+135	

Substantial changes in results were accomplished by implementing greater detail for any of the four assumptions; all had major effects on the estimates of total energy consumed and growth efficiency. Total metabolism changed very little, with only a modest reduction derived from the development of an optimal swimming model similar to but more extensive than that developed for salmon by Ware (1978). The most dramatic change was that expressed by a more than twofold increase in growth efficiency when *any* of the original assumptions were changed. That result has a profound message for models built around assumed efficiencies of growth often approximated as the "10% rule" of conversion efficiency widely used in trophic exchange modeling (Steele, 1974). The higher efficiency estimate is in fact regularly confirmed in controlled growth efficiency studies (Elliott, 1976b, 1979) and corresponds to Brett's (1982) estimate of 26% for the oceanic life of sockeye salmon. That total energy consumed and total metabolism changed to a lesser extent is a consequence of working with energy-budget models: growth was fixed, and the budgets must balance! Implementing an estimate of energy stored as fats and oils in the predators' flesh yielded increases in both the estimate of total energy consumed and because the specific dynamic action (SDA) component of total metabolism increases in proportion to food consumed, an increase in total metabolism. Swimming at optimal speeds decreased total metabolism and total energy consumed while increasing growth efficiency.

Stewart's analysis is specific to the conditions and objectives stipulated in the development of his model, but it is more general in several important ways. First, the danger of assuming a constant and usually low estimate of growth efficiency is apparent. Second, this parameter (growth efficiency) is subject to insidious bias and is usually expressed as a fractional conversion of prey biomass (B) (*e.g.,* as $0.1B$ or $0.2B$), which seems innocuous (. . . 0.1 is not much different than 0.2), but the quantitative difference is perpetuated at each step in the calculations. Third, the relatively conservative response of total metabolism makes it of lesser potential value as an indicator of the dynamics of energy budgeting processes by fishes in nature. Brett (1982) reached a similar conclusion.

Feeding rates and growth efficiencies can change dramatically with little apparent expression in total metabolic rates. Selection pressures for an optimal swimming speed can be of the same magnitude as those having to do with optimal prey choice (Werner 1979; Ware, 1982). Both can occur unless they are mutually exclusive, and in that case, the bifurcation of strategies can emerge. Where prey are of similar energetic value, swimming energetics become important; where prey are of dissimilar energetic value, prey choice may become the primary basis for selection pressure.

Model Validation and Application: An Example

Energetics models are usually developed to serve one or both of two general goals: autecologic questions dealing with critical periods in the life history of a species (*e.g.,* Ware, 1980), and synecologic studies of a predator's

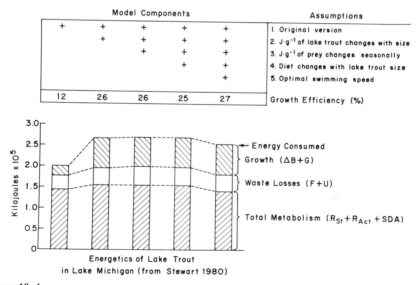

Figure 10–4
Simulated energy budgets for lake trout (*Salvelinus namaycush*) in Lake Michigan. Each change in the model is based on sequential changes in initial assumptions as detailed by Stewart (1980). See text for details.

impact on its food resources (*e.g.,* Stewart *et al.,* 1981; Majkowski and Waiwood, 1981; Kerr, 1982). The implicit assumption in either of these applications is that the energy-budgeting processes represented in the model are quantitatively correct. The appropriate test of that assumption requires independently derived measures of the unknowns (*e.g.,* feeding rates, metabolic rates, thermal history, growth rates, etc.).

Recent work afforded an opportunity to conduct a quantitative test of an energetics model developed for largemouth bass. Cochran and Adelman (1982) measured daily rations and growth rates for members of the age III+ cohort of largemouth bass in Lake Rebecca, Minnesota. Based on published laboratory studies (*e.g.,* Niimi and Beamish, 1974), Rice and colleagues (1983) constructed a bioenergetics model of growth by largemouth bass. Field measurements of feeding rates, initial fish size, and thermal history in Lake Rebecca were used as inputs to the model, and the simulated growth was compared with that independently measured (Cochran and Rice, 1982; Rice and Cochran, 1983). Results are represented in Figure 10-5; the modeled growth was within 2 standard errors of mean observed growth on seven of nine sampling dates. A visual estimate of model performance suggests good agreement with the observed data.

Finding an empirical way to evaluate the model-versus-data comparison is problematic. Because both are derived from data, it is difficult in the statistical sense to define the independent variable. This problem has been addressed by ecologists (Caswell, 1976) but remains unresolved. Rice and Cochran tested the model through a composite of several techniques. First they tested and rejected the null hypothesis argument developed by Kitchell

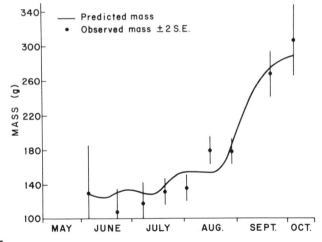

Figure 10-5
Predicted and observed mass (wet weight in grams) of age III+ largemouth bass (*Micropterus salmoides*) in Lake Rebecca, Minnesota. Observed data are from Cochran and Adelman (1982). Simulated weight is from an energetics model (Rice *et al.,* 1983). (From Rice and Cochran, 1983).

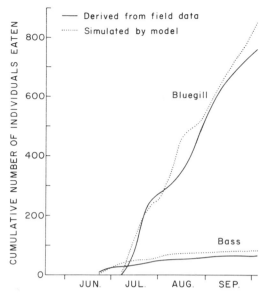

Figure 10–6
Estimates of cumulative predation rates on YOY (young-of-the-year) bluegill (*Lepomis macrochirus*) and largemouth bass by age III+ largemouth bass in Lake Rebecca, Minnesota. Direct field estimates (*solid line*) are from Cochran and Adelman (1982). Simulations (*dotted line*) are from the model developed by Rice and associates (1983). (From Cochran and Rice, 1982).

and Breck (1980), which states that observed annual growth is simply the result of temperature and allometric effects and is independent of short-term food-resource dynamics: bass growth in Lake Rebecca was not independent of seasonal changes in food availability. Next, they used a traditional statistical approach: the lack of fit test (Draper and Smith, 1966) indicated that there was no reason to doubt the adequacy of the model as a descriptor of the data. A partitioning of mean squared error presented by Theil (1961) and elaborated by Mincer and Zarnowitz (1969) was used to analyse agreement between predicted and observed growth. That analysis indicated that the differences between model results and field data were primarily due to random error rather than systematic bias. Finally, they calculated a reliability index (Leggett and Williams, 1981), which yields an estimate of model adequacy represented by a number equal to or greater than one (*e.g., if $k = 1.0$, there is perfect agreement, while a value of $k = 2.0$ indicates disagreement by a factor of 2); the k value for this test was 1.12. More specifically, 68% (*i.e., plus or minus 1 standard deviation) of all observations lie within ±12% of the model predictions.

Cochran and Rice (1983) further used the modeling approach to evaluate the impact of age III+ largemouth bass on their prey resources in Lake Rebecca. Cumulative predation on YOY bluegill and bass was estimated based on observed growth rates and simulated feeding rates, then compared with field estimates of predation rates. The results are summarized in Figure 10-6. Again, the simulated values were in close agreement with the observed values. Total predation calculated with the model was within 8.5% of that estimated by direct measurement in the field.

These analyses lead to one important conclusion: the energetics model assembled for largemouth bass is a remarkably good predictor of seasonally changing growth rates and of predatory impact. This is apparently the first example of direct and independent tests of this kind. The value of the modeling approach should be apparent. Given good and relatively easily made measures of growth rates and thermal history, the much more difficult and labor-intensive field estimates of *in situ* feeding rates can be replaced by an inexpensive and simple model simulation. Assumptions such as those dealing with predator activity levels or distribution, prey preferences and availability, and so on can be developed as testable hypotheses and independently evaluated with relatively modest effort. This example describes one replicate of an iterative process in model testing and evaluation. It is specific to one cohort of a species in one lake for one growing season. There is obvious need for other tests, but the results of the first are most encouraging.

OVERVIEW

This chapter attempts to define the basic ideas of energy budgeting and energetics models in ways that can lead to testable hypotheses. Examples developed include the following:

1. Alternative energetics strategies expressed in the rate constants for feeding and metabolism for otherwise similar species
2. The role of seasonal temperature variation and stochastic variability of food resources as a basis for coexistence of forms (genotypes) possessing only very small differences in physiological optima
3. The bifurcation of behaviors that can emerge where habitats are heterogenous with respect to food availability, temperature, and specific density
4. Independent evaluation of a model using field data

The sensitivity of parameters and assumptions made in developing the several energetics models considered suggests that the best uses of these models will derive from their ability to calculate other components of the energy-budgeting process when growth rates are known. Growth rates are relatively easy to measure and integrate the short-term variability of predator-prey dynamics with longer-term seasonal and ontogenetic changes. Because growth comes last in the energetics hierarchy, its variability is rich with information and potential insight. Growth can be predicted when other components of energy-budgeting processes are known. There are, however, logistics limitations as well as covariation to deal with in nature, where several unknowns are simultaneously operating. Models may then serve as the basis for developing testable, alternative hypotheses.

Ricker's (1979) excellent review of the many statistical attempts to model growth led him to say, "It now seems safe to conclude that no such simple relationship exists." The preferable alternative is to measure growth as accurately as possible and then to use the dynamics of growth rates as the basis for comparative study and the development of hypotheses regarding the survival value and fitness of other energetics processes, the role of stochastic and deterministic processes in the life history of fishes, and the quantitative role of fishes as predators in an ecosystem context.

Acknowledgments

Preparation of this chapter was supported in part by grants from the National Science Foundation, Regulatory Biology Program, and the National Oceanic and Atmospheric Administration, Office of Sea Grant, U.S. Department of Commerce, through an institutional grant to the University of Wisconsin. I thank Larry Crowder and Steve Kerr for their advice.

REFERENCES

Allen, J.R.M., and Wootton, R.J. 1982. The effect of ration and temperature on the growth of the three-spined stickleback, *Gasterosteus aculeatus*. *J. Fish. Biol.* 20:409–422.

Bailey, N.T.J. 1964. *The Elements of Stochastic Processes.* New York: John Wiley & Sons.

Beamish, F.W.H. 1974. Apparent specific dynamic action of largemouth bass, *Micropterus salmoides*. *J. Fish. Res. Board Can.* 31.1763–1769.

Bock, W.J. 1980. The definition and recognition of biological adaptation. *Am. Zool.* 20:217–227.

Brett, J.R. 1983. Life energetics of sockeye salmon, *Oncorhynchus nerka*. In *Behavioral Energetics: Vertebrate Costs of Survival*, edited by W.P. Aspey and S.I. Lustwick, Columbus, OH: Ohio State University Press. 29–63.

Brett, J.R., and Groves, T.D.D. 1979. Physiological energetics. In *Fish Physiology, Vol. VIII: Bioenergetics and Growth*, edited by W.S. Hoar, D.J. Randall, and J.R. Brett, 279–352. New York: Academic Press.

Caswell, H. 1976. The validation problem. In *Systems Ecology*, edited by H.H. Shugart, and R.V. O'Neill, 296–308. Stroudsburg, PA. Dowden, Hutchinson & Ross, 1979. Reprinted from Patten, B.C. (ed). 1976 *Systems Analysis and Stimulation in Ecology, Vol. IV.* 313–325. New York: Academic Press.

Cochran, P.A., and Adelman, I.R. 1982. Seasonal aspects of daily ration and diet of largemouth bass (*Micropterus salmoides*). *Environ. Biol. Fish.* 7:265–275.

Cochran, P.A., and Rice, J.A. 1982. A comparison of bioenergetics and field estimates of cumulative food consumption by largemouth bass (*Micropterus salmoides*). In *Gutshop '81*, edited by G. Calliet and C. Simenstad, 88–96. Seattle, WA: University of Washington Sea Grant Publications.

Crowder, L.B., Magnuson, J.J. and Brandt, S.B. 1981. Complementarity in the use of food and thermal habitat by Lake Michigan fishes. *Can. J. Fish. Aquat. Sci.* 38:662–668.

Crowder, L.B., and Magnuson, J.J. 1983. Cost Benefit analysis of temperature and food resource use: a synthesis with examples from the fishes. In *Behavioral Energetics: Vertebrate Costs of Survival*, edited by W.P. Aspley and S. Lustwick. Columbus, OH: Ohio State University Press. In press.

Draper, N.R., and Smith, H. 1966. *Applied Regression Analysis*. New York: John Wiley & Sons.

Elliott, J.M. 1976a. Energy losses in the waste products of brown trout (*Salmo trutta* L.). *J. Animal Ecol.* 45:561–580.

Elliott, J.M. 1976b. The energetics of feeding, metabolism and growth of brown trout (*Salmo trutta* L.) in relation to body weight, water temperature and ration size. *J. Animal Ecol.* 45:923–948.

Elliott, J.M. 1979. Energetics of freshwater teleosts. In *Fish Phenology: Anabolic Adaptiveness in Teleosts*, edited by P.J. Miller, 29–61. *Symp. Zool. Soc. Lond.* 44.

Gardner, R.H., O'Neill, R.V., Mankin, J.B., and Kumar, D. 1980. Comparative error analysis of six predator-prey models. *Ecology* 61:323–332.

Gooding, R.M., Neill, W.H., and Dizon, A.E. 1981. Respiration rates and low-oxygen tolerance limits in skipjack tuna, *Katsuwonus pelamis*. *Fish. Bull.* 79: 31–48.

Kerr, S.J. 1979. Prey availability, metaphoetesis, and the size structures of lake trout stocks. *Inv. Pesq.* 43:187–198.

Kerr, S.J. 1982. Estimating the energy budgets for actively predatory fishes. *Can. J. Fish. Aquat. Sci.* 39:371–379.

Kitchell, J.F. 1979. In search of an optimal environment. In *Predator-Prey Systems in Fisheries Management*, edited by F. Stroud and H.F. Clepper, 31–33. Washington, D.C.: Sport Fishing Institute.

Kitchell, J.F., and Breck, J.E. 1980. Bioenergetics model and foraging hypothesis for sea lamprey (*Petromyzon marinus*). *Can. J. Fish. Aquat. Sci.* 37:2159–2168.

Kitchell, J.F., Neill, W.H., Dizon, A.E., and Magnuson, J.J. 1978. Bioenergetics of skipjack tuna (*Katsuwonus pelamis*). In *Physiological Ecology of Tunas*, edited by G.D. Sharp and A.E. Dizon, 357–368. New York: Academic Press.

Kitchell, J.F., Stewart, D.J., and Weininger, D. 1977. Applications of a bioenergetics model to perch and walleye. *J. Fish. Res. Board Can.* 34:1922–1935.

Leggett, R.W., and Williams, L.R. 1981. A reliability index for models. *Ecol. Model.* 13:303–312.

Magnuson, J.J. 1970. Hydrostatic equilibrium of *Euthynnus affinis*, a pelagic teleost without a gas bladder. *Copeia* 1970:56–85.

Magnuson, J.J., Crowder, L.B., Medvick, P.A. 1979. Temperature as an ecological resource. *Am. Zool.* 19:331–343.

Magnuson, J.J., and Weininger, D. 1978. Estimation of minimum sustained speed and associated body drag of scombrids. In *The Physiological Ecology of Tunas*, edited by G.D. Sharp and A.E. Dizon, 293–311. New York: Academic Press.

Majkowski, J., and Waiwood, K.G. 1981. A procedure for evaluating the food biomass consumed by a fish population. *Can. J. Fish. Aquat. Sci.* 38:1199–1208.

Miller, P.J. 1979. A concept of fish phenology. In *Fish Phenology: Anabolic Adaptiveness in Teleosts*, edited by P.J. Miller, 1–28. *Symp. Zool. Soc. Lond.* 44.

Niimi, A.J., and Beamish, F.W.H. 1974. Bioenergetics and growth of largemouth bass (*Micropterus salmoides*) in relation to body weight and temperature. *Can. J. Zool.* 52:447–456.

Pitcher, T.J., and Hart, P.J.B. 1982. *Fisheries Ecology*. Westport, CN: AVI Publishing.

Rice, J.A., Breck, J.E., Bartell, S.M., and Kitchell, J.F. 1983. Evaluating the constraints of temperature, activity and consumption on growth of largemouth bass. *Environ. Biol. Fish.* In press.

Rice, J.A., and Cochran, P.A. 1983. Independent evaluation of bioenergetics model. Manuscript.

Ricker, W.E. 1979. Growth rates and models. In *Fish Physiology, Vol. VIII,* edited by W.S. Hoar et al., 677–743. New York: Academic Press.

Rottiers, D.V. 1978. The respiratory metabolism of the lake trout. Great Lakes Fishery Laboratory, Research Completion Report, Ann Arbor, Michigan.

Rottiers, D.V., O'Conner, D.V., and Edsall, T.A. 1978. The effects of temperature and food availability on food intake, growth and conversion efficiency of lake trout. Research Completion Report, Great Lakes Fishery Lab., Ann Arbor, Michigan.

Rottiers, D.V., and Tucker, R.M. 1978. Caloric content and proximate composition of Lake Michigan fishes. Research Completion Report, Great Lakes Fishery Laboratory, Ann Arbor, Michigan.

Sharp, G.E., and Dotson, R.C. 1978. Energy for migration in albacore (*Thunnus alalunga*). Fish. Bull. 76:447–449.

Sharp, G.D., and Francis, R.C. 1976. An energetics model for the exploited yellowfin tuna, *Thunnas albacores,* population in the eastern Pacific Ocean. *Fish. Bull.* 77:36–51.

Sharp, G.E., and Vlymen III, W.J. 1978. The relation between heat generation, conservation, and the swimming energetics of tunas. In *The Physiological Ecology of Tunas,* edited by G.D. Sharp and A.E. Dizon, 213–232. New York: Academic Press.

Stearns, S.C. 1980. A new view of life-history evolution. *Oikos* 35:266–281.

Steele, J. 1974. *The Structure of Marine Ecosystems.* Oxford: Blackwell Scientific Publications.

Stevens, E.D., and Neill, W.E. 1978. Body temperature relations of tunas, especially skipjack. In *Fish Physiology, Vol. VII,* edited by W. Hoar and D. Randall, New York: Academic Press.

Stewart, D.J. 1980. *Salmonid predators and their forage base in Lake Michigan: a bioenergetics-modeling synthesis.* Ph.D. thesis, University of Wisconsin-Madison.

Stewart, D.J., Kitchell, J.F., and Crowder, L.C. 1981. Forage fishes and their salmonid predators in Lake Michigan. *Trans. Am. Fish. Soc.* 110:751–763.

Theil, H. 1961. *Economic Forecasting and Policy.* Amsterdam: North-Holland.

Ursin, E. 1979. Principles of growth in fishes. In *Fish Phenology: Anabolic Adaptiveness in Teleosts,* edited by P.J. Miller, 63–87. *Symp. Zool. Soc. Lond.* 44.

Von Bertalanffy, L. 1957. Quantitative laws in metabolism and growth. *Q. Rev. Biol.* 32:217–231.

Ware, D.M. 1978. Bioenergetics of pelagic fish: theoretical change in swimming speed and ration with body size. *J. Fish. Res. Board Can.* 35:220–228.

Ware, D.M. 1980. Bioenergetics of stock and recruitment. *Can. J. Fish. Aquat. Sci.* 37:1012–1024.

Ware, D.M. 1982. Power and evolutionary fitness of teleosts. *Can. J. Fish. Aquat. Sci.* 39:3–13.

Warren, C.E. 1971. Biology and Water Pollution Control. Philadelphia: WB Saunders.

Webb, P.W. 1975. Hydrodynamics and energetics of fish propulsion. *Fish. Res. Board Can. Bull.* 190.

Webb, P.W. 1978. Partitioning of energy into metabolism and growth. In *Ecology of*

Freshwater Fish Production, edited by S.D. Gerking, 184–214. New York: John Wiley & Sons.

Weininger, D. 1978. *Accumulation of PCBs by lake trout in Lake Michigan.* Ph.D. Thesis, University of Wisconsin-Madison.

Werner, E.E. 1979. Niche partitioning by food size in fish communities. In *Predator-prey Systems in Fisheries Management,* edited by R. Shoud and H.E. Clepper, 311–322. Washington, D.C.: Sport Fishing Institute.

Wightman, J.A. 1981. Why insect energy budgets do not balance. *Oecologia* 50: 66–169.

Yeo, S.E. 1978. *Seasonal variation in food consumption and caloric content of the alewife,* Alosa pseudoharengus (Vilson), *in Lake Michigan.* M.S. Thesis, University of Wisconsin-Milwaukee.

Chapter 11
OPTIMIZATION OF LOCOMOTION
Daniel Weihs
Paul W. Webb

CONTENTS

INTRODUCTION

Effective use of available energy resources provides an important advantage for both short-term survival and evolutionary success. The class Pisces has developed various designs to fill different niches in the aquatic environment. In this chapter an attempt is made to obtain optimal conditions for various morphologic, kinematic, and behavioral patterns and to see to what degree and how fish have approached these optima. In all cases, optima are defined in terms of energy flux: rates of energy loss during an activity are minimized by various adaptations, and the ratio of the rate of gain to rate of expenditure is maximized. In terms of biomechanics, two criteria may then be examined: behaviors of high efficiency (minimum rates of energy expended for a given behavior) and behaviors at high rates of working (maximum success achieved by minimizing the time for a given behavior).

The energetic budget of an individual fish can be written (see also Chap. 10)

$$E_i = P + M + Q + (\Delta B + G) \tag{1}$$

where E_i is the energy input, P the propulsive rate of working, M the standard metabolic rate, Q denotes energy loss rates due to bodily activities unrelated to locomotion, ΔB the rate of energy going into growth, and G the energy for reproductive processes. The largest portion of metabolizable energy (up to 0.6 E_i), is burned in metabolism (Webb, 1978a; Brett, 1979; Brett and Groves, 1979; Elliott, 1979). Locomotion costs may represent a significant part of the energy budget or may increase net food intake; thus, optimizing locomotion would be expected to be of major importance (see Chap. 10).

Behavioral patterns conforming to the first criterion can now be defined as those that will maximize $G + \Delta B$ given the input E_i. For example, in long-range migration, fish can regulate speed such that the rate of energy expenditure per unit distance crossed is minimized, leaving more to $G + \Delta B$ (see section on optimal constant speed). The second criterion deals with cases in which the probability of a behavior being successful is a direct result of maximizing P or making P large, usually involving adaptations that can bring about high speeds or acceleration. An example here is rapid starting for escape by an attacked prey or the attacker's lunge. These adaptations will mainly be short-term, all-or-nothing type behaviors crucial to immediate survival but probably with small impact on the overall energy budget. This contrasts with the previous criterion, in which activities of long duration cause the efficiency effects to add up to significant contributions.

The scope of the subject matter of this chapter, locomotor optimization, is extremely wide but as yet largely unexplored. In the following discussions we do not attempt a detailed treatment of each topic, but rather indicate the current status and future potential of the subject area.

OPTIMAL DESIGN FOR LOCOMOTION

Performance (speed, acceleration, and endurance) depends on the balance between thrust and drag. It has been known for years that fish shapes have evolved in part in response to hydrodynamic requirements of streamlining for low drag, and other requirements. This observation has recently been refined, based on results of hydrodynamic studies of fish motions that indicate that there are at least two different functional trends, each leading to a different specialized form: one for long distance motion, the other for rapid lunging.

Definition of these two generic types of motion is required; thus, one observes periodic movements where a locomotory pattern is repeated cyclically for long periods, covering relatively long distances at constant average speed. Such periodic motion ranges from migratory movements of pelagic fish such as scombroids and salmonids to some forms of routine swimming and holding station, but has usually been called *steady* or *sustained swimming* in the literature, probably because it was measured in flumes and fishwheels where fish are forced to swim against a constant current. A more general and appropriate name for this type of locomotion is (as suggested above) *periodic motion*. Even constant-speed swimming is produced by periodic motions of body and fins (see Chaps. 6 and 7) that cause a slight "rippling" variation of speed. Add to this the *nage filée* (burst and coast; Houssay, 1912) routine swimming behavior of many species such as engraulids, gadids, and others in free-swimming situations, which in many cases is actually a more efficient way of swimming (Weihs, 1974; Videler and Weihs, 1982), and the periodicity of "steady" swimming is evident.

Typical adaptations for periodic motion are a relatively large percentage of red (aerobic) muscle and a thick, deep, and relatively rigid midbody area. The reasons for these adaptations will be discussed in detail in the following sections.

The other main type of motion is defined as *transient movements* and includes rapid starts and turns for lunging at prey and escape maneuvers that last tens, or at most hundreds of milliseconds. The morphologic requirements for effectiveness at performing these transient motions are radically different from those of the periodic motions; flexible elongate bodies with a large percentage of white muscle, large caudal fins, and a dorsoventral fin arrangement reminiscent of a double-tail are found. Pike and barracuda are typical of this fish shape. The kinematic description of locomotory motions appears in Chapters 6 and 7 and so will not be discussed in detail here.

Morphologic adaptations for higher efficiency can be subdivided into two main categories: adaptations to improve the thrust producing mechanism and adaptations to reduce water resistance to motion (drag reduction). These two categories are not completely exclusive because most modes of swimming cause an increase in drag over motion while not performing propulsive movements (Lighthill, 1971; Webb, 1971, 1975a). Alternatively, the adaptations can be classified as external versus internal. Most adaptations for improving thrust and reducing drag have been described in detail (Webb, 1975a; Bone, 1977), and optimal design criteria for transient and periodic swimming are summarized in Table 11-1. The following section therefore only briefly discusses the morphologic adaptations.

Improvement of Thrust Production and Efficiency

The main morphologic adaptation dedicated to thrust production occurred very early in the evolution of Pisces when specific organs developed to facilitate the transfer of momentum from the muscles to the surrounding water, i.e. fins (see also Evolutionary Trends). These organs have large, flattened surfaces enabling large masses of water to be moved by relatively small tissue volumes. Enlarging the geometric dimensions of the fins increases the forces produced when moving the fin, proportional to the square of the fin-span.

Table 11-1
SUMMARY OF MECHANICAL AND MORPHOLOGIC REQUIREMENTS
FOR MAXIMIZING TRANSIENT AND PERIODIC
SWIMMING PERFORMANCE*

TRANSIENT	PERIODIC
Mechanics	
Thrust is the sum of local effects along whole body length	Mean thrust is related to the rate of momentum shedding at the caudal-fin trailing edge
For fast-starts, resistance is equal to the product of virtual mass and acceleration rate; in powered turns, frictional drag is presumably large	Resistance is primarily caused by viscous effects in the boundary layer; surface friction and form drag predominates
Morphology	
Large, low aspect ratio tail (or double tail) maximizes thrust and turning moment	Deep, high aspect ratio tail maximizes thrust and minimizes drag
Deep caudal peduncle enhanced by posterior anal and dorsal fins increases thrust and turning moments	Small vertically flattened caudal peduncle (narrow necking) minimizes drag and destabilizing side forces causing recoil of the center of mass
	Large anterior body and/or depth minimize center of mass recoil and associated energy waste.
Flexible body allows large-amplitude lateral movements to maximize thrust and turning moments and to minimize turning radius	Streamlined anterior body minimizes drag but reduces body flexibility
Large proportion of myotomal muscle mass relative to body mass (*i.e.,* minimal dead weight to accelerate) minimizes acceleration resistance; large myotomal muscle mass maximizes turning moment	Large myotomal muscle mass maximizes sprint speeds because power requirements increase with velocity cubed

*Detailed discussion is contained in Lighthill (1969, 1970), Weihs (1972, 1973a), Webb, (1977, 1978b, 1982b and c) Webb and Smith (1980), and Chapter 6 in this volume.

This encouraged development of fins elongated in the spanwise direction both for fish producing forces by means of inertia (added mass) or lift (vorticity shedding) momentum transfer mechanisms (Lighthill, 1971; see Chap. 6).

Fins are presumed to have evolved from finfolds, but enlargements of these organs immediately cause bending to become an important factor in their operation. The bending deflection of a body subjected to a distributed load such as the water inertia is proportional to the span to the third power. Keeping the fins rigid thus requires strengthening, achieved by dermal plates in ostracoderms, fin rays in actinopterygians, and by thickening the enlargement of the fin base in selachians, in which cartilaginous structure does not withstand large bending moments (see Chap. 3).

The continuing development of fins as propulsors has led to the differentiation between fin duties, with specific fins being used for propulsive purposes, others being adapted to serve as stability and control surfaces. The major propulsive fins for high-speed swimming are positioned at the caudal end of the body in many cases (Chap. 6). This design, which is also prevalent in manmade vessels, has two distinct advantages over front-end or midbody propulsion. The net result of any propulsive action is to increase the water momentum in the opposing direction (to the rear). In any fin-type propulsion, where no mass is added (as opposed to say, rocket propulsion), this is observed as an increase in the rearward velocity of the water; thus, the water velocity over the body in other than rear-end propulsion is increased causing an increase in the viscous (boundary layer) drag, which is proportional to the velocity $^{1.5-2}$, depending on Reynolds number (Schlichting, 1968). This can be simply understood when one realizes that viscosity causes the water next to the skin to be at rest, relative to the skin; thus, when higher speed flow has to be stopped, more force has to be applied, resulting in higher drag.

Also, the flow into the rear-end propulsor is moving at less than the fish speed because the viscous "sticking" of the boundary layer to the fish body causes part of the water to move with the fish. Thus, for a given increase in the rearward velocity relative to the fin (*i.e.,* given thrust force), the absolute flow to the rear is slower, meaning that less energy is lost to the wake.

The development of the caudal fin as main propulsor in many fish has led to a revolutionary change in the method of thrust production. Paired fins usually produce drag-type momentum exchange by paddling, where the fin is pulled backward and broadside (Chap. 7), pushing the mass of water with it. Use of the vertical caudal fin in sinuous motion enables the application of aerodynamic lift-type momentum exchange; here the fin is moved while oriented at a small angle to its direction of motion (angle of attack), thus producing a force perpendicular to the direction of motion. This force, resulting from the circulation produced around the fin because of the unequal velocities on both sides, is the force producing the lift required by aircraft and will be called so here too, to minimize terminology; however, it is not to be confused with buoyancy forces. The advantage of lift force production is that much less energy need be expended to produce the same force as a paddle. This results from the fact that for motion at a small angle of attack, the ratio of lift-to-drag for a fin is much larger than one (*i.e.,* the useful force produced is much larger than the drag penalty, whereas in paddling these two are essentially equal). While the fish cannot use the full lift force produced by the fin and the force is at an angle to the direction of motion, the gain as compared to paddling is still enormous. It is interesting to note that this has recently been discovered by human swimmers, and Olympic coaches now teach a lift-type hand motion in the Australian crawl (Counsilman, 1968, p. 53).

When the main propulsive unit is not at the rear end (such as in labriform motion—see Chap. 7), the fins are usually shaped such that the main mass of water they move is outside of the boundary layer and interacts with it minimally. This avoids the inefficient momentum transfer resulting from flow in the boundary layer, which is moving with the fish body. The fins achieve acceleration of the water outside the boundary layer by evolving an elongate, triangular shape, narrow near the body, and placing the fins longitudinally close to the point of largest cross-section. The fin wake will then be relatively far sideways from the caudal body sections. Blake (see Chap. 7) has shown that this fin form also minimizes adverse effects of the negative angles of attack on the parts of the fin next to the body.

Extreme modification of caudal structures for optimization of thrust generation are seen in almost all fish species with lifestyles involving high-efficiency, continuous locomotion. This appears as high-aspect ratio, relatively stiff caudal fins (known as *lunate tails*). The advantages of the high-aspect ratio are exhaustively examined in Chapter 6 and so shall not be dwelt on here. Stiffer caudal fins have been shown (Katz and Weihs, 1978) to cause a large increase in available thrust at the price of a relatively small drop in efficiency. The stiffness thus required is obtained by close packing and fusing of many fin rays.

One can also mention here an attractive hypothesis that has yet to be proven. This is the double-tail idea, which suggests that fish such as pike (*Esox* sp.), cod (*Gadus* sp.) and others have evolved, in addition to the caudal propulsor, the dorsal and anal fins as propulsors in a configuration similar to the caudal fin (see Fig. 11-1). The propulsive wave that runs down the body (Chap. 6) causes each of these fins to produce lift forces, with a phase difference between the force produced by the two propulsors such that a relatively uniform thrust is produced. This thrust is also obtained at higher efficiency as some of the momentum lost to the wake of the "first tail" is used at the caudal fin.

The double-tail is especially effective for rapid starts. There the main thrust for acceleration is produced by a rapid sideward motion of the tail, producing lift forces in the direction of anticipated motion. The increase in tail fin area results in a higher potential for acceleration, albeit at higher cost (Weihs, 1973a).

Reduction of Drag

The second route to optimization of body shape and structure to energy-efficient motion is by adaptation for reduced drag while swimming. The streamlining of fishes was recognized early (see Chap. 1) and has even served as the basis of early attempts at aircraft design (Cayley, 1809).

The basic fusiform, elongate fish shape (Webb, 1982b) is an adaptation toward reducing the energetic cost of motion through the water. The evolved ellipsoidal shape has thickness ratios (ratio of maximum dimensions in the longitudinal and vertical directions) of between 3 and 7, which have been shown to minimize drag (Hess, 1976). These optimal shapes should be axisymmetric around the fish longitudinal axis (*i.e.,* bodies of revolution). Actual fish

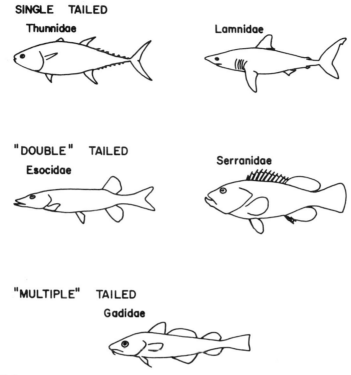

SINGLE   TAILED

Thunnidae

Lamnidae

"DOUBLE"   TAILED

Esocidae

Serranidae

"MULTIPLE"   TAILED

Gadidae

Figure 11-1
Single, double, and multiple tail arrangements. The single-tail caudal fin is typical of periodic sustained swimmers with carangiform swimming mode. Double-tailed fish are rapid starters (*i.e.,* transient swimmers). The gadidae and similar arrangements are probably based on anguilliform force production along the whole body in periodic motion.

shapes are thus a compromise between the round cross-section for drag and the deepening of cross-sections required for inertial (added mass) propulsion, as well as turning, and other motions. Scombroids, for example, have almost circular cross-sections because the body is not oscillated for propulsion, and their dorsal fin, which serves for maneuvers, is retractable. On the other hand, species that spend more time moving slowly and maneuvering tend to have deep and narrow body cross-sections.

The distribution of body thickness in the longitudinal direction also indicates an attempt to minimize form drag. Scombroids have the shoulder (point of maximum body depth) situated at a point over 60% of the body length from the nose, with a rather rapid reduction of cross-sectional area afterward. This again is reminiscent of the shapes obtained in recent studies of bodies with minimum drag for a given enclosed volume. Most nonscombroid fish flex most of their body for locomotory purposes so that an optimal stretched-straight configuration is of less use. The oscillatory motion generates lateral flows, which result in increased drag. Additional drag also occurs because of flow separation and vortex production that occur as the propulsive wave travels backwards on the parts of the body with instantaneous concave shapes; thus, the drag during swimming is increased to three to five times the drag when the fish is stretched out straight (Alexander, 1967; Lighthill, 1971; Webb, 1971, 1975a).

Many sharks (which swim in an almost anguilliform mode) tend to have elliptical cross-sections changing from horizontal near the head to vertical at the shoulder (which is near the middle of the body) and back to a horizontal section near the caudal peduncle. This reduces the form drag caused by moving the front and rear parts of the body sideways for propulsive purposes (Weihs, 1981) by delaying and reducing the effects of separation.

Other adaptations to reduce form drag are grouped together as the carangiform mode of swimming. Here the propulsive motions for straight-line, sustained swimming are concentrated at the rear part of the fish, the amplitude of lateral motions growing toward the caudal fin. Extremes of this adaptation are observed in scombroids, where only the rear third of the body is moved. This part of the body has additional lateral drag-reducing adaptations, including finlets, which reduce form drag by delaying lateral separation of flow (Aleyev, 1977, p. 231), and the caudal peduncle, which has an elliptical shape with horizontal long axis similar to the sharks mentioned above.

Numerous drag-reduction properties have been attributed to fish mucus (see Webb, 1975a; Bone, 1977 for reviews), but virtually none of those functions have been adequately substantiated. An exception is recent observation by Daniel (1981), who showed that mucus reduced frictional drag and suppressed vortex formation in fish.

MIGRATION

Migration is the movement of an animal over extended distances, usually greater than 10^4 body lengths, toward a specific goal. Animals frequently migrate to avoid climatic extremes, to improve food resources, and for reproduction. In extreme cases, such as Pacific thunnids (Sharp and Dotson, 1978) and Atlantic eels and cod (Harden–Jones 1968), distances traveled may be thousands of kilometers (millions of fish lengths). Depending on the species, this distance must be traveled most economically or in least time. Demands for economy at any speed will always be important, especially as many migrant fish do not feed enroute. Active migrations (and not just planktonic motion following currents, eddies, etc.) belong to the class of periodic motion almost by definition. The morphologic adaptations for periodic motion were discussed above, and here we look at behavioral options such as speed adjustment, schooling, and so on.

Optimal Constant Speed

The first and simplest behavioral parameter a fish can control is its swimming speed, relative to the water mass. In cases of swimming in shallow or confined waters where an external spatial reference is available, the speed controlled can also be the absolute value. Looking initially at constant-speed swimming, the energy optimization principle can be stated as follows: find the constant swimming speed at which the rate of energy expended per unit distance is minimal. This approach, first presented by Weihs (1973b), can be described simply by assuming that no feeding, evacuation, or growth take place during the period of swimming analyzed; thus, the only contributions to the energy flux are the locomotory and resting metabolic requirements. The energy per unit time required for locomotion at constant speed (or almost constant speed, neglecting the small variations due to the periodic mode of propulsion) is

$$\eta P = TV \tag{2}$$

where η is the propulsive efficiency, T the (average) thrust, which is equal and opposite to the drag, and V the swimming speed relative to the water. The total rate of working is

$$E = P + M = (K/\beta)\, C_{Do}\, V^{3-\alpha-\delta} + M \tag{3}$$

where the relation between drag and velocity and the empirical (Kliashtorin, 1973) relation between efficiency and aerobic swimming speed are substituted into P. K, β, and C_{Do} are constants for a given fish. $K = (\rho A)/2$ where ρ is the density of the surrounding water, and A a characteristic area that is taken here as the fish volume$^{2/3}$. β is an empirical proportionality constant relating efficiency and an empirical power of the swimming speed ($\eta = \beta V_\alpha$), and C_{Do} is the reduced drag coefficient independent of velocity. The drag coefficient $C_D = C_{Do} V^{-\delta}$ where δ has values empirically found to be 0 to 0.3. The distance crossed by the fish per unit time is numerically equal to the average swimming speed. The distance traversed per unit energy used is the distance crossed per unit time, divided by the energy expended in the same unit of time (*i.e.*, V/E). The optimal speed V_o fulfills the mathematical condition

$$d(V/E)/dV = 0 \tag{4}$$

which leads to

$$V_o = [\beta M / K C_{Do}(2-\alpha-\delta)]^{1/(3-\alpha-\delta)} \tag{5}$$

by substituting V_o into equation 3 one sees that the ratio of standard metabolism to propulsive rates of working at the optimal speed is

$$(M/P)_o = 2\text{-}\alpha\text{-}\delta \tag{6}$$

α has values of $0.7 \le \alpha \le 1.0$, such that the ratio M/P takes values of $1.3 < M/P < 0.7$. The rate of energy consumption at optimal speed is thus predicted to be 2 ± 0.3 times the standard metabolic rate. This value is in good agreement with data from Winberg (1956), Kerr, (1971), and Ware (1975, 1978). Figure 11-2 shows the change in distance crossed per unit energy used as a function of speed.

This approach can be carried further to include size effects (Weihs, 1977). Applying various empirical relationships for the scaling of the quantities appearing in equation 5, it was predicted that

$$V_o \simeq \text{const. } L^{0.43} \tag{7}$$

with the constant having a numerical value of approximately 0.5 when V_o is measured in meters per second and L is the forklength in meters. Ware (1978) independently obtained the same exponent (to both significant figures) of size

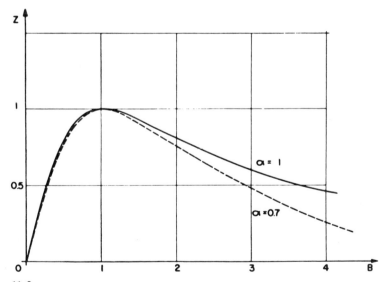

Figure 11-2
The ratio of the distance traversed per unit energy expenditure rate (Z) over the maximum value of this parameter (obtained at the optimal cruising speed) as a function of speed divided by the optimum speed (B) for $\alpha = 0.7$ and $\alpha = 1.0$. As a result of the nondimensional form, this curve also describes the ratio of energy intake rate over expenditure (again Z) during filter feeding. The actual speeds are different. (From Weihs, 1975b)

dependence of the optimal speed. He analyzed sockeye salmon data with the empirically obtained constant being about 8% larger than the one quoted above in one case and about 40% larger in another. The constants obtained in equation 7 were obtained essentially by using data on trout (Webb, 1971), salmon (Brett, 1979), and some other fishes swimming in flumes. All of the fish were in the 0.3 m to 0.7 m size range; thus, to test the validity of the predicted size dependence, data on large as well as very small fish are required. Fish that are much smaller than the range above (less than 0.05 m) are less likely to be involved in directed migrations, so the data on large fish is essential. Such data has been lacking because it is difficult to study large fish under controlled conditions that include metabolic measurements. A first such attempt has appeared recently (Weihs, *et al.,* 1981) where voluntary swimming speeds for two species of carcharhinid sharks were measured in a large tank. The measured fish were fully acclimatized to the tank, having been in it for months and even years. The conclusion was that the relationship in equation 7 is surprisingly accurate, taking into account the multiplicity of parameters and the assumptions involved.

Migration in the Presence of Currents and Tides

The optimum speeds discussed in the previous section were calculated and measured (as far as possible) for uniform relative motion between fish and water mass. Under natural conditions, uniform relative motion corresponds to motion in still waters. Many migrations take place in areas where constant or tidal currents with speeds of up to 1.5 m/sec are traversed. In many cases, migrating fish will adapt their paths to make use of such currents (Harden–Jones, 1968).

In a recent attempt to generalize the results of the previous section to include the effect of currents, Trump and Leggett (1980) predict that the optimum speed relative to the water mass will be V_0 (equation 5 or 7) plus the average current speed, so that the absolute speed relative to ground still stays V_0. Trump and Leggett's analysis does not address some basic problems such as how the current speeds (especially in constant currents) are estimated by the fish and what course the fish should choose when the current is at an angle to the required direction of motion. The problem of motion optimization in currents of a general nature must still be seen as unsolved.

Specific cases such as selective tidal stream transport have been shown to be a means of minimizing the energy cost of migration (Weihs, 1978) and quantitatively proven to exist (Harden–Jones *et al.,* 1978). Here migratory routes such as that of plaice (*Pleuronectes platessa* L.) and sole (*Solea solea*; de Veen, 1967) in the North Sea are in a zone of rapid tidal currents (0.7 m/sec to 1.2 m/sec; *i.e.,* 2 to 3 body lengths/sec). When tidal current speeds are much larger than V_0, as in the case above, gains of 50% or more in energy needed to cross a given distance are possible for fish moving in midwater when the tidal current is in the direction of motion and going to the sea bottom and waiting while the tide is moving in the opposite direction.

Burst and Coast Swimming

A common mode of locomotion among many migratory species is a two-phase periodic behavior in which one phase includes one or more locomotory cycles of the body and fins causing acceleration (the burst phase) followed by a comparable period of coasting with no propulsive motions (the coast phase). At the end of the coasting period, the speed has slowed to the initial value, and another burst and coast cycle begins. This behavior, which seems rather clumsy and complicated at first sight, has been shown (Weihs, 1974) to lead to large energy savings for sustained (aerobic) swimming over a long distance; thus, the burst-and-coast swimming mode should be seen as an additional route to the minimization of energy consumption during migration. The hydrodynamic drag of the flexing fish body is three to five times larger than when stretched out while coasting at the same speed (Alexander, 1967; Webb, 1975a), so any distance crossed while coasting is economical. This is the key factor leading to energy saving by this two-phase motion. For obvious reasons, coasting must alternate with periods of acceleration so that the burst-and-coast behavior is obtained.

Quantitative analysis of the benefits of this behavior shows (Weihs, 1974) that the gains in efficiency are only functions of the initial and final speeds of the beat phase, and the ratio α of drag when swimming actively to coasting drag. The optimal conditions are obtained at relatively low average speeds. The increase in efficiency is greater when α is bigger and when the burst phase becomes shorter; thus, fish swimming in the anguilliform mode (see chap. 6) stand to gain more from this two-phase swimming, and optimal burst phases include only one or two propulsive cycles.

Burst-and-coast swimming was recently also shown to be energetically advantageous for anaerobic high-speed sprints for gadids (Videler and Weihs, 1982). Here also, the greatest gains are obtained at the low end of the sprint speed range.

A variant of two-phase swimming developed by negatively buoyant fish has been observed (Olla *et al.,* 1972) and was analyzed by Weihs (1973c). This includes a phase of passive gliding at constant speed, using the submerged weight to produce a component of force countering the hydrodynamic drag. As a result, the fish sinks obliquely at the gliding angle to greater depth. The second phase starts by the fish moving diagonally upward, this time swimming actively, and lasts until the fish reaches its original depth. Swimming oscillations then stop, and another glide phase starts. As with burst-and-coast swimming, the gains obtained here result from the difference between drag when swimming and coasting. Optimal gains in range for a given energy store can be twofold.

Glide-and-swim gains can be optimized by two distinct categories of adaptations: first, increase the ratio of swimming to gliding drag (for example, anguilliform swimmers such as flatfish); second, minimize the gliding drag together with increased submerged weight. The ratio of these at any speed gives the glide angle. Minimizing gliding drag does not necessarily increase the ratio of swimming to gliding drag. For example, the low gliding drag shape of thunnids is expected to reduce swimming drag to a much greater extent. There is an incentive for fish using the second approach to evolve low-drag shapes with high density; this is predominantly found in predatory, highly active scombroids and sharks (Magnuson, 1978).

Schooling

A different type of adaptation for efficient long-distance motion involves cooperative interactions of many individuals in a school. Many reasons for schooling have been suggested (Cushing and Harden–Jones, 1968; Shaw, 1978), such as benefits in search and escape. Here the hydrodynamic advantages of schooling are discussed.

Synchronized motion in tight formations can be shown (Weihs, 1973d, 1975a) to reduce the thrust (and thus the energy) required to move at any given sustained speed. When a fish swims by body and caudal fin oscillation it sheds a wake consisting of a series of vortices in two staggered rows (Lighthill, 1969). Each of these vortices induces velocities in the surrounding water in the same direction of rotation as the vortex and with strength inversely proportional to the distance from the vortex. As a result, a mean velocity in the direction opposite to the fish motion is induced directly behind the fish, while diagonally behind (outside of the vortex "street"), a forward velocity appears (Fig. 11-3).

A fish situated directly behind its predecessor would experience a higher relative velocity and would have to work harder. In the diagonal position, however, less effort is required than for a solitary fish moving at the same absolute speed. The best position has been predicted (Weihs, 1975a) to be laterally midway between two fish of the preceding row. In this formation one fish helps another with no direct gain to itself; however, by staying close to neighbors of the same lateral row and moving in antiphase synchrony (moving the tail in a direction opposite to the two closest neighbors), a channelling effect is produced that can increase the thrust produced by given bodily motions, again increasing the effectiveness of swimming in schools. Similar channelling effects can be obtained with neighbors vertically above and below, resulting in an elongate diamond shape as the basic optimum structure of a fish school. Since this model was suggested, Breder (1976), reanalyzing some data on *Trachurus symmetricus* of Hunter (1966), has shown that the

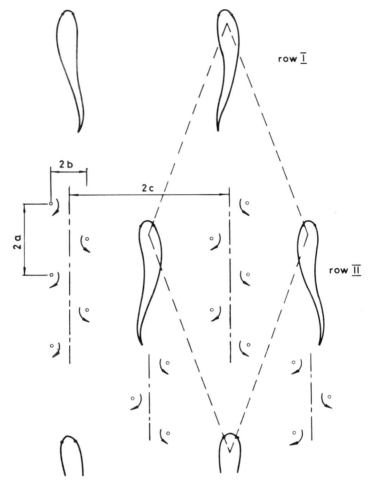

Figure 11-3
Part of a horizontal layer of fish within a school and the discrete vortices shed (*hollow circles*).
Arrows show direction of flow velocity induced by the vortices; broken lines indicate a diamond.
Fish in row I induce a forward velocity on fish diagonally behind them in row II; row-II fish help
each other (and themselves) by a channelling effect. (2a is wave length of propulsive wake; 2b is
width of wake (maximal tail lateral excursion); 2c is lateral distance between neighboring fish of
the same row; (from Weihs, 1975a)

mean measured location of individuals approximate the diamond shape.
Partridge and Pitcher (1979) did not find such formations in saithe, (*Pol-
lachius virens*), herring (*Clupea*), and cod (*Gadus morhua*), but more recently
(Partridge, personal communication) observed lateral positioning for hydro-
dynamic advantage in single-row hunting schools of Atlantic bluefin tuna
(*Thynnus thynnus*).

FEEDING

Feeding is the basic activity that determines the rate of energy input to the fish. It is also a behavior subject to optimization such that the ratio of energy gain rate to expenditure rate is maximized, in turn maximizing the rate of energy gain for growth and reproduction. Food sources are all possible animal, vegetable, and derived detrital material on the water surface, on the bottom, or in the water column. Irrespective of the origin and distribution of food, feeding involves two common phases: food must first be located (search) and then consumed. Optimal locomotor tactics to maximize the probability of encountering food are relatively independent of the food type; however, locomotor optima might be altered by sensory capabilities, although such interactions have not been examined. In contrast, mechanisms for consumption are commonly more specific depending on variable characteristics such as spatial location, size, escape potential, defenses, and schooling of food items.

Search

The rate at which fish encounter vulnerable food items depends on the rate and pattern of search and food distribution. In some circumstances this phase of feeding may be relatively unimportant. For example, food may come to some predators such as esocids (Pitcher, 1980) and fish with lures as in antennariid anglerfish (Grobecker and Pietsch, 1979); active search is then largely limited to moving to new ambush sites. In other situations, food distribution is contagious and predictable; because of topographic features such as reefs, vegetation, and upwelling areas or due to diurnal migrations. Search distances are then minimal as foragers learn food locations. Sometimes food must be followed or stalked, and these situations may involve numerous different behaviors and locomotor modes, but all of these movements may be slow and are unlikely to impact substantially on the fish's energy budget. None of these behaviors are likely to be limited by structural and physiological systems.

In contrast, searching is of primary importance in homogeneous habitats when functional design is expected to impact on foraging efficiency. Homogeneous habitats may be defined as those where reaction distances of fish to food particles are small compared to topographic references. The search is probably the dominant phase of feeding for zooplankton particulate feeders (O'Brien, 1979) and probably many pelagic carnivores (Sharp and Francis, 1976).

For all searches where the distribution of food particles or patches is unknown, the general problem is to sample the largest volume of water at the least rate of energy expenditure (Weihs, 1975b). The solution is explicitly developed below with respect to filter feeding and results in optimal speeds similar to those for migration. It therefore follows that optimal designs and behavior maximizing constant-speed swimming efficiency (see sections on Optimal Design for Locomotion and Migration) are also optimal for searching for food. In addition, some correlation would be expected between the uncertainty of food distribution and body form. Certainly, scombroids feeding on patches of unpredictable distribution are highly specialized for cruising, while esocids, taking advantage of predictable food distributions have very little capacity for search (Beamish, 1978; Diana, 1980).

Filter Feeding

Filter feeding is defined here as feeding on prey of much smaller size than the predator. Filter-feeding prey range from microscopic phytoplankton and zooplankton of typical sizes in the range of tens to hundreds of micrometers ($\leq 10^{-2}$ cm) up to krill and other crustaceans of similar size. Predator species range in size from engraulids (10^{-1} m) to whales and large sharks (10 m) eating the larger prey. The ratio of predator-to-prey lengths for filter feeding is not less than 10^2. For example, Leong and O'Connell (1969) show that anchovy (*Engraulis mordax*) of length 10 cm to 15 cm filter feed on nauplii of length 6.5×10^{-4} m, (*i.e.,* a predator-to-prey length ratio of 150 to 250) but bite on individual adults 3.7×10^{-3} m (size ratio of 30 to 40). This results in two characteristics of filter feeding that influence the optimization procedure:

1. Large numbers of individual prey particles must be collected (*i.e.,* no specific maneuvers directed at a prey unit are to be expected)
2. Prey escape attempts do exist, but the predator does not take them into account, and they can be neglected in analyzing the feeding behavior.

The factors influencing filter feeding are thus prey concentration (in terms of units, mass, or nutritional value), prey patchiness, and on the predator's side, its capability for sensing and collecting the available prey and the effort required. Most of these can be quantified within one crucial dependent parameter, the nutritive value of prey per unit water volume filtered. This will be designated as F, a function of prey number, density, size, and composition. Then

$$F = n \, V_p \, Q_P(1 - \zeta p) \tag{8}$$

where n is the number of prey particles per unit water volume, V_P and Q_P are the prey volume and nutritive content, respectively, and ζ_P is the sum of the specific dynamic action, fecal, and nitrogenous losses normalized by Q_P. The net energy intake per unit time for swimming at speed V is F times the volume covered by the mouth

$$E_i = F \; V \; A \tag{9}$$

where A is the intake area, which is usually smaller than the mouth area (due to deceleration of the flow near the mouth). This virtual area depends on mouth shape as well as the filtering resistance of gill-rakers.

The optimum filtering speed can be now established, by looking for the speed V at which the ratio E_i/E (energy intake to expenditure) is highest. This is obtained in a similar way to the optimum cruising speed, taking the value of E from equation 3 and equating the derivative of E_i/E, with respect to the speed V, to zero. The optimum speed is obtained when the ratio of swimming to resting rates of working is (Weihs, 1975b)

$$(M/P)_o = 2\text{-}\delta\text{-}\alpha \tag{10}$$

This is the same solution as that for long-distance economic cruising (see Fig. 11-2). The optimum feeding speed has therefore the same functional dependence on the various physical parameters as does the cruising speed found earlier when discussing migration; the value of the optimum feeding speed will be somewhat higher than the cruising speed, however, because M must be defined as energy expenditure unrelated to locomotion. M will be larger owing to feeding excitement (Brett and Zala, 1975 for example). In addition, the drag coefficient for swimming with flow through a widely opened mouth is different than that for closed-mouth swimming.

Thus, the optimum feeding speed (V_{fo}) at a temperature of 15°C is predicted

$$V_{fo} \simeq 0.69 \; L^{0.43} \tag{11}$$

where length is in meters and speed in m · sec^{-1}

Ware (1978) has also examined optimal feeding speeds from a different point of view, taking into account factors such as prey density over a large range, prey handling time, and capture success ratios. His analysis spans the range from filter feeders to particulate feeders. While the regression coefficient relating V_{fo} and L in Ware's analysis varied with the additional factors, the same exponents of L, as in equation 11, are found for typical cases. Ware (1978) also considered the importance of burst-and-coast locomotion. As expected from Weihs (1974; see section on burst-and-coast swimming), Ware found that the mean feeding speed using this behavior is higher than for constant-speed swimmers. Recent work by Durbin and associates (1981) shows that Atlantic menhaden with fork length about 25.8 cm swam at 41.3 cm/sec at 20°C, while the optimum feeding speed (equation 11) is 38.5 cm/sec. The agreement is good, especially when taking the temperature difference into account.

Particulate Feeding

Particulate feeders are macrophagous fish that consume items that are individually sensed and seized. They are separated from filtering microphagous feeding fish when the predator-to-prey length ratio is about 100 or less as mentioned in the section on filter feeding. The food particles fall into two major categories of elusive and nonelusive items. The optimal locomotor tactics to maximize net surplus energy of fish feeding on nonelusive food do not differ substantially from those for filter feeders. Locomotor tactics are markedly different only when prey are active and attempt to escape from a predator.

The optimal strategy for consuming elusive prey remains one that maximizes net surplus energy, but the situation is complicated because the prey has an objective of escaping, opposite to that of the predator. This is the classic basis of interception games (*e.g.,* Isaacs, 1975) when the general strategy of the predator is to minimize the duration of an interaction while that of the prey is to extend the duration; therefore, neither the predator nor the prey is likely to move at the speeds that are optimal for consuming nonelusive items.

Observations on locomotor strategies in predation situations are fragmentary; nevertheless, many optimal tactical components can now be recognized and their generality assessed. Several fruitful areas for research can therefore be identified. Locomotor strategies are most distinct for particulate feeders taking other fish, so general principles are considered for piscivorous predator-prey interactions. Interactions are considered primarily for two patterns of attack: strikes characteristic of predators such as esocids and chases common in piscivores like scombroids.

STRIKES

A strike is a single attempt to reach the prey, usually including a bite (Chap. 9) and followed by a catch, a chase, or abortion of the attack. A fundamental principle is that predator locomotor tactics should be based on the expectation that prey will attempt to escape. The prey's escape response is a fast start, usually a C-start, initiated by the Mauthner cell (Eaton and Bombardieri, 1978; Eaton *et al.,* in press). The initial Mauthner-controlled stage is stereotyped, while in subsequent non-Mauthner controlled stages (R.C. Eaton, personal communication), behavior is variable (Weihs, 1973a; Webb, 1975b).

Other features of the motor response are illustrated in Figure 11-4, which shows that the body bends into C-shapes as the anterior and posterior of the body make large amplitude excursions and the center of mass moves least; the initial trajectory of the center of mass is predictable because of recoil; and

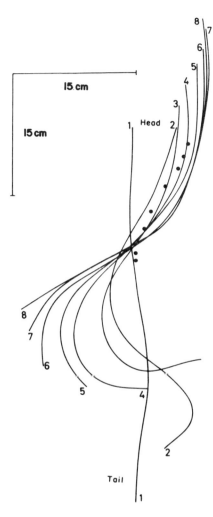

Figure 11–4
Stages in a standing fast-start of 33-cm trout. The numbered lines are tracings of centerline positions of the fish at successive intervals of 1/40s. The full circles mark the positions of the fish's center of mass. The starting process is comprised of three stages. In stage 1 (frames 1 to 3) the body is bent into a C or J shape; in stage 2 (frames 4 to 7), the body bend travels backward over the body, the stage ending in a J or C shape opposite to that in stage 1. Most of the acceleration takes place in stage 2 at an angle to the original orientation of the fish owing to the heads reaction in stage 1. Stage 2 is followed by a variable stage 3 where either stage 2 is repeated or periodic swimming or coasting commences. (From Weihs, 1973a)

during the first two fast-start stages, the center of mass moves a relatively small distance, about 10 cm in 70 msec for 10-cm fish at 15°C (Webb, 1976, 1978b and c). The most effective locomotor tactics for the predator to intercept the prey in the least time with the greatest likelihood of capture are strike at the center of mass as a target, strike at an angle to the prey body axis so that the attack and initial escape trajectories coincide, and strike to intercept while movements are stereotyped in stage 1 and failing that, before stage 2 is completed (*i.e.*, strike as quickly as possible).

Some of these locomotor tactics appear to be common in piscivorous fish; others are not possible because of morphologic limitations when other factors appear to compensate. For example, several teleost predators (*Esox, Micropterus dolomieui, Salmo gairdneri* and *Ambloplites rupestris*) with variable predatory behavior aimed strikes at minnows (*Pimephales promelas*) at a point 0.31 to 0.39 *L* from the nose. The center of mass of the prey was 0.35 ± 0.04 *L* from the nose (P. W. Webb, unpublished). McPhail (1977) also found characin predators attacked characin prey in this general region. The center of mass is not known to the predator, but commonly lies at a point 0.3 to 0.4 × length, measured from the nose and close to the point of maximum body depth (Houssay, 1912; Webb, 1978b). These morphologic features, together with others such as the eyes, probably act as target cues. In chases, such targets are presumably unimportant because predator-prey orientation is fixed along a common axis.

The escape trajectory of the center of mass is initially at a large angle (80° to 90°) to the initial axis of the prey's body. This is because recoil is proportional to acceleration (Weihs, 1973a), and the Mauthner cell triggers a maximum response. Many teleost predators attack prey from the side when attack and escape paths tend to coincide, but some predators have other preferred strike directions. For example, yellow perch (*Perca flavenscens*) maneuver to attack the prey from the head, probably to facilitate swallowing the prey (Hoogland *et al.*, 1956; Nursall, 1973).

The third optimal tactic based on prey motor responses is to strike quickly before unpredictable motor behavior can develop and before the prey center of mass is displaced substantially from the strike path. This may also be important if predator response latencies to prey maneuvers are large. The ability to achieve rapid closure with the prey is constrained, in part, by predator morphology. This tactic is therefore expected to be affected by predator body form and biomechanical scope for locomotion but has not been the subject of critical experimental evaluation.

A given distance can be covered in the least time by a predator starting from rest using a fast start. The predator must reach a specific target in space; therefore S-starts are optimal because recoil forces are better balanced along the body length and fish can accelerate in any chosen direction (Webb, 1976; Webb and Skadsen, 1980). S-start kinematics have been observed in all fish predators, both larval and postlarval forms striking at fish and zooplankton prey. In addition, predators should adopt an S-posture before starting its strike because the hydromechanical efficiency increases throughout a fast start (Weihs, 1973a; Webb, 1979). It is therefore not surprising to find the adoption of a prestrike S-posture in both larval and postlarval fish attacking a variety of elusive prey, for example, piscivorous esocids (Hoogland *et al.,* 1956; Neill and Cullen, 1974; Christiansen, 1976; Kashin, 1977; Eaton and Bombardieri, 1978; Webb and Skadsen, 1980; Rand and Lauder, 1981), cornet fish (Fistulariidae) and trumpet fish (Aulostomidae; Hobson, 1974), fish larvae (Rosenthal, 1969; Rosenthal and Hempel, 1970; Hunter, 1972; Beyer, 1980), plankivorous stickleback (*Gasterosteus aculeatus*), lake trout (*Salvelinus namaycash*), and sunfish (Centrarchidae) (Tugendhat, 1960; Kettle and O'Brien, 1978; O'Brien, 1979; Vinyard, 1982).

S-starts and use of a prestrike S-posture require good body flexibility and are not possible for more rigid fish. Among actinopterygians, reduced vertebral number (Greenwood *et al.,* 1966; Gosline, 1971) and flexibility (Aleyev, 1977) are common phylogenetic trends, so more advanced teleosts are most likely to use other locomotor options in predation; however, the evolution of protrusible jaws and suction is also a major feature of actinopterygian phylogeny (Lauder, 1982; Chap. 8), providing for rapid extensions of the bite and hence representing a different strategy to intercept prey in minimal time. Indeed, bite extension might be energetically more economical than fast starts in closing the final distance between the predator and its prey.

Extension of the bite by suction is not independent of locomotion. Weihs (1980) has shown that the suction field extends forward in a moving fish and that the greater the speed, the greater the extension; thus, high strike speeds are desirable in strikes (and chases) by suction feeders. Where the body is rigid high speeds probably require that a strike be initiated from a longer distance.

These three strike tactics (striking from the side of the prey, at an appropriate target, and at a high closure speed) define the optimum strategy for a biting predator to minimize the duration and maximize the probability of catch success in a strike. In order to maximize its chances of success, prey should attempt to maximize the interaction time. This occurs when the prey responds to an attack initiating a chase or detering the predator from continuing.

CHASES

A chase is a series of one or more uninterrupted strikes by a predator toward its prey. It is usually initiated by a prey response to the predator. Chases are an important or the dominant phase of predation for many fish piscivores with low flexibility or poor suction, but with high speed and maneuverability; carangids and many scombroids almost exclusively chase down prey (Major, 1977, 1978; Sharp and Dizon, 1978), and less specialized cruisers such as the salmonids often follow an unsuccessful strike with a chase.

The same optimization principles apply to chases as to other feeding techniques. The general strategies are the same as for a strike: the predator should minimize the duration of a chase, the prey attempting to maximize it. Quantitative studies on chases are few, but some of the boundaries on chase interactions are becoming increasingly clear, providing the beginnings of a framework for study of this neglected biomechanical field. Most useful information currently applies to prey tactics, probably because it is prey behavior that initiates a chase and all subsequent maneuvers, as predators follow to intercept at the present prey position without anticipation of future positions (Lanchester and Mark, 1975).

The overall duration and minimum length of a chase appear to be small. Refuge in the form of bottom rubble, vegetation, other fish in schooling species, and even the air, is typically within 1 m to 2 m distance (Nursall, 1973; Neill and Cullen, 1974; Major, 1977, 1978). Christiansen (1976) found that northern pike (*Esox lucius*) would only chase prey if there were 3 m to 4 m of clear water without refuges. Typical prey could travel at maximum speeds of 10 to 20 lengths · sec^{-1} or 1 to 2 m · sec^{-1} (Wardle, 1975; Popova, 1978) and hence travel a 3-m to 4-m distance in 1 to 4 sec. Major (1978) found that chases by the predatory jack (*Caranx ignobilis*) attacking schooling Hawaiian anchovy (*Stoleophorus purpureus*) lasted about 1 to 3 sec.

Chases therefore appear to be relatively short but high-speed interactions. It is known that speed and maneuver (turning radius) are related, and optimal escape tactics must take this into account. Howland (1974) has analyzed relationships between speed and turning radius and determined the threshold relationships favoring prey escape. In Howland's model, the predator and prey are points initially traveling along a common path at speeds V_P and V_Q, respectively. The prey starts a turn of constant radius R_Q and the predator responds with a turn of constant radius R_P, with $R_P > R_Q$ (Fig. 11-5). If the dimensionless relative speed (v), and turning radius (r), are calculated by normalizing with V_P and R_P, respectively

$$v = V_Q/V_P \text{ and } r = R_Q/R_P \qquad (12)$$

The prey can escape a larger and hence faster (Beamish, 1978) predator when the prey's turning radius is sufficiently small, such that

$$v \geq r^{0.5} \qquad (13)$$

The prey's maneuver must, of course, be appropriately timed to begin within some minimum starting distance. Escape then occurs as the prey enters a safe zone delimited by the predator's larger minimum turning radius at V_P, forcing the predator to stop and reorient for another attack. This clearly extends the duration of an interaction favoring prey escape (Howland, 1974).

The applicability of Howland's model to fish chases is unclear. Flexible fish are able to turn at very high rates with small turning radii (Webb, 1976), so the safe zone would be of limited size and exist for a short time. The model would be expected to apply to more rigid fish, but Major (1978) found that Hawaiian anchovy attacked by jacks were invariably caught after entering the safe zone, but escaped by straight-line flight. Unfortunately, Major's observations were made by eye on large numbers of individuals from two schooling species, so that resolution of events in the detail required was impossible. Clearly, there is a need for more data on speed and maneuverability in predation interactions. In addition, for schooling predators, an individual's safe zone might leave prey vulnerable to the other predators.

Predation interactions ultimately occur between individuals of different

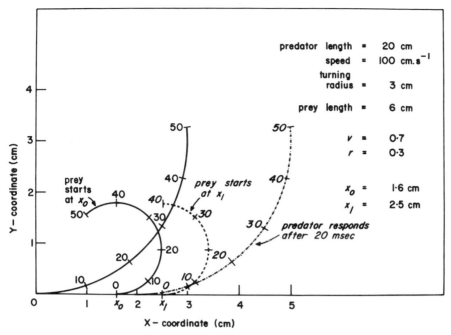

Figure 11-5

Chase trajectories, seen from above, for a hypothetical predation interaction between fish, based on a model of optimal tactics by Howland (1974). (Times are shown in msec.) The situation described by Howland in which prey can escape is illustrated by the solid lines. The prey starts turning when the distance from the predator is x_o and crosses into the safe zone enclosed by the predator's smallest turning radius appropriate for its speed within 30 msec. If the prey starts to maneuver too early when the distance separating it from the predator is x_1, the prey cannot enter the safe zone and may be captured (*dotted line*); however, if the predator has a response latency of >20 msec (*chain dotted line*), the range of starting distances where escape is possible is extended and prey can still escape into the safe zone starting from x_1. Trajectories are based on observed performance of smallmouth bass (*Micropterus dolomieui*) and fathead minnow (*Pimephales promelas*) (P.W. Webb, unpublished data).

sizes. Howland (1974) considered how size would affect locomotor tactics in a chase. He argued that the minimum turning radius of a fish is determined when the centrifugal force equals the turning moment. Using the analogy of aerodynamic forces on control surfaces, Howland deduced

$$k \, A_c \, V^2 = m \, V^2 / R \qquad (14)$$

where A_c is control surface area, m is mass, and k is constant.

For geometrically similar fish, $m \propto L^3$ and $A_c \propto L^2$ and therefore $R \propto L$. Webb (1976) confirmed this for fast starts of rainbow trout, and the same result is probably applicable to turns during chases because fast starts and turns are mechanically similar (Weihs, 1972, 1973a). For geometrically similar fish, r (equation 12) will be equal to the length of the prey divided by that of the predator. For geometrically dissimilar fish, r would be expected to be proportional to some product of their relative body areas (Howland, 1974; Webb, 1983).

The scaling relationships also lead to a prediction of minimum speeds for fish of a given size that favor prey capture. For geometrically similar fish, $R \alpha$ L and speed should scale with length raised to some exponent ≥ 0.5 to favor prey capture. There are no accurate data to test this prediction for sprint speeds of fish. Somero and Childress (1980) have shown that activities of two key enzymes in glycolysis, the metabolic pathway by which power is made available for spring swimming, scale with $L^{4.3}$ to $L^{4.7}$. If these activities reflect potential to generate power, maximum sprint speeds would be proportional to $L^{0.8}$ to $L^{0.9}$.

FEEDING ON ZOOPLANKTON

Many of the principles developed above for fish also apply to planktivores consuming individual zooplankters. Searching is the dominant phase of zooplankton predation (O'Brien, 1979), and strategies for optimal rates of food location will be the same as for other searchers and filter feeding as discussed above. Maximization of surplus energy can also be controlled by the predator's decisions to ignore certain species or concentrations. Planktivores can recognize different prey species and may ignore faster individuals (Drenner et al., 1978; O'Brien, 1979; Vinyard, 1980). Slower prey may also be ignored rather than chased if an escape attempt is made (Webb, 1982a).

Suction is the usual mode of capture for particulate planktivores, and those fish with more protrusible jaws and better suction are most effective against elusive prey (McComas and Drenner, 1982). Predators presumably have no particular target on the prey owing to the small size of the prey compared to the predator. Plankton morphology would be expected to influence escape trajectories, but there appears to be no evidence that predators anticipate these differences; however, fish do use different tactics to intercept elusive prey. Sacramento perch (*Archoplites interruptus*) use large-amplitude C-starts to catch elusive prey (*Daphnia magna*) but slowly approach and take nonevasive prey (*Diaphanosoma brachyurum*; Vinyard, 1982). Centrarchids adopt S-postures preparatory to taking faster prey (O'Brien, 1979), but the S-shapes are of small amplitude because these fish have relatively few vertebrae, reducing flexibility. As with piscivores it is clear that experimental studies are desirable to evaluate particulate zooplankton strike tactics and predator functional morphology.

EVOLUTIONARY TRENDS

Recognition of the existence of distinct optimal body forms for periodic and transient propulsion provides some basis for evaluating trends in the evolution of fishes. The earliest known fish, the Agnatha, were a diverse group of armored fish (hence their name, ostracoderms). Romer (1966) considers that "the trunk and the tail appear as a relatively small locomotor appendage, useful in transporting the feeding apparatus to a favorable location," and that "the locomotion of the oldest vertebrates must have been of the relatively ineffective and uncontrolled type seen in a frog tadpole." Romer further visualizes the diversity in ostracoderm morphology as numerous "experiments" in swimming and stabilization. Despite of their apparent clumsy ways and structural variability, some trends were established among the ostracoderms that continue throughout the evolution of fish. One trend was toward expansion of the caudal area by bending the body axis and extending the trailing-edge fin flap, which would favor improved transient swimming (Webb and Smith, 1980).

Several different caudal morphologic experiments have been tried among fishes, including the heterocercal and hypocercal tails and the later, diphycercal tail in the sarcopterygii. Of these, the heterocercal tail dominated, probably because of its additional role in dynamic buoyancy regulation in negatively buoyant fish (Webb and Smith 1980; see also Chap. 5).

A further trend among all the early fishes is the reduction of armor (Moy–Thomas and Miles, 1971). Loss of armor occurs with or following the appearance of a large caudal area that would enhance acceleration. This loss of armor would reduce acceleration resistance (Webb and Skadsen, 1979; Webb, 1982c) and hence may be considered a further adaptation to improve transient swimming performance.

The evolution of jaws was a major step in fish evolution. Following the appearance of jaws, there is less variation in body and fin patterns so that early gnathostomes preview the scope of body forms seen in modern fishes. The early gnathostomes were typically fusiform, with an expanded low aspect ratio tail, two pairs of fins (pectorals and pelvics), an anterior dorsal fin, and various other median appendages. This form probably provided the best compromise between requirements for periodic and transient swimming (Webb, 1977, 1982b).

In all lineages there are some recurring trends associated with fin systems that improve stabilization and control functions, strengthen skeletal elements to improve the magnitude of propulsive forces, improve buoyancy regulation, and of course, provide more flexible and powerful jaw mechanisms (see Chaps. 4 and 7; reviews by M.L. Moss, 1977; S.A. Moss, 1977; Thomson, 1976; Thomson and Simanek, 1977; Lauder, 1980, 1982; Webb, 1982b). Within this diversity of fishes, two major lines are identified: cartilaginous fish, represented by the elasmobranchs, and the ray-finned fishes, the actinopterygians. (The smaller crossopterygian and dipnoan groups of the osteichthyes are not considered here.) The bony fish differ from elasmobranchs in that the skeleton is made of bone and historically there was a swimbladder. Bone is stronger than cartilage in bending and together with neutral buoyancy, this skeletal basis provides for much of the tremendous actinopterygian locomotor radiation from anguilliform to thunniform caudal fin modes and all but rajiform noncaudal modes.

Actinopterygian evolution may be considered as a series of radiations about a recurring generalized carnivore having a more or less laterally flattened fusiform body, a large caudal area, two sets of paired fins, an anterior (stabilizing) dorsal fin, and various other posterior median fins (Webb, 1982b). Successive radiations are based on changes in the axial skeleton that would withstand progressively larger compressive and bending forces. The recurring generalized form is that providing a compromise between periodic and transient performance criteria, although experimental evidence indicates that the transient feature is most important (Webb, 1977, 1982b). Such generalists are possible because of collapsible fins or fin specialization, largely owing to the bony fin skeleton, that permit controlled variation in the longitudinal body-depth distribution for both transient and periodic swimming. Optimal forms for periodic (*e.g.*, scombroids) or transient propulsion (*e.g.*, esocids) occur particularly in later radiations.

Another trend in actinopterygian evolution is toward slow swimming and attendant fine control over maneuver, again attributable in part to neutral buoyancy and flexible fins. The most recent teleosts (the acanthopterygians) show optimal forms for slow swimming: the pectoral fins have migrated dorsally from their primitive ventral position, and the pelvic fins have migrated forward to lie more or less beneath the pectoral fins. These locations provide for a wide variety of propulsive and control forces (Harris, 1937, 1953; Alexander, 1967; Gosline, 1971, 1980) that have been important in penetrating numerous structurally complex habitats (*e.g.*, reefs, rooted vegetation, etc.); however, it appears that specialization for slow, noncaudal swimming has been made at some cost to sprint performance (Hobson and Chess, 1978; Webb, 1982b).

Trends in bony fish evolution pertinent to locomotion are therefore related to increased magnitude of propulsive forces (especially for the production of angular and linear acceleration movements), and compromises between optimal designs for slow, noncaudal swimming versus caudal propulsion.

Less is known of cartilaginous fish. The group appears to have emphasized anguilliform caudal propulsion in sharks and rajiform pectoral swimming in skates and rays (Lindsey, 1978). The evolution of cartilaginous fish is also poorly known, in part because cartilage is poorly fossilized; nevertheless, evolutionary trends appear to emphasize periodic swimming and benthic life, both probably largely attributable to the absence of a swimbladder. Elasmobranchs are characteristically dorsoventrally flattened over much of their length, this being most advanced in the specialized benthic Batoidimorpha and Squatinidae. No quantitative studies have been performed on swimming in skates and rays.

The sharks (Selachimorpha) have long, flexible fusiform bodies and swim in the anguilliform mode (Thomson and Simanek, 1977; Webb and Keyes, 1982). The cross-sectional shape varies along the body in such a way as to minimize drag (Weihs, 1981). The general form and fin plan of sharks is remarkably uniform, the insertion of fins along the body and relative fin size being remarkably constant (Thomson, 1976; Thomson and Simanek, 1977). Sharks characteristically have large gaps between the first and second dorsal fins and the caudal fin. In more pelagic species, the second dorsal fin is frequently small. Webb and Keyes (1982) have shown that this fin organization, coupled with characteristic anguilliform body movements, could result in interactions between median fins enhancing thrust and efficiency (Lighthill, 1970). This is only applicable to periodic swimming at uniform speed, which is the usual mode of locomotion in sharks (Thomson and Simanek, 1977). In benthic species, fin areas tend to be larger (Thomson and Simanek, 1977), and transient swimming is probably of greater importance; however, the body-to-fin areas are always small compared to bony fishes, and it is probably that sharks lack the transient swimming performance capabilities of bony fish.

Acknowledgments

The authors thank the National Science Foundation (grant PCM-8006469) for support during the preparation of this chapter.

REFERENCES

Alexander, R. McN. 1967. *Functional Design in Fishes.* London: Hutchinson University Library.

Aleyev, Y.G. 1977. *Nekton.* The Hague, Netherlands: Junk.

Beamish, F.W.H. 1978. Swimming capacity. In *Fish Physiology,* edited by W.S. Hoar and D.J. Randall, vol. 7, 101–187. New York: Academic Press.

Beyer, J.E. 1980. Feeding success of Clupeoid fish larvae and stochastic thinking. *Dana* 1:65–91.

Bone, Q. 1977. Muscular and energetic aspects of fish swimming. In *Swimming and Flying in Nature,* edited by T.Y. Wu, C.J. Brokaw, and C. Brennen, 493–528. New York: Plenum Press.

Breder, C.M., Jr. 1976. Fish schools as operational structures. *Fish Bull.* 74:471–502.

Brett, J.R., and Groves, T.D.D. 1979. Physiological energetics. In *Fish Physiology,* edited by W.S. Hoar, D.J. Randall, and J.R. Brett, vol. VII, 279–352. New York: Academic Press.

Brett, J.R. 1979. Environmental factors and growth. In *Fish Physiology,* edited by W.S. Hoar and D.J. Randall, vol. VIII, 599–675. New York: Academic Press.

Brett, J.R., and Zala, C.A. 1975. Daily pattern of nitrogen excretion and oxygen consumption of sockeye salmon (*Oncorhynchus nerka*) under controlled conditions. *J. Fish Res. Board Can.* 32:2470–2486.

Cayley, Sir George. 1809. On aerial navigation. *Nicholson's J.* 24:163–174.

Christiansen, D.G. 1976. Feeding and behavior of Northern pike (*Esox lucius* Linnaeus). M.Sc. Thesis, Department of Zoology, University of Alberta, Edmonton, Canada, 302 p.

Counsilman, J.E. 1968. *The Science of Swimming.* Englewood Cliffs, NJ: Prentice-Hall.

Cushing, D.H., and Harden-Jones, F.R. 1968. Why do fish school? *Nature* 218: 918–920.

de Veen, J.F. 1967. On the phenomenon of soles (*Solea solea*) swimming at the surface. *J. Cons. Int. Expl. Mer* 31:207–236.

Daniel, T.L. 1981. Fish mucus: In situ measurements of polymer drag reduction. *Biol. Bull.* 160:376–382.

Diana, J.S. 1980. Diel activity pattern and swimming speeds of northern pike (*Exos lucius*) in Lac Ste. Anne, Alberta. *Can. J. Fish. Aquat. Sci.* 37:1454–1458.

Drenner, R.W., Strickler, J.R., and O'Brien, W.J. 1978. Capture probability: The role of zooplankter escape in the selective feeding of planktivorous fish. *J. Fish. Res. Board Can.* 35:1370–1373.

Durbin, A.G., Durbin, E.G., Verity, P.G., and Smayda, T.J. 1981. Voluntary swimming speeds and respiration rates of a filter feeding planktivore, the Atlantic menhaden. *Fish. Bull.* 78:877–886.

Eaton, R.C., Lavender, W.A., and Weiland, C. Identification of Mauthner-initiated response patterns in goldfish: Evidence from simultaneous cinematography and electrophysiology. *J. Comp. Physiol.* In press.

Eaton, R.C., Lavender, W.A., and Wieland, C. In press. Identification of Mauthner-initiated response patterns in goldfish: Evidence from simultaneous cinematography and electrophysiology. *J. Comp. Physiol.*

Elliott, J.M. 1979. Energetics of freshwater teleosts. *Symp. Zool. Soc. Lond.* 44: 29–61.

Gosline, W.A. 1971. *Functional Morphology and Classification of Teleostean Fishes.* Honolulu: University Press of Hawaii.

Gosline, W.A. 1980. The evolution of some structural systems with reference to interrelationships of modern lower teleostean fish groups. *Japan. J. Ichthyol.* 27:1–28.

Greenwood, P.H., Rosen, D.E., Weitzman, S.H., and Myers, G.S. 1966. Phyletic studies of teleostean fishes, with a provisional classification of living forms. *Bull. Am. Museum Nat. Hist.* 131:343–355.

Grobecker, D.B., and Pietsch, T.W. 1979. High-speed cinematographic evidence for ultrafast feeding in antennariid anglerfishes. *Science* 205:1161–1162.

Harden-Jones, F.R. 1968. *Fish Migration.* London: Edward Arnold.

Harden-Jones, F.R., Arnold, G.P., Greer Walker, M., and Scholes, P. 1978. Selective tidal stream transport and the migration of plaice (*Plauronectes platessa* L.) in the southern North Sea. *J. Cons. Int. Expl. Mer* 38:331–337.

Harris, J.E. 1937. The mechanical significance of the position and movements of the paired fins in the teleostei. *Tortugas Lab. Pap.* 31:173–189.

Harris, J.E. 1953. Fin patterns and mode of life in fishes. In *Essays in Marine Biology*, edited by S.M. Marshal and P. Orr, 17–28. Edinburgh; Oliver and Boyd.

Hess, J.L. 1976. On the problem of shaping an axisymmetric body to obtain low drag at large Reynolds numbers. *J. Ship Res.* 20:41–60.

Hobson, E.S. 1974. Feeding relationships of teleostean fishes on coral reefs in Kona, Hawaii, *Fish. Bull.* 72:915–1031.

Hobson, E.S., and Chess, J.R. 1978. Trophic relationships among fishes and plankton in the lagoon at Enewetak Atoll, Marshall Islands. *Fish. Bull.* 76: 133–153.

Hoogland, D., Morris, D., and Tinbergen, N. 1956. The spines of sticklebacks (*Gasterosteus* and *Pygosteus*) as a means of defense against predators (*Perca* and *Esox*). *Behavior* 10:205–236.

Houssay, S.F. 1912. *Forme, puissance et stabilité des poissons.* Paris: Herman.

Howland, H.C. 1974. Optimal strategies for predator avoidance: The relative importance of speed and manoeuvrability. *J. Theoret. Biol.* 47:333–350.

Hunter, J.R. 1966. Procedure for analysis of schooling behavior. *J. Fish. Res. Board Can.* 23:547–562.

Hunter, J.R. 1972. Swimming and feeding behavior of larval anchovy, *Engraulis mordax. Fish. Bull.* 70:821–838.

Isaacs, R. 1975. *Differential Games.* Huntington, N.Y.: Krieger Publishing.

Kashin, S.G. 1977. Behavior of some fishes during hunting. *Zool. Zh.* 56:1328–1339. (In Russian)

Katz, J., and Weihs, D. 1978. Hydrodynamic propulsion by large amplitude oscillation of an airfoil with chordwise flexibility. *J. Fluid Mech.* 88:485–497.

Kerr, S.R. 1971. A simulation model of lake trout growth. *J. Fish Res. Board Can.* 28:815–819.

Kettle, D., and O'Brien, W.J. 1978. Vulnerability of arctic zooplankton species to predation by small lake trout (*Salvelinus namaycush*). *J. Fish. Res. Board Can.* 35:1495–1500.

Kliashtorin, L.B. 1973. The swimming energetics and hydrodynamics characteristics of actually swimming fish. *Promyslovaya. Okeanol. Podvod. Tekh.* 6:1–19.

Lanchester, B.S., and Mark, R.F. 1975. Pursuit and prediction in the tracking of moving food by a teleost (*Acanthaluteres spinomelanurus*). *J. Exp. Biol.* 63:627–645.

Lauder, G.V. 1980. On the relationship of the myotome to the axial skeleton in vetebrate evolution. *Paleobiology* 6:51–56.

Lauder, G.V. 1982. Patterns of evolution in the feeding mechanism of actinopterygian fishes. *Am. Zool.* 22:275–285.

Leong, R.J.H., and O'Connell, C.P. 1969. A laboratory study of particulate and filter feeding of the northern anchovy (*Engraulis mordax*). *J. Fish. Res. Board Can.* 26:557–582.

Lighthill, M.J. 1969. Hydromechanics of aquatic animal propulsion. *Ann. Revs. Fluid Mech.* 1:413–446.

Lighthill, M.J. 1970. Aquatic animal propulsion of high hydromechanical efficiency. *J. Fluid Mech.* 44:265–301.

Lighthill, M.J. 1971. Large-amplitude-elongated-body theory of fish locomotion. *Proc. R. Soc. Lond.* 179B:125–138.

Lindsey, C.C. 1978. Form, function, and locomotory habits in fish. In *Fish Phy-*

siology, edited by W.S. Hoar and D.J. Randall, vol. 7, 1–100. New York: Academic Press.

Magnuson, J. J. 1978. Locomotion by scombrid fishes: Hydromechanics, morphology and behavior. In *Fish Physiology,* edited by W.S. Hoar and D.J. Randall, vol. 7, 230–313. New York: Academic Press.

Major, P.F. 1977. Predator-prey interactions in schooling fishes during periods of twilight: A study of the silverside *Pranesus insularum* in Hawaii. *Fish. Bull.* 72:415–426.

Major, P.F. 1978. Predator-prey interactions in schooling fishes, *Caranx ignobilis* and *Stolephorus purpureus. Animal Behav.* 26:760–777.

McComas, G.F., and Drenner, R.W. 1982. Species replacement in a reservoir fish community: silverside feeding mechanics and competition. *Can. J. Fish. Aquat. Sci.* 39:815–821.

McPhail, J.D. 1977. A possible function of the caudal spot in characid fishes. *Can. J. Zool.* 55:1063–1066.

Moss, M.L. 1977. Skeletal tissues in sharks. *Am. Zool.* 17:335–342.

Moss, S.A. 1977. Feeding mechanisms in sharks. *Am. Zool.* 17:355–364.

Moy-Thomas, J.A., and Miles, R.S. 1971. *Palaeozoic Fishes.* Philadelphia, PA: W.B. Saunders.

Neill, S.R. St. J., and Cullen, J.M. 1974. Experiments on whether schooling by the prey affects the hunting behavior of cephalopods and fish predators. *J. Zool. Lond.* 172:549–569.

Nursall, J.R. 1973. Some behavioral interactions of spottail shiners (*Notropis hudsonius*), yellow perch (*Perca flavensens*), and northern pike (*Esox lucius*). *J. Fish. Res. Board Can.* 30:1161–1178.

O'Brien, W.J. 1979. The predator-prey interaction of planktivorous fish and zooplankton. *Am. Sci.* 67:572–581.

Olla, B.L., Samet, C.E., and Studholme, A.L. 1972. Activity and feeding behavior of the summer flounder (*Paralichthys dentalus*) under controlled laboratory conditions. *Fish. Bull.* 70:1127–1136.

Partridge, B.L., and Pitcher, T.J. 1979. Evidence against a hydrodynamic function for fish schools. *Nature (Lond.)* 279:418–419.

Pitcher, T.J. 1980. Some ecological consequences of fish school volumes. *Freshwater Biol.* 10:539–544.

Popova, O.A. 1978. The role of predaceous fish in ecosystems. In *Ecology of Freshwater Fish Production,* edited by S.D. Gerking, Oxford: Blackwell Scientific Publishing, 215–249.

Rand, D.M., and Lauder, G.V. 1981. Prey capture in the chain pickerel Esox niger: Correlations between feeding and locomotor behavior. *Can. J. Zool.* 59:1072–1078.

Romer, A.S. 1966. *Vertebrate Paleontology.* Chicago: University of Chicago Press.

Rosenthal, H. 1969. Untersuchungen uber das beutefanguerhalten bei Larven des Herrings (*Clupea harengus*). *Marine Biol.* 3:208–221.

Rosenthal, H., and Hempel, G. 1970. Experimental studies in feeding and food requirements of herring larvae (*Clupea harengus* L.). In *Marine Food Chains,* edited by J.H. Steele, 344–364. Berkeley, CA: University of California Press.

Schlichting, H. 1968. *Boundary-layer Theory,* 6th ed. New York: McGraw-Hill.

Sharp, G.D., and Dizon, A.E. 1978. *The Physiological Ecology of Tunas.* New York: Academic Press.

Sharp, G.D., and Dotson, R.C. 1978. Energy for migration in albacore (*Thunnus alalunga*). *Fish. Bull.* 76:447–449.

Sharp, G.D., and Francis, R.S. 1976. An energetics model for the exploited yellow fin tuna *Thunnus albacores* population in the eastern Pacific Ocean. *Fish. Bull.* 74:36–50.

Shaw, E. 1978. Schooling fishes. *Am. Sci.* 66:166–175.

Somero, G.N., and Childress, J.J. 1980. A violation of the metabolism-size scaling paradigm: Activities of glycolytic enzymes in muscle increase in larger-size fish. *Physiol. Zool.* 53:322–337.

Thomson, K.S. 1976. On the heterocercal tail in sharks. *Paleobiology* 2:19–38.

Thomson, K.S., and Simanek, D.E. 1977. Body form and locomotion in sharks. *Am. Zool.* 17:343–354.

Trump, C.L., and Leggett, W.C. 1980. Optimum swimming speeds in fish: The problem of currents. *Can. J. Fish Aquat. Sci.* 37:1086–1092.

Tugendhat, B. 1960. The normal feeding behavior of the three-spined stickleback (*Gasterosteus aculeatus* L.). *Behaviour* 15:284–318.

Videler, J.J., and Weihs, D. 1982. Energetic advantage of burst-and-coast swimming of fish at high speeds. *J. Exp. Biol.* 97:169–178.

Vinyard, G.L. 1980. Differential prey vulnerability and predator selectivity: Effects of evasive prey on bluegill (*Lepomis macrochirus*) and pumpkinseed (*L. gibbosus*) predation. *Can. J. Fish. Aquat. Sci.* 37:2294–2299.

Vinyard, G.L. 1982. Variable kinematics of Sacramento perch (*Archoplites interruptus*) capturing evasive and non-evasive prey. *Can. J. Fish. Aquat. Sci.* 39: 208–211.

Wardle, C.S. 1975. Limit of fish swimming speed. *Nature (Lond.)* 255:725–727.

Ware, D.M. 1975. Growth, metabolism and optimal swimming speed of a pelagic fish. *J. Fish. Res. Board Can.* 32:33–41.

Ware, D.M. 1978. Bioenergetics of pelagic fish: Theoretical change in swimming speed and ration with body size. *J. Fish. Res. Board Can.* 35:220–228.

Webb, P.W. 1971. The swimming energetics of trout. *J. Exp. Biol.* 55:484–520; 521–540.

Webb, P.W. 1975a. Hydrodynamics and energetics of fish propulsion. *Bull. Fish. Res. Board Can.* 190:1–159.

Webb, P.W. 1975b. Acceleration performance of rainbow trout, *Salmo gairdneri,* and green sunfish, *Lepomis cyanellus. J. Exp. Biol.* 63:451–465.

Webb, P.W. 1976. The effect of size on the fast-start performance of rainbow trout (*Salmo gairdneri* Richardson) and a consideration of piscivorous predator-prey interactions. *J. Exp. Biol.* 65:157–177.

Webb, P.W. 1977. Effects of median-fin amputation on fast-start performance of rainbow trout (*Salmo gairdneri*). *J. Exp. Biol.* 68:123–125.

Webb, P.W. 1978a. Partitioning of energy into metabolism and growth. In *Ecology of Freshwater Fish Production,* edited by S.D. Gerking, 184–214. Oxford: Blackwell Scientific Publishers.

Webb, P.W. 1978b. Fast-start performance and body form in seven species of teleost fish. *J. Exp. Biol.* 74:211–216.

Webb, P.W. 1978c. Effects of temperature on fast-start performance of rainbow trout (*Salmo gairdneri*). *J. Fish. Res. Board Can.* 35:1717–1422.

Webb, P.W. 1979. Mechanics of escape responses in crayfish (*Orconenctes virilis*, Hagen). *J. Exp. Biol.* 79:245–263.

Webb, P.W. 1982a. Responses of northern anchovy, *Engraulis mordax*, larvae to predation by a biting planktivore, *Amphiprion percula*. *Fish. Bull.* 79:727–735.

Webb, P.W. 1982b. Locomotor patterns in the evolution of actinopterygian fishes. *Am. Zool.* 22:329–342.

Webb, P.W. 1982c. Fast-start resistance of trout. *J. Exp. Biol.* 96:93–106.

Webb, P.W. 1983. Speed, acceleration, and manoeuvrability of two teleost fishes. *J. Exp. Biol.* 102:115–122.

Webb, P.W., and Keyes, R.S. 1982. Swimming kinematics of sharks. *Fish. Bull.* 80: 803–812.

Webb, P.W., and Skadsen, J.M. 1979. Reduced skin mass: An adaptation for acceleration in some teleost fishes. *Can. J. Zool.* 57:1570–1575.

Webb, P.W., and Skadsen, J.M. 1980. Fast-start locomotion and the strike tactics of *Esox*. *Can. J. Zool.* 58:1462–1469.

Webb, P.W., and Smith, G.R. 1980. Function of the caudal fin in early fishes. *Copeia* 1980:559–562.

Weihs, D. 1972. A hydrodynamical analysis of the fish turning manoeuvres. *Proc. R. Soc. Lond.* 182B:59–72.

Weihs, D. 1973a. The mechanism of rapid starting the slender fish. *Biorheology* 10:343–350.

Weihs, D. 1973b. Optimal fish cruising speed. *Nature (Lond.)* 245:48–50.

Weihs, D. 1973c. Mechanically efficient swimming techniques for fish with negative buoyancy. *J. Marine Res.* 31:194–209.

Weihs, D. 1973d. Hydromechanics of fish schooling. *Nature (Lond.)* 241:290–291.

Weihs, D. 1974. Energetic advantages of burst swimming of fish. *J. Theoret. Biol.* 48:215–229.

Weihs, D. 1975a. Some hydrodynamical aspects of fish schooling. In *Swimming and Flying in Nature*, edited by T.Y. Wu, C.J. Brokaw, and C. Brennan, vol. 2, 703–718. New York: Plenum Press.

Weihs, D. 1975b. An optimum swimming speed of fish based on feeding efficiency. *Israel J. Technol.* 13:163–167.

Weihs, D. 1977. Effects of size on sustained swimming speeds of aquatic organisms. In *Scale Effects in Animal Locomotion*, edited by T.J. Pedley, 333–338. New York: Academic Press.

Weihs, D. 1978. Tidal stream transport as an efficient method for migration. *J. Cons. Int. Explor. Mer.* 38:92–99.

Weihs, D. 1980. Hydrodynamics of suction feeding of fish in motion. *J. Fish. Biol.* 16:425–433.

Weihs, D. 1981. Body section variations in sharks—an adaptation for efficient swimming. *Copeia* 1981:217–219.

Weihs, D., Keyes, R.S., and Stalls, D.M. 1981. Voluntary swimming speed of two species of large carcharhinid sharks. *Copeia* 1981:220–222.

Winberg, G.G. 1956. Rate of metabolism and food requirements of fishes. *Fish. Res. Board Can. Trans. Ser.* No. 194.

SYMBOLS

A	area	P	propulsive rate of working
ΔB	energy used in growth	Q_p	prey nutritional (energy) content
C_D	drag coefficient		
C_{Do}	drag coefficient defined for equation (3)	R_P	predator turning radius
		R_Q	prey turning radius
E	rate of working	r	R_Q/R_P
E_i	food energy input	T	average thrust
F	nutritional (energy) value of prey per unit volume of water filtered	V	swimming speed
		V_{fo}	optimal feeding speed
G	energy for reproduction	V_o	optimal swimming speed
K	$\rho A/2$ (see equation 3) and following text	V_P	predator swimming speed
		V_Q	prey swimming speed
k	constant	v	V_Q/V_P
L	length	$\alpha\beta\gamma$	constants; see equation (3)
M	metabolic energy losses due to non-locomotor activity	η	propulsive efficiency
		ξ	energy losses from E_i specific dynamic action, feces and nitrogenous wastes
m	mass		
n	number of prey per unit volume of water		

EPILOGUE: TOWARD A MORE FULLY INTEGRATED FISH BIOMECHANICS

James Lighthill

The editors of this volume are to be congratulated on their success in compiling a comprehensive survey of current knowledge about the biomechanics of fishes in a form that to a remarkable extent integrates the biological and the mechanical aspects of the subject. Working together, a zoologist with very extensive mechanics knowledge and experience and an authority on fluid mechanics with a long-standing involvement in biology, the authors were able to ensure that practically every part of this book achieved a necessary interdisciplinary integration. Furthermore, the book's strategic plan, with specialized surveys on musculature and connective tissue, gas and heat transfer, and energetics of locomotion and feeding, culminating in a chapter surveying whole-animal problems from the standpoint of various optimality considerations, lays a strong foundation for construction of a still more fully integrated fish biomechanics that can be viewed as part of the background to fish evolution.

The more complete integration that is needed will demand *both* an extension of available knowledge within each of the component areas of the subject *and* a more complete success in combining these different bodies of knowledge (alongside data in other fields from neurobiology to paleozoology) in order to throw greater light on major problems of locomotor control and fish evolution. Admittedly, the present book's chapter cross-referencing allows the reader to make valuable steps in mentally combining material from different specialized fields. Chapter 2 on fish muscle, for example, ensures that readers of later chapters (on areas of study in which a crude categorization of fish musculature color remains usual) can interpret what is written there in terms of more detailed knowledge of fast glycolytic and fast oxidative-glycolytic muscle and of the fast and slow aerobic types of muscle, together with information on their characteristic types of innervation and data on the progressive recruitment of muscle-fiber types as swimming speed increases. Each chapter enhances the interpretation of other chapters.

Nevertheless, almost every contributor has admitted (with appropriate honesty) ignorance of at least one topic, which besides being of key importance for the specialized area concerned, is crucial for wider synthesis. Indeed, the highly informative Chapter 1, on the history of fish biomechanics, ends with the comment that "much remains to be done. . . ." The valuable

372

contribution of Chapter 3, on skeletal mechanics, the force trajectories for muscles of different types, and the importance of skin extensibility and stiffness for fish swimming, concludes with a section describing missing links in the arguments. Chapter 4 outlines the nature of fish circulatory flows characterized by the absence of an intervening pump between the gas-exchange complex and the systemic circulation and analyzes the blood flow in the "sheetlike" lamellae of the gills; however, after beginning an application of boundary-layer analysis to the water flow through the gills, the author recognizes that this topic requires more advanced hydrodynamic analysis and further experimentation. Beyond these requirements, there is a need for quantitative estimation of the benefits of countercurrent gas exchange in the gills and similarly (one may add), within the retia mirabilia responsible (in many fishes) for the secretion of swimbladder gas (Chap. 5) and as heat exchangers (Chap. 8) responsible for maintaining elevated body temperature in the convergent groups of sharks and teleosts, the Lamnidae and the Thunnidae.

In another part of Chapter 5, the analysis of ecologic influences on the selection of buoyancy-control mechanisms is particularly valuable; yet, where hydrodynamic lift (and/or an upwardly directed component of *propulsive* force) is selected (as with the two groups just mentioned), the interesting analyses of the advantages of beat-and-glide swimming (see also Chap. 11) have not been sufficiently accompanied by observational identification of the groups that adopt this maneuver. By contrast, widespread use of burst-and-coast swimming in neutrally buoyant fish is better documented (Chap. 11).

The chapters on locomotion (6 and 7) offer some admirable hydromechanic analyses of propulsion in certain groups of fishes, including (Chap. 6) many of the "energy speculators" (Chap. 10; fishes that by continual active locomotion exploit environments offering a sparse food supply). In particular, these fishes include the Lamnidae and the Thunnidae and the other lunate-tailed fishes in which the balance of thrust and drag characteristic of steady swimming is achieved with physically separate organs: the body surface, specialized for low drag (Chap. 11), and the lunate tail, specialized for efficient thrusting (Chap. 6). Similar advantages for efficiency are emphasized (in relation to environments where this confers a benefit) in Chap. 7, in a discussion of the extensive use of lift-based forms of oscillatory, paired-fin swimming.

A completely opposite type of swimming in which thrust is generated by undulations of the body surface as a whole (the same surface that is responsible for drag), is adopted by *Anguilla,* and this book makes no attempt to resolve the long-standing difficulties (Lighthill, 1975) opposing any attempt to analyze anguilliform swimming.* In this partly resistive mode of

---

*Needless to say, the corresponding analyses for microorganisms are irrelevant at the Reynolds numbers characteristic of fish locomotion.

motion, the effect on posterior flow fields of disturbances shed from anterior cross-sections is very hard to estimate, although it seems unlikely to promote efficiency. This motion has to be studied in view of the knowledge of the extremely long migrations (thousands of kilometers) undertaken by *Anguilla*.

For the carangiform swimming of elongated fishes, the longitudinal force balance (thrust versus drag) is admirably treated in Chapters 6 and 11, but there is no discussion of lateral force balance. Such an omission is serious because in carangiform undulations, where much less than a whole wavelength of undulation is present at any one instant, the main threat to potentially good thrusting efficiency lies in the undulation's capacity for generating unbalanced side-forces. By contrast, propulsion by undulations of one or more median fins attached to nonundulating body (as analyzed excellently in Chap. 7) generally involves more than a whole wavelength of undulation at any one instant. In such a case, there is at any one instant a broad balance between side-forces to the right and to the left. Such a balance is notably absent in carangiform swimming; it is essential to recognize that carangiform movements of the posterior part of the body are capable of creating large lateral forces on that part of the body that are equal and opposite to the *rate* at which those movements impart lateral momentum to the water. A significant amount of general yaw and sideslip of the fish body would be imparted by those forces (enough so that they would come into equilibrium with the system of forces opposing that yaw and sideslip), and very substantial energy dissipation could result.

In Chapter 6, the local lateral momentum of the water contiguous with the fish body is specified by Equations 12 and 13 and the equation between them. These equations make plain one source of the above-mentioned danger: where the oscillation amplitude $h(x,t)$ rises very steeply as x increases, the gradient with respect to x in Equation 12 will be very large. Consequently, the associated oscillations in the momentum-per-unit-length (mV) will be large unless the fish has adopted a substantial reduction in m (through a reduction in the cross-section depth b) near the location of steep amplitude gradient. It may be appropriate to view the association of carangiform swimming with a major reduction in cross-section depth around the caudal peduncle in the light of the very large oscillations in lateral water momentum (leading to very large unbalanced side-forces) that would otherwise result.

Even so, considerable side-forces must remain (in particular, those associated with shedding of lateral momentum from the posterior end of the fish) are unavoidable, and these give a selective advantage to shapes that minimize yaw and sideslip. Lighthill (1977) has quantitatively analyzed the advantages of configurations with "deep and relatively rigid midbody area," which Chapter 11, identifies as being characteristic of fishes that are long-distance swimmers.

Specific avowals of significant gaps in knowledge, again, appear in later chapters. The very interesting Chapter 8, on heat transfer, concludes with a comment that "this review documents our ignorance," while certain hydro-dynamic questions are left unresolved in the admirably systematic Chapter 9, on food capture. These gaps exist particularly in relation to the method of capture (Chap. 8, Section A) that combines a high-velocity attack with rapid mouth-opening to trap prey in the oral cavity. No doubt this method is used by some of the species characterized by continual activity and by others of the type described in Chapter 11 as specialized for a rapid-lunge attack. (These are the fishes for which the authors of Chap. 11 suggest a most interesting hypothesis regarding potential advantages of a pair of medial fins just anterior to the caudal fin; they are also the fishes that may often strike at the prey's center of mass to minimize the effectiveness of the C-shape escape attempt. . . .) Hydrodynamic analysis could perhaps determine a kind of "capture cross-section" for this type of attack, indicating the accuracy of aim required for success. Another area of uncertainty, to which Chapter 9 makes explicit reference, is concerned with the quantitative estimation of the advantages of jaw protrusion to suction feeders. Finally, Chapter 10, on energetics, precedes its valuable contrasting of energy budgets estimated for 'energy savers' and 'energy speculators' with a clear admission that there are *no* field studies in which all components of the budgets have been measured for any fish species.

Nevertheless, all of the areas of uncertainty or ignorance that have so far been mentioned pale beside the major unresolved problem of fish locomo-tion biomechanics. This is a problem of understanding the detailed neurologic and muscular control-and-feedback mechanisms that create each of the different modes of fish locomotion when opposed by the water's characteristic reactive and resistive loadings. The present work suggests great opportunities for future researchers to advance beyond the detailed information on innervation and musculature, the biomechanics of skin and other connective tissue, the hydromechanics of fish swimming modes, and all the other material in the book to carry out new types of experiments and make new theoretical analysis that will allow questions to be answered within the framework of more fully integrated fish biomechanics.

REFERENCES

Lighthill, J. 1975. *Mathematical Biofluiddynamics*. Philadelphia: Society for Industrial and Applied Mathematics.

Lighthill, J. 1977. Mathematical theories of fish swimming. In J.H. Steele (ed.). *Fisheries Mathematics*, pp. 131–144. New York: Academic Press.

AUTHOR INDEX

E

Eales, J. G., 175
Eastman, J. T., 144, 171
Eaton, R. C., 356, 358, 366
Ebeling, A., 148, 173
Edgerton, H. E., 13, 26, 30, 216, 244
Edsall, T. A., 337
Egberink, B. P., 308
Egginton, S., 46f, 51, 52f, 53t, 55, 56f, 57f
Ehrlich, L. W., 136
Eichelberg, H., 58, 64
Eisenberg, B. R., 54, 64
Ellington, C. P., 238, 241, 244
Elliot, J. M., 313, 314, 324, 330, 336, 366
Elshoud-Oldenhave, M. J. W., 287, 291, 309
Emerson, L., 64
Erskine, D. J., 252, 256, 258–259, 259f, 260, 263, 270, 276

F

Fänge, R., 140, 142, 172
Farmer, G. J., 28, 31
Farquhar, G. B., 23, 31
Farrell, A. P., 113 121, 118f, 134
Fechhelm, R. G., 262, 263, 264, 275, 277
Ferguson, G. G., 100, 134
Fierstine, H. L., 76, 90, 204, 204t, 210
Fischer, E., 62, 64
Fischer, G., 3, 31
Fisher, T. R., 113, 134
Fitzpatrick, L. C., 249, 251, 262, 276
Flitney, F. W., 38t, 44, 49, 50f, 51, 64
Flood, P. R., 67
Focant, B., 64
Forster, G. R., 171
Forster, R. E., 134
Forbes, R. J., 5, 31
Fox, R. S., 28, 31
Foxon, G. E. H., 26, 30
Francis, R. S., 326, 337, 353, 369
Francois-Franck, C. A., 9, 13, 25, 29, 31
Frank, O., 24, 31
Franklin, D. L., 24, 25, 32, 135
Freadman, M. A., 60, 64, 169, 172
Fromm, P. O., 261, 262, 278
Frost, B. W., 160t, 161, 176
Fry, F. E. J., 27, 31, 250, 251, 260, 261, 264, 277, 278
Fung, Y. C., 119, 134, 137

G

Gabrielson, G., 276
Gadd, G. E., 21, 31
Galbraith, M. G., 302, 309
Gardner, R. H., 313, 322, 336
Gates, D. M., 278
Gee, J. H., 142–143, 153–157, 154f, 163, 166–168, 155t, 158t, 162t, 172, 174, 176
Gee, P. A., 143, 157t, 162t, 163, 172
Gerardin-Outhiers, N., 65
Gerday, Ch., 61, 64
Gibbs, R. H., 172
Gibbs-Smith, C. H., 6, 31
Gillis, J. M., 61, 64
Goldspink, G., 39, 45, 53, 58, 59, 64, 65, 66, 182, 210, 243
Goodyear, R. H., 160t, 172
Gooding, R. M., 125t, 134, 267, 269, 270, 270f, 277, 317, 318, 319, 326, 328, 336
Gordon, J. D. M., 142, 175
Gordon, J. E., 74, 90
Gosline, W. A., 289, 309, 359, 364, 366
Graham, J. B., 142, 163, 172, 254, 261, 266, 267f, 268–269, 272, 277, 278
Gray, J., 17–19, 18f, 19f, 32, 207, 210, 226, 244
Green, J. M., 165, 172
Greene, C. W., 9, 32
Greenwalt, C. H., 223, 244
Greenwood, P. H., 359, 366
Greer-Walker, M., 36, 54, 59, 64, 162, 172, 366
Grillner, S., 69, 90
Grimes, P. W., 173
Grimstone, A. V., 114f, 121, 135
Grobecker, D. B., 280, 287, 309, 353, 366
Gross, D. R., 136
Groves, T. D. D., 251, 252, 269, 276, 313–316, 318, 324, 327, 335, 340, 365
Guernsey, D. L., 276
Gunn, D. L., 250, 251, 260, 277
Guth, L., 40, 64
Guyton, A. C., 95, 135

H

Haddle, G. P., 295, 309
Haedrich, R. L., 176
Hagiwara, S., 47, 64
Hales, D. C., 302, 310
Hales, S., 5, 32, 93, 135
Hall, D. J., 304, 311
Halliburton, W. D., 7f, 8, 9f, 32

SUBJECT INDEX

SYSTEMATIC INDEX